The book opens with
changes which have
African agriculture in Rhodesia since the
beginning of colonization. A detailed
analysis is given of two tribal trust lands —
the most common form of agricultural
settlement for Africans in that country —
including government policies and administrative control of these areas, voluntary
and forced adjustment to land shortage,
and the economic resources and productivity of peasant cultivators. Settlements
under individual land tenure (the purchase areas) are examined, as are government policies with regard to these farms,
the internal transformation of these
communities and their economic resources and productivity. The third section
of the book deals with irrigation schemes,
a new government controlled settlement
type, and the reaction of the people to
irrigation farming. Case histories of
farmers are added to each section to
provide practical illustrations of the
problems faced by Africans engaged in
agriculture in Rhodesia.

The book analyses the factors making for
success and failure in agricultural development among Rhodesian Africans
and shows that one of the major reasons
for low productivity is the too tight control
by government, its many restrictions on
African peasants, and its suppression of
many schemes originating from voluntary
agencies, such as the churches, if these
do not align themselves with government
policies.

Dr. A. K. H. Weinrich (Sister Mary
Aquina, O.P. of the Dominican Convent,
Salisbury, Rhodesia) is Senior Lecturer in
Social Anthropology at the University of
Rhodesia. She has published books and
articles on Independent African Churches
and on the tribal areas of Rhodesia.

AFRICAN FARMERS IN RHODESIA

Master farmers and their wives discuss modern farming techniques in the Shoko Museamwa community

AFRICAN FARMERS IN RHODESIA

OLD AND NEW
PEASANT COMMUNITIES IN
KARANGALAND

A. K. H. WEINRICH
(Sister Mary Aquina O.P.)

Published for the
INTERNATIONAL AFRICAN INSTITUTE
by the
OXFORD UNIVERSITY PRESS
LONDON   NAIROBI   CAPE TOWN
1975

Oxford University Press, Ely House, London W1

GLASGOW   NEW YORK   TORONTO   MELBOURNE   WELLINGTON
CAPE TOWN   IBADAN   NAIROBI   DAR ES SALAAM   LUSAKA   ADDIS ABABA
DELHI   BOMBAY   CALCUTTA   MADRAS   KARACHI   LAHORE   DACCA
KUALA LUMPUR   SINGAPORE   HONG KONG   TOKYO

ISBN 0 19 724194 8

© *International African Institute 1975*

*Printed in Great Britain by
Ebenezer Baylis and Son Limited
The Trinity Press, Worcester, and London*

This book is dedicated to my friend,
Sister Mary Matthia Stigler, O.P.,
who conducted this research together
with me.

PREFACE

This book is based on research carried out in Rhodesia between 1962 and 1969. Originally I intended to collect agricultural data as background information for a study of tribal politics. These agricultural findings I published in 1964.[1] That short study, however, aroused my interest in African agriculture and between 1966 and 1968 I carried out a careful survey of labour organization and agricultural productivity in two tribal trust lands and two purchase areas. By 1968 the Rhodesian government had invested large sums of money in African irrigation schemes, so I decided to include two of these in my research project.

Throughout the research I asked myself which factors were responsible for high and low agricultural output. That climatic and ecological conditions rank high was clear to me, but I had noticed that even in identical environments productivity varied greatly. I therefore tried to choose peasant communities in which ecological factors were kept constant. This was possible for the tribal trust lands and purchase areas, but when I tried to select two irrigation schemes the Ministry of Internal Affairs, who are responsible for these areas, restricted my choice. After lengthy negotiations they allowed me access to two irrigation schemes, one of which was situated in a completely different climatic region of Rhodesia and was, moreover, occupied by a different tribal people. Hence several factors were introduced which complicated a strict comparison.

This book is the third of three studies in which I have dealt with that part of rural Rhodesia known as Karangaland. The first book, *Chiefs and Councils in Rhodesia*, was published in 1971 by Heinemann, London, and the second, *Black and White Elites in Rural Rhodesia* was published in 1973 by the Manchester University Press. Since in the first book I dealt with political

[1] Sr. Mary Aquina, 1964.

events which, if the actors could be identified, might cause them
embarrassment with the Rhodesian government, I used fictitious
names for all the communities and also for all the people. To keep
these people and communities anonymous, I have used the same
fictitious names in this study.

I hope that this book will in a small way help to a better understanding of peasant problems in Rhodesia and help administrators
to improve the living conditions of Africans in the rural areas of
Rhodesia.

A. K. H. Weinrich
(Sr. Mary Aquina, O.P.)

Dominican Convent,
Salisbury,
Rhodesia
1974

Note When this book was written, Rhodesia shared a common currency
with Great Britain. Since then Rhodesia has adopted its own currency,
under which $2 equalled £1 before the £ was devalued. Throughout
the book the money units are those of the old English £.

TABLE OF CONTENTS

PART III

IRRIGATION SCHEMES

LIST OF ILLUSTRATIONS

LIST OF DIAGRAMS

INTRODUCTION

(1) PLANNING ECONOMIC CHANGES

Ever since the first Five-Year-Plan was formulated in Russia, some ten years after the Bolshevik revolution of 1917 which tried to transform the semi-colonial country of the tsars into a modern industrialized state, planning has become a respected government function in almost all countries on the road to economic development. In 1963 an international conference of the Rehovot was held in Israel and it devoted most of its time to agricultural planning in developing countries.[1] A book by Leys, *Politics and Change in Developing Countries*,[2] studies in detail the theory and practice of development through government planning. Literature on the subject is too voluminous for any individual to wade through.

The interest in centralized economic planning results from the sudden awareness that in the twentieth century geographical distances have lost their meaning and that developed and under-developed countries have become neighbours whose fate is closely linked. A kind of universal responsibility has emerged, and the United Nations has become the meeting place where development plans are made and help is discussed.

In addition to underdeveloped and developed countries there are some which are neither totally developed nor underdeveloped, but where small sections of the population have developed an economy similar to that in developed nations, but where the large masses of the people still live at, or just above, subsistence level. Many Latin American countries, as well as Rhodesia and South Africa, belong in this category. It might be thought that these countries would be even more urgently aware of the need for planning to raise the poorer sections to the level of their richer neighbours, yet it seems that in such countries less centralized planning takes place than in totally underdeveloped countries.

[1] Conference de Rehovot, Israel, 1963.   [2] Leys, 1969.

The reason seems to be that the economically advanced sections of these countries gain advantages from their superior position and that they are therefore inclined to leave changes to slow evolutionary processes. In most of these countries subsistence cultivators have already become peasants because they are drawn into the modern cash economy. They visit nearby estates and towns, desire the goods they see, and willingly offer their labour to pay for them. The owners of factories, mines or landed estates, welcome this development because they need labour as well as customers for their goods. Through this constant interaction of more advanced and backward people, subsistence agriculture is slowly transformed so that, where it once stood opposed to commercialized farming and industry, a continuum is evolving on which ever larger sections of backward communities move towards the cash economy.

Changes in an economic system only take place when new methods of production become available and are either thought desirable or are forced upon a community. Changes can be hastened when a political authority imposes them on its people. Such imposition can cause resentment, but if the political authority possesses sufficient power of coercion, it is likely to succeed in changing peasant agriculture.

Agricultural planning in developing countries is to a large extent based on the decision and determination of their governments to change the agricultural practices of peasants in order to increase production and so raise local living standards. Some governments stress persuasion and cooperation, others use force to bring about economic changes. The speed with which peasant societies move towards industrialism depends partly on the development policies of their governments, partly on the governments' financial ability to assist the people in increasing their production; but the most important factor is the people's assessment of their governments' motives in introducing economic changes. If a popular government, responsible to a peasant electorate, advises on agricultural changes, the response may be more wholehearted than if a government whose support lies outside the peasant sector orders certain changes for reasons which do not immediately seem profitable to peasant cultivators. Schemes with national or long-term effects, like the erection of contour ridges to preserve the natural resources of the country, will probably not obtain immediate support.

If changes in peasant agriculture are government directed and have to be accomplished in a short time, a responsible government must take over the direction of the change and assist peasants with advice, credit and marketing facilities; otherwise major social disturbances are likely to occur.

To turn now to Rhodesia, few people would question the need for changes in Rhodesia's peasant agriculture. Whether the present government's policy in introducing changes is good or even practicable is another question. It is the intention of this book to examine government policy and test its effectiveness in the light of the actual needs of peasant agriculture as I see them in Rhodesia; thus I am not writing a comparative study of peasant evolution on a continental or even world-wide scale, but am concerned rather with a very peculiar situation of agricultural development in the Third World. For Rhodesia is a country in which 95 per cent of all people are Africans and less than 5 per cent of European origin, yet where the small European community controls both the political and the economic destiny of the country and possesses 50 per cent of all agricultural land.

The Rhodesian government claims to adhere to western values and to be opposed to socialism. Economic planning, which is so characteristic of socialist states, should therefore be absent in this country. Yet for many decades successive Rhodesian governments have given directions to African peasant communities and since 1965, when the international community imposed economic sanctions on Rhodesia, the government has found itself forced to direct in even greater detail the economic life of the country. Since then the Rhodesian economy has become a directed economy to a much larger extent than any economy of the western world. This direction is especially felt in the most recent type of African agricultural settlement.

Rhodesia knows three types of African agricultural settlement, all of which are government controlled. This means that no economic changes can take place in African agriculture without the explicit or implicit consent of civil servants. Some of these settlements have closer links with the African past than others; some are more orientated towards the modern cash economy. All of them include peasants who prefer traditional African values to the values of their European neighbours, and all also include peasants who prefer modern to traditional values. Hence Rhodesia's African peasants can be placed on a continuum, ranging from economic traditionalists to successful cash crop farmers. In some types of settlement the more conservative, in others the more progressive peasants predominate.

The three types of African agricultural settlement in Rhodesia are known as tribal trust lands, purchase areas and irrigation schemes. The traditional tribal system no longer exists, though the old people still recall with nostalgia the life of the past. Tribal trust lands are modifications of the traditional tribal system and may be regarded as its direct descendents. They are the most important type of peasant settlement and account for the largest number of African cultivators. In tribal trust lands African life has undergone fewer changes than in the other settlement types.

Purchase areas are settlements in which African peasants can buy tracts of land so become owners of their farms. The fact that some Africans have accepted the concept of individual land tenure, alien to the tribal system, shows European influence on these peasant farmers.

Irrigation schemes are scheduled production schemes erected in tribal trust lands. On these schemes the methods of production are those of European agriculture and are completely alien to traditional methods of cultivation. Yet irrigation schemes are situated within tribal areas and so tribal values may be expected to influence the lives of plotholders.

In a free society people are at liberty to move from one type of settlement to another. Preferences, ability and economic pressures determine choice of residence. This leads to a high degree of satisfaction among the people. Unfortunately, Rhodesia is not a free society. Here government controls all movement of Africans between the various types of agricultural settlement and only on obtaining a government permit can a peasant shift from a tribal trust land to a purchase area or to an irrigation scheme. Progressive peasants who prefer to purchase their own land may be unable to do so and may be forced to intensify land use in tribal areas if they want to augment their family income from agriculture. Inability to move may thus lead to economic stratification in each of the agricultural settlements.

The aim of this book is to provide a deeper understanding of peasant agriculture in Rhodesia and to work out the factors which lead to greater satisfaction and security among African peasants, to higher family incomes and to a better use of the land. To provide the reader with some information with which to judge the hypothesis advanced at the end of this Introduction, a brief sketch is here given of the traditional tribal system as reconstructed from the memory of the old people, of alterations in this system which gave rise to the structure of present tribal trust lands, of further alterations which produced purchase areas, and finally of irrigation schemes which were created in order to cope with a population explosion in African areas. The detailed analysis of these settlement types in the subsequent chapters of this book elaborates this sketch.

(2) THE TRADITIONAL TRIBAL SYSTEM OF THE KARANGA

An outline of the traditional tribal system, which no longer exists in its past form, is here given to show the origin of modern peasant settlements in Rhodesia. The inheritance of the past is important because the past has shaped the outlook of the people and their values, and any radical departure from traditional practices is likely to cause insecurity and arouse opposition.

During the nineteenth century the country between the Limpopo and Zambezi rivers, known today as Rhodesia, was only thinly occupied by shifting cultivators. Small compact settlements, surrounded by fields, were scattered over the land and wide open spaces between these settlements were used as hunting grounds. Local chiefs were often little more than village headmen and exerted what authority they could over the land surrounding their settlements. Some chiefs controlled several villages and the village headmen who owed allegiance to them were closely related to them. The land farthest away from village settlements was practically no-man's-land and boundaries were only vaguely recognized because people were few and land was plentiful.

With plentiful land resources at the disposal of a small population, people felt no need to claim private ownership over specific tracts of land. The land was vested in the chiefs and as long as a family owed allegiance to a chief, the chief provided it with land to grow crops and herd its cattle. Unless a person committed a public crime, such as witchcraft or treason, and was expelled from the community, he was assured of a share in the tribal arable and grazing land.

Plentiful land resources not only obliterated the need for private ownership, they also created no need for intensive cultivation; and since agricultural surpluses could not be put to any use but had to be given away, people cultivated only small fields of about one acre for each member of the community. Whenever the soil fertility declined, they moved as a group to another area which had not been cultivated for many years.

This system of shifting cultivation was highly suited to the life of the people. The problems of declining soil fertility did not confront them because when the yields of village fields declined, the elders decided on a move, and this decision was the only agricultural regulation the people knew.

The traditional village consisted of an extended family, usually a group of brothers and their dependants, and the chiefdom was a village writ large: ideally all men were related by unilineal descent to each other and to their chief. Consequently the closer men lived to each other, the closer were their kinship ties. In the economic sphere neighbours could be relied upon to join work parties whenever labour requirements exceeded the available family labour because people were not only neighbours to each other but also kinsmen.

In addition to cultivators, traditional communities possessed some part-time craftsmen, skilled in mat making, pottery, iron work and herbalism, who engaged in their specialized crafts in their spare time. Items of their crafts were bartered within the community. There was little incentive for anyone to leave his chiefdom and relatively few new ideas came into the community so that the way of life of the people changed only very slowly.

This brief and simplified account of the past tribal system shows that African cultivators formed self-sufficient communities during the last century with no outside aid either available to them or required. All depended on an exchange of services and equipment within the community. The output per acre was low, but because land was plentiful there was no need to raise the yield. The profit motive was non-existent because there was no use to which a surplus could be put. Since no markets existed, the output per household was geared to meet family requirements, including allowances for beer brewing and some tribute to chiefs. Storage facilities were minimal. Not only did the people produce little; production costs were also low, consisting merely of some seed kept back from the previous harvest, together with family labour or the labour by kinsmen. Since the people lived at subsistence level, differential living standards were unknown.

Africans in Karangaland still hark back to this memory of their past, and at least the traditionalists among them evaluate any changes recommended or enforced by government according to the degree to which they depart from this memory. The greater the departure from the basic traditional values, the greater is the insecurity Africans experience and the greater the opposition with which planned changes are received.

(3) THE MODIFIED TRIBAL SYSTEM

The common form of agriculture in Africa today is still communal land tenure, though under modified tribal systems. Many studies have described how former subsistence cultivators adapted themselves under colonial rule to situations in which authority was partially removed from their traditional leaders and new economic opportunities were opened up outside their tribal economy, causing former subsistence cultivators to engage simultaneously in agriculture and labour migration. Watson's study of the Mambwe in Zambia[1] and van Velsen's study of the Lakeside Tonga in Malawi[2] are examples.

The African population of Rhodesia also adapted itself to political and economic changes. Yet in the colony of Southern Rhodesia, and in Rhodesia at the present, certain factors have operated which did not apply in many other African colonies: Rhodesia has always had a substantial European population which was and still is determined to live in Africa without mixing with the African people. This determination of the white people brought about a division of the land into African and European occupied areas and soon set severe limits to African agricultural expansion. The first factor, therefore, which modified the traditional tribal system in Rhodesia, was the government policy of separate development.

A second factor which modified the traditional way of life was the superimposition on chiefs of civil servants who administered, controlled and modified the rural system in conformity with government regulations. But because government did not abolish traditional rulers these were able to exert a conservative influence which ran counter to that of civil servants.

A third factor is partially the result of the first, partially a result of the introduction of health services into African communities. For with the alienation of land to Europeans and a lowering of the

[1] Watson, 1958.   [2] van Velsen, 1967.

African mortality rate, the population soon increased to such an extent in the greatly reduced tribal areas that the land could no longer support its people under the traditional system of land use. Shifting cultivation had to give way to continuous cultivation and if the people were to be sufficiently fed, continuous cultivation had to be accompanied by soil conservation techniques and modern farming methods unknown to traditional agriculture.

A fourth and most important factor modifying the traditional system was the development in Rhodesia of industry. Townsmen developed large industrial plants which required markets, and in the country unskilled labourers were needed on mines and white-owned farms. As the African agricultural system became less and less capable of meeting the economic needs of the people, needs which expanded through contact with western culture, more and more men left the rural areas for wage employment. Wage employment in turn diversified the skills of the rural population and many Africans learned new crafts, such as building and carpentry; others acquired formal education and became teachers and clerks. Such men could be employed in both town and country and most tried to combine wage employment with agriculture, thus substantially adding to their family income. At times government supported the drift to towns,[1] at times it tried to arrest it through 'influx controls', depending on the state of the national economy.

These four factors, government policy, administrative control of tribal areas, demographic changes and contact with the wider Rhodesian economy set in motion further changes in African agriculture. Government control over natural resources led to the occasional resettlement of local communities and these resettlements affected the composition of villages. Government tried to keep the tribal system intact, but through population movements people often ceased to be related to their chiefs. The number of strangers, that is unrelated men, increased in villages and even whole villages or sections of chiefdoms were moved into the areas of chiefs with whom they had no traditional links. This affected the basic pattern of cooperation in agricultural tasks and kinship bonds were supplemented by bonds of common neighbourhood.

By the mid-twentieth century labour migration withdrew

---

[1] During the first years of European settlement Africans were not interested in wage employment and the British South Africa Company had to impose taxes on them in order to force them out of their villages into European employment.

large numbers of men from their homes, made cooperation beyond the nuclear families essential and traditional work parties increased in importance. But in these broadly based production units agricultural skills remained at a low level because the absence of men, who were responsible for economic planning, prevented, or at least retarded, change.

Change was arrested for other reasons as well. Since tribal trust lands are the direct successors of the traditional tribal system, the farming techniques well adapted to shifting cultivation were carried over into the system of permanent farming. Then, as land became scarce for cultivation, it also became scarce for grazing, and cattle herds had to be reduced in size below the needs of individual peasant households. With the introduction of ploughs, oxen became essential draft animals, and with lowering soil fertility manure became essential for sustained crop production. Shortage of draft animals and manure can be made up by tractor ploughing and artificial fertilisers, yet these require more money than most peasant cultivators possess. Cooperative societies can be formed and used to obtain loans for fertiliser, but few peasants in tribal trust lands are interested in such commercialized credit. They do not fully understand the workings of a commercial credit system and if they have taken out a loan they seldom set aside money to repay it. As a result they are not reckoned credit-worthy in the future.

With little investment in the land production costs are low, and without the obligation to repay credit, peasants are free to sell their surpluses in the open market to the highest bidder. Most families in the tribal areas harvest very small surpluses and these are generally sold to their less successful neighbours. Since few peasant families can live on agriculture alone, most combine it with wage labour.

Membership in a modified tribal system is acquired by birth and the fact of being born in a tribal trust land had in the past given a man a guarantee of being able to cultivate land. But land shortage is now making it impossible to give every tribesman a field to cultivate and this causes increasing insecurity in rural areas, for without land Africans feel 'diminished human beings'.[1]

In this book members of tribal trust lands engaged in agriculture are called peasant cultivators.

[1] This statement, made by a Basutho to Wallman, is equally valid for Africans in Rhodesia. See Wallman, 1969, p. 109.

(4) SYSTEMS OF INDIVIDUAL LAND TENURE

Systems of individual land tenure occur in Africa under two different sets of circumstances. They occur either under intense pressure on land when peasants lay claim to very small acreage and hand these down to their children, such as is done among the Chagga in Tanzania or the Kikuyu and Gishu in Kenya[1]; or they occur when land is not too scarce and enterprising men can clear larger areas to establish their own farms. This happened among the Ndembu,[2] the Plateau Tonga[3] and the Lala[4] in Zambia. In these instances peasant farmers did not buy the land, as is the case in Rhodesia, but their labour and capital investment in the land was recognized by their neighbours as giving them a permanent and individual claim to it. No government intervention ever occurred in these instances which evolved naturally from developing peasant agriculture.

In Rhodesia the situation is very different because individual land tenure among African peasants did not evolve naturally but was brought about by government policy. The purpose of creating purchase areas was to prevent wealthier Africans, who wanted to buy land in the open market on the same basis as Europeans, from doing so if this land was situated in the neighbourhood of European farms. Thus individual land ownership for Africans was introduced in Rhodesia as a means of strengthening the policy of separate development.

Purchase area farms are sufficiently large to guarantee their owners an annual profit. To preserve this potential affluence of African farm owners, government allows no subdivision of their land and keeps the population in purchase areas constant by syphoning off all surplus population to tribal trust lands. Population pressure, so typical of tribal areas, is therefore no problem on the farms.

As government creations purchase areas are administered by civil servants, but democratically elected committees are encouraged to take part in the local administration so that peasant farmers have a say in the running of their communities.

Although farm owners live in the same Rhodesian society as peasant cultivators and have the same labour market outside agriculture open to them, they are prevented from participating in

[1] Allan, 1965, pp. 370 and 373.   [2] Turner, 1957, pp. 10 and 41.
[3] Allan & Gluckman, 1948; Johnson, C. E., 1956.   [4] Long, 1968.

labour migration because of their full-time engagement in agriculture. Consequently their contacts with the wider economy are confined to agricultural transactions: the purchase of farming implements and fertilizer and the sale of their own produce.

Since peasant farmers were selected by government officials for their interest in agriculture and their farming skills, farm owners may be expected to be receptive to modern farming techniques and, having adequate land resources, they could risk adopting innovations. Yet conservative factors counteract these possibilities. Farm owners have spent most of their lives in tribal areas and so bring with them many values and attitudes common to African peasant communities. Few, if any, of them have been born on farms. Consequently their long previous stay in tribal villages often hinders any impulse towards modernization and, having plenty of land at their disposal, they can cultivate it as extensively as their ancestors did in the past. Hence agricultural skills may be greater on the farms than in tribal trust lands, but readiness to change may be only moderate.

New settlement patterns too cause unexpected problems. Farm owners build their individual homesteads in the centre of their farms so that neighbours live far apart from each other and are no longer ready at hand to assist when their help is needed. Moreover, neighbours have their own work to do so that the production unit can no longer be a neighbourhood group but has to be the individual family, supplemented, where need arises, by hired labour.

With larger acreages at their disposal, farm owners can raise larger herds of cattle than tribal people and are therefore adequately provided with draft power and manure. For the purchase of additional artificial fertilizer money is generally available from the sale of surplus crops or through credit offered by cooperative societies.

Marketing is partially free and partially directed by the repayments of loans by means of 'stop-orders' so that compulsory cooperative marketing has become a feature in purchase areas. With economies of scale within their reach, African farm owners should be able to produce large harvests, especially since with private ownership and access to larger financial resources some investment in the land is possible. Because of their security in the land and potentially high incomes, farm owners may be regarded as the best placed section of African peasants in Rhodesia.

Farm owners in purchase areas are referred to in this book as peasant farmers.

(5) IRRIGATION SCHEMES

Irrigation schemes have become a most important means for economic planning in underdeveloped countries. Growing crops under strict control according to tested agricultural techniques should guarantee a large output. Many African countries have experimented with irrigation schemes. Some of the best known are the irrigation scheme in Mwea, Kenya,[1] the Gezira scheme in the Sudan[2] and the Niger project in West Africa.[3] In most African countries irrigation schemes were planned as 'essential bases of an agricultural revolution'.[4] In Rhodesia, irrigation schemes were introduced by government to relieve the rapidly increasing population pressure on tribal lands. Several district commissioners said to me that these schemes were not started to make Africans rich but to prevent social unrest. They must therefore be seen as plans for subsistence, and not as plans for the economic advance of irrigation farmers.

Land set aside for irrigation is taken from tribal trust lands to allow, on small pockets of land, population densities to exceed 2,000 persons per square mile. Unlike the Niger scheme, most Rhodesian irrigation schemes for Africans are relatively small. They are exclusively administered by civil servants and plotholders are discouraged from forming their own authority structures. Irrigation schemes, then, are government administered and admission and expulsion is by civil servants. Plotholders are mainly drawn from landless rural Africans who are offered a living on the condition that they conform to the instructions of the scheme personnel.

The reason for strict supervision on irrigation schemes is the need for high technical competence which few African peasants possess. The working schedules of schemes are tight because on most schemes two crops are grown per season and this can only be achieved by rigid work discipline. Consequently plotholders cannot be absent from their schemes as labour migrants, and so they have no additional income to irrigation farming. Moreover, since all contacts with the wider Rhodesian economy are channelled

[1] Chambers, 1969.   [2] Kamarck, 1967, pp. 121–122.
[3] Dumont, 1966, pp. 53–54.   [4] Dumont, 1966, p. 32.

through the scheme personnel, plotholders are to a large extent encapsulated in their schemes.

The administrators of irrigation schemes demand that plotholders live on, or immediately adjacent to, the irrigated land so that they are always at hand when their work is required. This generally necessitates the separation of nuclear families from their wider kinship groups.

Since irrigation plots allocated to African peasants are small, averaging about three acres per family, most work can be performed by a man and his wife with an occasional hired labourer. Hence cooperation among neighbours is seldom required. If, in addition, part of the work is done by machinery and contract labour, few skills are required of plotholders. This reduces them to unskilled labourers working at the instruction of the scheme personnel. This situation is likely to cause feelings of insecurity among the people similar to those experienced by unskilled labourers in European employment. Like wage labourers, moreover, plotholders are unprepared by their previous tribal farming experience for irrigation farming, and consequently can be expected to be as willing to accept most far-reaching changes in their work situation as are Africans in European employment.

Irrigation schemes are highly capital intensive, more than any other form of agriculture practised in Rhodesia. Commercial credit must therefore be available to plotholders on a large scale; in fact, it must not only be available but must be compulsory, for if plotholders do not invest heavily in the irrigated land, its output will be so low as not to cover production costs. To recover credit, sales are organized by the scheme personnel and as a consequence the freedom of the plotholders to sell their crops to the highest bidder is greatly reduced.

Under intensive cultivation and irrigation, output per acre is very high, especially if cash crops, such as cotton, are grown. However, production costs are also high so that the profit of plotholders may be low. With complete control by civil servants, hard work and low profits, the attraction of irrigation schemes is likely to be very small. Plotholders often regard themselves as the poorest of peasants, and since their tenure depends on their willingness to cooperate with the scheme personnel, they feel insecure. They therefore look with envy at their neighbours in the tribal trust land who enjoy much greater freedom and security.

(6) HYPOTHESIS

This brief sketch of the traditional and modern tribal system in Rhodesia, of purchase areas and irrigation schemes, indicates that four major factors determine the life of African peasant communities.

(i) In all agricultural settlements of African peasants government policy and control play a major role in the social and economic life of the people. It appears that government's ideology of racial segregation is given greater importance than plans to raise the living standards of the African people. Hence government policies for individual settlement types must be carefully examined. If ideological considerations override economic concerns, a settlement type may prove an agricultural failure.

(ii) Participation by the people in the administration of their communities may be an important factor making for satisfaction and a sense of belonging. Where local participation is discouraged, insecurity and a sense of alienation may prove detrimental to economic progress and a full community life.

(iii) Where population densities increase to such an extent that with given methods of production a community can no longer feed itself, people must either adopt new agricultural methods or experience great insecurity. Hence dry land may have to be irrigated or former peasants may be pushed off the land. With adequate land resources pressure for the adoption of new agricultural techniques may be reduced.

(iv) Population pressure may be temporarily relieved by labour migration, or permanently by emigration. If migrants bring back goods or knowledge of the wider society, a peasant community may profit from their absence, and contact with the wider society may cause further changes in peasant settlements. Communities with little contact with the outside world may remain more conservative in their values, and changes may more often be imposed on them by civil servants than sought by the people themselves.

These four major factors give rise to further variations in Rhodesian peasant settlements.

(a) Settlement patterns, determined by government officials, affect the labour supply. Families living on isolated homesteads may experience acute labour shortage which may prevent a full exploitation of their farming land.

(b) Settlers on modern farming schemes are government selected so that men can be chosen who possess the required skills or other personal characteristics.

(c) Output per acre is generally determined by investment. If personal savings or credit is available, or even forced on peasants, agricultural yields may be high.

(d) Readiness to invest will depend on a peasant's break with tradition and acceptance of modern values. If peasants are settled in new communities far away from their tribal homes, changes may be more readily accepted.

(e) Access to markets and freedom to select among potential buyers may create an eagerness to increase output. Controlled marketing may cause apathy.

These suggestions are based on the brief sketch of Rhodesian peasant settlements. They are tested in the following chapters of this book. If they prove true, purchase areas ought to be the most favoured form of settlement among Africans because peasant farmers are allowed greater freedom and initiative than any other type of Rhodesian peasant. Conversely, irrigation schemes ought to be the most disliked because of the extreme control of all economic activities by the scheme personnel. Tribal trust lands ought to occupy an intermediate position.

Potential income should be highest in the purchase areas because of the large acreage at the peasant farmers' disposal. It should be lowest in tribal trust lands because under dry land cultivation small acreages may not suffice to support large families. Plots on irrigation schemes, planned by government to feed small families, ought to provide a meagre though secure income to plotholders if these comply with all the rules of the scheme personnel. If, however, plotholders are negligent or use wrong cultivation methods, they may not only reap low yields but also lose their high investment in the land.

Output per acre should be highest on irrigation schemes because of the intensive cultivation of the wet land. It should be lowest in purchase areas because with adequate land resources and a possible labour shortage no intensive cultivation can be practised. Output per acre should be higher in tribal trust lands than in purchase areas because peasant cultivators must aim at growing their own food, however small their land-holdings are, so that they must either cultivate their land more intensively or starve—or seek a living outside agriculture and so move partly or totally out of the peasant economy.

The final chapter of this book will re-examine these issues, refine this hypothesis and suggest some means of improving peasant agriculture in Rhodesia.

CHAPTER I

EVOLUTION AND REVOLUTION IN AFRICAN AGRICULTURE

(1) 1890–1923: EXPROPRIATION OF AFRICAN LAND

In 1889 the British South Africa Company was granted a Royal Charter to settle in, and administer, the land north of the Limpopo river. In 1890 Cecil Rhodes sent a pioneer column from South Africa, which crossed the Limpopo and established the town of Salisbury, the future capital of the new country.

Immediately after occupation, the company granted large tracts of land to the pioneers and to syndicates without taking into account the distribution of the African population.[1] Within a short time some 15 million acres out of 96 million were given to Europeans.[2] This land alienation, accompanied by harsh administrative practices by company agents, caused bitter frustration among the African people and when in 1893 the pioneers invaded the country of the Ndebele, a tribe living to the west of the newly occupied territory, war broke out. This war was won by the superior weapons of the European settlers and Ndebeleland came under the control of the British South Africa Company.

After the war, in 1894, a Land Commission was set up to find a solution to the conflicting interests of Africans and European settlers in Ndebeleland. The commission recommended that land be set aside for exclusive African occupation. The British South Africa Company accepted this suggestion and allocated to the Ndebele two large tracts of land, the Gwaai and Shangani reserves, which covered an area of over two million acres. But this land was waterless, had never been inhabited by the Ndebele and the Ndebele refused to settle there. The Ndebele homeland on the high veld was declared a European area.[3] This division of land between Europeans and Africans established an important principle which still dominates life in Rhodesia.

The 1894 settlement did not satisfy the Ndebele. They saw in white occupation a threat to their very subsistence and in 1896

[1] Quinton Report, 1960, para 9. [2] Palmer, 1968, p. 6.
[3] Quinton Report 1960, para. 11–12; Palmer, 1968, pp. 11–12.

rose in rebellion and were soon followed by their eastern neighbours, the Shona. Both rebellions were crushed by superior white
force. In 1898 Mashonaland was united with Matabeleland and
the whole country became known as 'Southern Rhodesia', in
honour of Cecil Rhodes. The provisions of the 1894 Order-in-
Council were extended to the whole territory.[1] In addition to the
right of Africans to land in special reserves, the so-called 'Cape
Clause' which had formerly applied to Mashonaland only,[2]
became valid for the whole of Rhodesia. It stated that Africans
had the right to hold or dispose of land on the same conditions as
non-Africans outside the reserved land.

To implement the Order-in-Council, native commissioners,
that is administrative officers placed over the indigenous African
population, were asked to demarcate African areas throughout
Rhodesia. This was a difficult task because native commissioners
did not know what land had been alienated to Europeans. Only a
small section of the alienated land had been used for crop production and ranching; the rest was lying idle and was indistinguish-
able from African land. By 1902 suggestions for reserve boundaries
reached the Executive Council and in 1908 these were approved
by the Colonial Secretary 'with the important reservation that
they were to be regarded as provisional and be subject to possible
further considerations'.[3]

In 1907 a party of the British South Africa Company directors
toured Rhodesia and in 1908 they established an estates department designed to promote European settlement.[4] The estates
department found that it needed more land to promote white
settlement and requested readjustment of the original land distribution, arguing that some reserves were too large and some too
small. These readjustments were to be made for the benefit of the
European, rather than the African community, and the administrative officials were aware of this. One of them, the acting Native
Commissioner of Chilimanzi, wrote: 'Because there are a few
thousand acres of good ground there is no reason why the whole
(Serima) reserve should be thrown open and the natives turned
out of their homes, where they have been living ever since we
occupied the country.'[5]

[1] Quinton Report, 1960, para. 14.
[2] Yudelman, 1964, p. 63. In the old records the indigenous prefixes are added,
so that, e.g. Ndebeleland becomes Matabeleland.
[3] Palmer, 1968, p. 14.   [4] Ibid., p. 18.   [5] Quoted in Palmer, 1968, p. 20.

The aims of the estates department, as well as the African population increase from 500,000 at the turn of the century to an estimated 712,000 in 1913, caused uneasiness in government circles and led to the establishment by the British Government of the Southern Rhodesia Native Reserve Commission in 1914.[1] This commission, however, came under the direct pressure of the estates department. In its final report it suggested numerous alterations to the existing 20·5 million acres of reserve land: it advocated that more than 5·6 million acres be added and slightly less than 6·7 million acres be deducted from the African area, reducing it by about 1·1 million acres.[2] The head of the estates department commented favourably that the commission had 'shown a willingness to meet the view of this Department wherever possible', and that 'the greater part of the land . . . recommended [for inclusion into African reserves] is of inferior quality and therefore more suited for native than for European occupation; further it is hoped that the native reserve land to be returned to the Company will prove of greater extent and superior quality'.[3]

This readjustment of reserve boundaries to the disadvantage of the indigenous population caused apprehension among Africans. Many refused to adopt modern agricultural techniques, recommended since 1911 by some native commissioners,[4] in case good crops would lead to further alienation of African land.[5]

Discontent and bitterness among African peasants increased still more when those Africans, who had continued to live on their ancestral land once it had been alienated to Europeans, were forced off the European farms and told to move into the reserves.

(2) 1923–1941: RIGID SEGREGATION OF AFRICAN AND
EUROPEAN AGRICULTURE

In 1923 Rhodesia was granted responsible government. Company rule came to an end and for the first time the settlers elected their own parliament. With internal self-government, the land question resumed its importance. Many Europeans displayed 'intense

[1] Quinton Report, 1960, para. 16.
[2] Palmer, 1968, p. 26.
[3] Quoted in Palmer, 1968, p. 28.
[4] Cf. *The Native Affairs Committee of Enquiry*, quoted in Floyd, 1959, p. 19. and Palmer, 1968, p. 32.
[5] Palmer, 1968, p. 24.

hatred ... at the idea of Africans buying land in their midst',[1] though by 1925 only nineteen farms, totalling less than 47,000 acres, had been sold to Africans.[2] Europeans desired a complete segregation of African and European areas and pressed for the abolition of the Cape Clause in the early Order-in-Council.

In 1925, therefore, a land commission was appointed under the chairmanship of Morris Carter 'to enquire into ... the expediency and practicability of setting apart defined areas outside the boundaries of Native Reserves (a) within which natives only shall be permitted to acquire ownership of or interest in land and (b) within which only Europeans shall be permitted to acquire ownership.'[3]

Morris Carter, chairman of the commission, had been Chief Justice in Uganda and Tanganyika where he had favoured the development of European plantations and the reduction of African land. Later, in 1932, he headed the Kenya Land Commission which prevented Africans from acquiring land in the White Highlands of Kenya.[4]

The land commission proposed that some 7·5 million acres of land be set aside as native purchase areas and, at the request of the Chief Native Commissioner, recommended that this land adjoin the reserves 'so that the progressiveness of individual landowners could infiltrate into the reserves'.[5] The commission also suggested that well over 17 million acres be reserved for future European purchase, and just less than 17·8 million acres, in remote and tsetse infested areas, be left unassigned for the time being. Only some 88,000 acres were classified as 'semi-neutral areas' where members of either race could purchase land.[6]

The establishment of purchase areas caused many difficulties. Thirteen of the twenty-three native commissioners stationed throughout Southern Rhodesia mentioned that they found it almost impossible to find suitable areas for progressive African peasants since most of the land had already been alienated, and the land which was left was unsuitable for farming. Consequently four million acres of the land finally designated as purchase areas consisted of five large, remote and low-lying areas in the very north and south of the country.[7] This meant that almost 60 per cent of all land set aside for purchase areas was hardly suited to

[1] Palmer, 1968, p. 34.   [2] Ibid., p. 34.   [3] Quinton Report, 1960, para. 24.
[4] Palmer, 1968, p. 41.   [5] Ibid., 35.   [6] Quinton Report, 1960, para 28.
[7] Palmer, 1968, pp. 42–43.

agricultural development because of poor ecological conditions and distances from markets. The planned abolition of the Cape Clause promised to be disadvantageous to African peasant farmers.

The proposals of the Morris Carter Commission were legalized by the Land Apportionment Act in 1931 and this Act became the charter of white Rhodesians. It rigidly segregated the land between Africans and Europeans, thus complying with the desire of European farmers. It classified all African areas as 'scheduled areas' which were especially protected under the constitution.[1] The land distribution under this Act is set out in Table 1.

TABLE I

Land Categories under the Land Apportionment Act[2]

European Area	49,149,174
Native Reserves	21,600,000
Native Purchase Areas	7,464,566
Unassigned Land	17,793,300
Forest Area	590,500
Undetermined Land	88,540
Total	96,686,080

One of the most important aspects of the Land Apportionment Act was the abolition of the Cape Clause and the creation of purchase areas. Under the Act a native land board was established which could sell land in purchase areas to African peasant farmers.[3] But although the native land board had some 7·5 million acres at its disposal, sales proceeded very slowly. By 1938, 552 African peasants had been given farms under the Act; by 1944 their number had increased to 1,785[4]; by the early 1960s one million acres had been given to some 6,500 peasants[5]; and by 1968, 8,410 peasant farmers owned, or were in the process of acquiring some 3,100,000 acres.[6] This slow increase in purchase area farms was due to the unsuitability of much of the land set aside for African purchase, to the work required to survey the land before it could be brought into the market, and also to the fact that much of the land was illegally occupied by Africans living under chiefs in adjacent tribal areas.

[1] Quinton Report, 1960, para 33.
[2] Ibid., para. 48.
[3] Ibid., para 35.
[4] Smith, 1966, p. 15.
[5] Yudelman, 1964, p. 72.
[6] Elkington, 1968, p. 5.

Apart from this land classification, the years between 1923 and 1941 saw various changes in African agriculture. By 1931 the African population of Southern Rhodesia had increased to 1·3 million, that is by 11 per cent, though in the reserves it had increased by 27 per cent due to the large emigration of Africans from European farms.[1] With the plough larger areas were cultivated, though less intensely than they had been under hoe cultivation because only light and cheap ploughs were purchased by African peasants. By 1920 Africans owned some 16,000 ploughs.[2] Consequently land pressure became acute in African areas and soil fertility fell.

In order to raise African agricultural production, the department of native agriculture was established in 1926,[3] and E. D. Alvord, an American Methodist missionary, was appointed as 'Agriculturalist for Instruction of Natives'. He trained the first African agricultural demonstrators and sent them into the reserves to teach African peasants better farming techniques. His aim was to encourage some enterprising Africans to adopt modern farming methods so that, seeing their success, other Africans would follow their example. Yet the African response was exceedingly slow. Many Africans feared that the scheme was designed to test the fertility of African land in order to alienate it to Europeans.[4]

Alvord's demonstrators succeeded in instructing the first African cultivator in 1928. This man applied the new method to one of his 32 acres of land and in 1929 he reaped more from this one acre than from the rest of his land. He was greatly impressed and decided to cultivate in the future less land than he had done in the past, but to cultivate it more intensively. In 1932 he told some 2,300 Africans who had come to attend his 'pre-harvest meeting', how he had achieved his success. Thereafter pre-harvest meetings were held annually and at one such meeting the Chief Native Commissioner and Alvord awarded him a 'master farmer's certificate'.

This success inaugurated the master farmer training scheme which has played an important role in African agriculture ever since, because nearly all the efforts of agriculturists to improve African agriculture have been channelled through it.

The pre-harvest meetings later developed into 'green crop

[1] Palmer, 1968, p. 39.   [2] Smith, 1966, p. 6.
[3] Pendered and von Memerty, 1955, p. 100.   [4] Palmer, 1968, p. 51.

shows' at which Africans, who were adopting modern farming techniques, exhibited their produce.[1]

By 1950, 1,665 Africans had become master farmers, and by 1965 the number had increased to 14,626. Yet these 14,626 farmers represented only 3·2 per cent of all African cultivators, though another 26 per cent had adopted some aspects of modern farming, such as the use of fertilizer.[2]

In 1953 a master farmer's certificate became an essential prerequisite for obtaining a purchase area farm,[3] and remained so until the early 1960s. The issue of a certificate altered the function of master-farmer training which until that time had been aimed at spreading modern techniques in tribal areas. Many of the new men who came forward to obtain a master farmer's certificate did so in order to move out of the reserves. A sample of 286 master farmers in the year 1960 showed that 40 per cent had joined the training scheme to purchase a farm, and only 60 per cent to learn better farming techniques.[4]

The initial efforts to improve African agriculture met with distrust and reluctance by African cultivators, and with opposition from European farmers. These feared African competition for the limited markets of the early 1930s. When Alvord encouraged Africans to grow maize, European farmers loudly complained, and in 1934 the training of agricultural demonstrators was temporarily suspended.[5]

Alvord also tried various other means to improve African agriculture. In 1929 he persuaded a subchief of Selukwe reserve to 'centralize' his arable land[6] and found that this led to great local improvements. In the past cultivated fields had been haphazardly placed in village surroundings and cattle were allowed to graze in between them. This made herding difficult and cattle frequently destroyed crops. In separating grazing from arable land Alvord hoped to safeguard the crops and make herding easier. By 1936, 1·2 million acres had been centralized, by 1938 this figure had doubled,[7] and by 1957 over ten million acres had been centralized.[8] Centralization was generally welcomed by African cultivators because they saw its immediate advantages for cattle herding. However, it deprived their land of manure because centralization increased the distance between the cattle byres and the fields,

[1] Smith, 1966, p. 13.   [2] Ibid., p. 29.   [3] Jordan, 1966, p. 4.
[4] Ibid., p. 9.   [5] Palmer, 1968, p. 51.   [6] Mason, 1960, p. 65.
[7] Palmer, 1968, p. 51.   [8] Floyd, 1959, p. 106.

and few peasants made the effort to cart cattle manure to their
fields.

(3) 1941–1962   AUTHORITARIAN PLANNING OF AFRICAN
AGRICULTURE

With the rigid division of Rhodesia into African and European
areas and the rapidly increasing African population—by 1941
the African population was estimated to be about 1·5 million[1]—
agricultural reform measures became more urgent.

The ever increasing cattle population in African areas also
caused grave concern. The increase in African owned cattle is set
out in Table 2.

TABLE 2

African Owned Cattle in the Reserves

Year	Estimated Number of Cattle[2]
1901	44,000[3]
1911	330,000
1926	1,197,000
1932	1,755,000
1938	1,555,000
1943	1,824,000

The Chief Native Commissioner in his annual reports urged
his staff to persuade African peasants to de-stock, but efforts in
this direction met with little response due to the value placed on
cattle in African life. Investment in cattle is the only form of
saving known to traditional African society. The Natural Resources
Act of 1941 gave statutory powers to administrators to de-stock
areas in which the carrying capacity of the land had been exceeded.
The cumbersome legislation of the Act, however, made its en-
forcement difficult,[4] and by 1943 forty-two out of ninety-two
reserves were found to be overstocked.[5]

[1] *Population Census* 1961, p. 3.
[2] Mason, 1960, pp. 65–66.
[3] *Report of the Advisory Committee*, 1962, Table 55, p. 164. Throughout the
1940s and 1950s the African cattle population remained more or less stationary
at about 1·9 million head.
[4] Holleman, 1969, p. 49.
[5] Smith, 1966, p. 17.

In addition to encouraging de-stocking, native commissioners were ordered to see to soil conservation, water development, physical communication, agricultural extension services, the marketing of grain, and to the resettlement of whole communities. In short, paramount importance was given to increasing African agricultural production.[1]

The real impetus to these measures was given by the Commission on Native Production and Trade in 1944. The commission calculated that under optimum conditions of high rainfall, the practice of crop rotation, the use of manure, and proper marketing facilities, a peasant with six acres and a herd of six head of cattle could reap ten bags per acre and expect a cash return of between £18 and £23[2] per annum after his subsistence needs had been met. The commission admitted that in low rainfall areas several times this acreage would have to be cultivated to obtain the same amount of cash.[3]

Many of the recommendations of this commission were later turned into law. The most important legislation, based on the commission's report, was the Land Husbandry Act of 1952. Mason describes this Act as a tool which 'was to enforce what so far had merely been a matter of persuasion'.[4] The change from persuasion to force was necessitated by the rapid natural increase of the African population which by 1951 was estimated to be 2·3 million.[5]

The purpose of the Land Husbandry Act was 'to provide for the control of the utilization and allocation of land cocupied by Africans and to ensure its efficient use for agricultural purposes; to require Africans to perform labour for conserving natural resources and for promoting good husbandry; and for matters connected with the foregoing'.[6]

The Act regulated the grazing of cattle in African areas and controlled the rights of African peasants to cultivate land in their reserves. Careful planning and large sums of money went into the implementation of the Act which was 'one of the boldest and technically best prepared measures of agrarian reform in Africa'.[7] The tribal areas were surveyed and village units demarcated for both arable and grazing areas. Then individual fields were allocated to those peasants who, under this new legislation, were entitled to land.

---

[1] Holleman, 1969, p. 32.   [2] See Note on p. viii.   [3] Holleman, 1969, p. 51.
[4] Mason, 1960, p. 69.   [5] *Population Census*, 1961, p. 3.
[6] Preamble to the Land Husbandry Act.   [7] Holleman, 1969, p. 66.

This implementation encountered much opposition, especially from those who did not qualify for a land right, for the Act ruled that only those were allowed to farm in African areas who had done so in the previous season. This disqualified many labour migrants. Consequently political agitation prevented the final implementation in many areas and often the agricultural staff had to be satisfied with demarcating the land assigned to whole villages; individual allocation was left to headmen.

In some areas land improvement followed the implementation of the Act; in others opposition was so strong that people refused to cooperate. After ten years of persuasion and force government ceased its attempt to implement the Act in the remaining districts of Rhodesia, and even ignored the non-conformity to its regulations of those peasants who lived in areas in which the Act had already been implemented.

The revolutionary aspect of the Land Husbandry Act is summarized as follows in the Quinton Report: 'The passing of the Native Land Husbandry Act . . . was a landmark in the intensification of African agriculture. . . . Although the Southern Rhodesia Constitution precludes a farmer in a Native Reserve from receiving freehold title to any of the land involved, nevertheless his rights are registered and are negotiable.'[1] The Act, therefore, aimed at a gradual transition from communal to individual land tenure. Land, which in the past had been vested in the chief and allocated by him to individual peasants for the period they lived in his area and needed it, had now come into a market controlled by government officials. Though no 'land' itself was sold, the 'right' to cultivate a particular piece of land could now be purchased for money. By 1963 over 700 'land rights' had changed hands, 442 in the Victoria province alone.[2] This is less than 0·15 per cent of all land rights allocated to African peasants in Rhodesia. Also 'grazing rights', that is the number of animal units a peasant was allowed to graze on communal land, were sold separately from actual livestock. By 1963 their number amounted to 19,600. This is about 1·08 per cent of all grazing rights held by Africans. The price of the right to cultivate one acre of land varied between £4 and £10, and the price for the right to graze one head of cattle varied between £5 and £12.[3]

A circular of the Secretary for Native Affairs set out the

[1] Quinton Report, 1960, para. 56.   [2] Holleman, 1969, p. 333.
[3] Ibid., p. 334.

recommended acreage for peasant cultivators and the number of cattle required for farming above subsistence level according to rainfall regions. Case studies presented in the later chapters of this book fall within the rainfall regions of 25 to 28 inches. The circular states that in such a region a standard holding should include eight acres of land and six animal units, that is six adult head of cattle or their equivalent. It estimated that for every head of cattle some ten to twelve acres of grazing were required.[1]

Another outcome of the Native Production and Trade Commission in 1944 was the passing of the Cooperative Act of 1956. The first four purchase areas registered their cooperative societies in the same year that the Act was passed. Some time later cultivators in the reserve also formed their first cooperative societies. By the end of 1960 twenty-two societies had registered; they had a membership of 1,870 and a share capital of £3,966.[2]

In 1958 a revolving fund, known since 1964 as the Agricultural Loan Fund, was established to grant loans to African peasants. Long-term loans of up to £150 were granted for permanent improvements, and were repayable over ten years at 5 per cent interest; medium-term loans of up to £100 were granted for equipment and livestock, and were repayable over five years at 5 per cent interest; short term loans of up to £25 were granted for fertilizer, seed and other farming expenses, and repayable in one year at ½ per cent interest per month. All purchase area farmers and members of cooperative societies, as well as African peasants in the reserves who had been allocated land under the Land Husbandry Act, were eligible for these loans. By 1961 over £180,000 had been loaned out to African peasants, of which 56 per cent had been given out on short-term loans, 26 per cent on medium-term loans, and 18 per cent on long-term loans. The repayment of loans was sometimes delayed.[3] Only a very tiny fraction of African peasants availed itself of these loan possibilities.

The establishment of cooperative societies and of the Agricultural Loan Fund which made credit available to Africans was something new in Rhodesia and foreshadowed developments which were to take place during the following decade.

---

[1] Quoted in Floyd, 1959, p. 142.
[2] *NAD Form Service Information Sheet* No. 17, 1961.
[3] Johnson, 1964e, p. 214.

(4) 1962–1971: EXPERIMENTS WITH AFRICAN AGRICULTURE

By 1961 the African population was estimated to be 3·8 million,[1] of whom 463,000 were cultivators in tribal areas.[2] African reserves had a population density of some 35 persons per square mile, and purchase areas of 19 persons per square mile.[3] African land was in very poor condition and improvements were urgently required.[4] Throughout the 1960s the Natural Resources Board and other bodies warned about soil erosion and overstocking.[5] They even suggested that reserves were rapidly turning into deserts.[6]

Not only reserves, but also purchase areas caused concern. Purchase area farms varied in size between fifty and a thousand acres, depending on local rainfall, the majority being about 240 acres in area. But few farms, whatever their size, were satisfactorily developed, and only a small proportion of the farm owners had paid the full price of their land. Of 8,110 peasant farmers in 1968, only 2,281 had obtained their title deeds, 2,608 were well on the way to obtaining them, but 3,221 were still on lease agreement.[7] The Director of Conservation and Extension stated that purchase area farmers could be divided into three categories, those with a gross output of over £500, those with a gross output of between £300 and £500, and those with a gross output of below £300. He noted that the latter category was the largest.

Though the Minister of Lands stated that the bar to the advancement of purchase area farmers was not lack of good land but reluctance to make good use of it,[8] the President of the African Farmers Union stated that three-quarters of the purchase area farms given to Africans were uneconomic.[9] Moreover, African peasant farmers claimed to suffer from labour shortage caused by the absence of their sons as labour migrants,[10] for land inspectors did

[1] *Population Census*, 1961, p. 3.

[2] Smith, 1966, p. 29.

[3] Mitchell, J. C. 1962 *The Sociological Background to Agricultural Development*. Unpublished paper, Dept of Sociology, University College of Rhodesia & Nyasaland. (Roneo.)

[4] In 1972 (August 10th) *The Rhodesian Herald* reported that only 15 per cent of all tribal land was designated as arable. The tremendous demands on such limited agricultural land makes improvement almost impossible.

[5] e.g. *The Sunday Mail* 22.10.1967; *The Rhodesia Herald* 7.2.68, 1.3.68, 16.5.68.

[6] *The Rhodesia Herald*, 23.10.69.

[7] *Ibid.*, 10.10.68.　　　　　　　　　[8] *Ibid.*, 10.10.68

[9] *Ibid.*, 21.9.67.　　　　　　　　　[10] *Ibid.*, 22.9.67.

not allow grown-up children to build their own homesteads on their fathers' farms but ordered them to leave their parents to prevent the subdivision of farms into smaller and smaller units.

After the research for this book had been concluded, a new blow struck African farmers when in 1972 the administration of purchase areas was handed over to the Ministry of Internal Affairs. This ministry stated that the intention behind the transfer was not to leave purchase areas 'out of the current and planned development of the whole African area'[1] but African farmers saw the situation differently. In 1970 they had been assured by the Minister of Agriculture that they would stay with his ministry, and they had applauded him. Now they were greatly disturbed. They had 'pulled themselves some way towards the individualism on which the cash economy is based'[2] and now feared to be pushed back into tribalism. They also deplored a 'divided authority', since they foresaw that the district commissioner's development plans—and he was to be responsible for the administration—might differ from those of the agricultural experts on whose technical advice and help they depended.

With African agricultural output still at a low ebb after many years of authoritarian control, government realized that it had failed to improve African agriculture through force. Consequently the Land Husbandry Act was officially abandoned in 1962,[3] after some £17 million had been spent on its implementation.[4] Freedom for experimentation was now granted to a variety of bodies.

This new era was ushered in by a reorganization of African administration. African agriculture, till then part of the Native Affairs department, was set up as the new Ministry of Agriculture which in 1963 amalgamated with the European service. The Native Affairs department itself became the Ministry of Internal Affairs. Reserves were renamed tribal trust lands, and native commissioners were called district commissioners. The separation of African agriculture and administration continued until 1969, when both branches were again united, and control over African agriculture passed to district commissioners.[5] The seven years of independence saw a diversification of agricultural activities, and

---

[1] *Rhodesia Herald*, 22.6.1972.
[2] *Ibid.*, 23.6.1972.
[3] Departmental Circular 309; cf. Holleman, 1969, p. 220.
[4] Smith, 1966, p. 24.
[5] Secretary for Internal Affairs (S.I.A.), 1970, p. 1.

the reincorporation of agriculture with administration was greatly
regretted by agricultural extension workers and African peasants
alike.[1]

(a) Extension Advice by Agriculturalists

Because of the growing population pressure in many tribal
trust lands, government undertook land reclamation in formerly
uninhabitable areas. In the Gokwe district for example, which
was dry and infested with tsetse fly, government built roads and
sank boreholes, and made efforts to eliminate the fly. As soon as
water was provided, even before the fly was eliminated, it encouraged African peasants to settle. Between 1963 and 1968 some
80,000 Africans arrived in Gokwe. Agriculturalists showed them
how to grow cotton, and in 1968 they sold crops worth £1 million.[2]

Freed from the control of administrators, agriculturalists
intensified their research, and as soon as possible passed on their
findings to African peasants. They persuaded them to adopt non-
traditional crops, especially Turkish tobacco and cotton. In 1967
two hundred farmers in the Gatooma district produced cotton
worth £16,800.[3] By 1968 their number had increased to 500, and
they produced cotton to the value of £24,000.[4]

Successes were especially conspicuous in animal husbandry.
Agriculturalists encouraged Africans to stall feed their cattle, an
entirely new idea to African peasants. The scheme caught on first in
the Victoria province in 1963, when two farmers fattened thirteen
head of cattle which they sold to the Cold Storage Commission
for good prices. In 1965 Africans sold 800 fattened cattle to the
Cold Storage Commission, and in 1967 they sold 5,490 head. During
the 1968–69 season, the Secretary for Agriculture estimated that
some 8,000 head of cattle were fattened in African areas, 3,600
of them in the Victoria province alone.[5] The scheme became
popular because of the high prices fetched for stall-fed cattle.
Whereas the average price for an ox sold in a tribal trust land was

---

[1] Cf. for example *The Sunday Mail* 11.5.69, 6.4.69, 29.6.69; *The Rhodesia
Herald* 11.3.69, 14.3.69, 1.5.69, 8.5.69, 12.9.69. On July 8th, 1971, *The Rhodesia
Herald* reported: 'the vacuum left by the withdrawal of Conex in 1969 had not
been filled. The present agricultural service of the Ministry of Internal Affairs
was decidedly inferior to that of the old Department of Native Agriculture in
1963.'

[2] S.I.A., 1969, p. 1.

[3] S.I.A., 1969, p. 3.

[4] S.I.A., 1969, p. 2.

[5] Secretary for Agriculture, 1970, p. 50.

said to be about £10, the fattened cattle were reported to bring in on the average some £60. They required additional feeding costing £7, and therefore showed a profit of about £43 per beast.[1]

Agriculturalists recorded another success by spreading interest in young farmers clubs which were first formed in 1960. In 1962 there existed 25 clubs in the whole of Rhodesia, by 1969 they numbered over 300 and had a membership of about 10,000 African youths.[2] Eighty-seven per cent of the clubs operated in the Victoria province. The Young Farmers Club constitution pledges its members to cooperate with any body engaged in agriculture in order to further farming interests. In 1966 an agricultural expert stated that the clubs had made a great contribution to improved peasant farming.[3]

Not only agriculturalists, but also Christian missionaries showed interest in improved peasant farming. The Catholic church began holding annual harvest festivals for the Association of Young Farmers and Natural Resources Clubs. In 1970 the Mashonaland branch held this festival in the Catholic cathedral in Salisbury, where it received a broad press coverage.[4]

(b) Credit Facilities

Of greater importance than support for young farmers clubs was the Catholic church's endeavour to make credit facilities available to African peasants. A missionary was sent to America to study experiments with credit unions in economically poor communities. On his return in 1963 he started a savings club with twenty Africans who promised to contribute at least three pennies a week. That year the club held £3. By 1970, 75 such clubs had been established throughout Rhodesia. They had a membership of about 4,000 and held savings of £50,000.[5]

By 1965 the first two of these clubs became credit unions. By 1970 their number had increased to thirteen. These had a

---

[1] *The Rhodesia Herald* 27.10.66, 24.2.67; *The Sunday Mail* 6.4.69. The average price of £10 per beast in a tribal trust land seems to be a low estimate by *The Rhodesia Herald*. My own observation is that the average price is nearer to £15. Also £60 as the average price for a head of fattened cattle seems rather high. Most seem to be sold at about £42. This reduces the average profit recorded by the press to about £20, but is still a great gain.

[2] *The Sunday Mail*, 6.4.69.

[3] Smith, 1966, p. 33.

[4] *The Rhodesia Herald*, 19.7.70.

[5] Credit Union National Council, p. 3.

membership of 1,746 and a share capital of £40,769.[1] Credit unions only allow peasants to draw money for expenditure considered worthwhile by the union. Preference is given to the purchase of seed, fertilizer, and capital equipment, especially ploughs,[2] though money may also be drawn to pay school fees and bridewealth.[3]

Since many people regard lack of capital as the major obstacle to intensive peasant farming, civil servants and other Rhodesians too tried to make money available to Africans. Agriculturalists laid special emphasis on the cooperative movement and by 1965 there existed 169 African cooperative societies: 44 in the purchase areas, 112 in tribal trust lands and 13 in other areas, mainly on irrigation schemes.[4] By 1969 there were 267 cooperative societies: 55 in purchase areas, 190 in tribal trust lands, 20 on irrigation schemes and two on mission lands.[5] Cooperative societies not only sold the surplus crops of their members; through their control of the African Loan Fund they also made loans available to their members. Until 1969 the administration of loans became one of their most important functions.

In areas where no cooperative societies were formed, 'district loan committees' were set up to provide money for African peasants from the African Loan Fund. By 1965, 160 such committees were created.[6]

By the mid 1960s the African Loan Fund had become popular for a short time. It had increased the ceiling of its loans: purchase area farmers could obtain short-term loans of up to £50 at 7 per cent interest, medium-term loans of up to £200 at $7\frac{1}{4}$ per cent interest, and long-term loans of up to £300 also at $7\frac{1}{4}$ per cent interest. Tribal trust land peasants could obtain short-term loans of up to £35 at 7 per cent interest and medium-term loans of up to £100 at $7\frac{1}{4}$ per cent interest, but no long-term loans.[7] With the extension of loan facilities however, serious problems of repayment arose. By 1965 there were 9,500 peasants in arrears with a total of

---

[1] Weinzierl, 1970, p. 10 and S.I.A., 1970, p. 31.

[2] By 1966 some three-quarters of all African cultivators owned their own ploughs. Smith, 1966, p. 29.

[3] Weinzierl, 1970, p. 6.

[4] Smith, 1966, p. 26.

[5] S.I.A., 1970, p. 31. By 1971 the number of Cooperative Societies in tribal trust lands had increased to 226. *The Rhodesia Herald*, 14.7.71.

[6] Smith, 1966, p. 27.

[7] Thorpe, 1968, p. 3.

£60,194 and by 1967, 13,943 peasants were in arrears with £236,031.[1]

To prevent further evasions of loan repayment the Ministry of Internal Affairs decided in 1969 to brand the cattle of African peasants who took out loans. Africans strongly objected to this security measure because they feared that the brand would make government the owner of their herds. Consequently only 21 per cent of all peasants who had taken out loans in 1968 did so in 1969, and the total money paid out in loans dropped from £233,000 to £48,965.[2] The boycott of the loan fund greatly reduced the input of fertilizer; in some purchase areas crop yields fell by 75 per cent.[3]

In addition to the African Loan Fund of the government, a commercial finance company, called the 'African Loan and Development Company', also made loans available to Africans in purchase areas, especially in regions with higher rainfall.[4] Some money was also lent to Africans in tribal trust lands. The company was formed in 1961 and began lending money in 1962. The demand made on the company by African peasants grew rapidly from 270 peasants who obtained £14,000 during the 1964–65 season to 900 who obtained £140,000 during the 1967–68 season. The company noted that with its financial help for seed and fertilizer, African peasants were able to increase their agricultural output fourfold.[5] In 1967 the company made headlines in the press when it reported that one peasant, who with financial assistance from the company had irrigated half an acre of land to grow tomatoes, had made a profit on that half acre of £185.[6] Yet like the government, this commercial company too encountered difficulties when Africans failed to repay their loans, and during the 1970–71 season it only handed out £110,000 to 650 African peasants.[7]

(c) Assistance by European Farmers

Help was also forthcoming from individual European farmers who lived close to African areas. In 1962 some of these expressed concern at the low yield of their African neighbours on land which they thought could bring as high a return as their own.

[1] Ibid., p. 4.
[2] S.I.A., 1970, pp. 18, .33, 28.5
[3] The Rhodesia Herald.70.
[4] Kirkpatrick, 1968, p. 23.
[5] Ibid., pp. 24–25.
[6] The Rhodesia Herald, 19.8.67.
[7] Ibid., 21.4.71.

They discussed the matter first among themselves, and then with the African peasants.[1] By 1964 some 31 Africans promised to co-operate, and the 'African Farming Development' company was founded. The 31 Africans cultivated between themselves 212 acres and in 1965 made an average profit of £170 each. The next year 64 peasants joined the scheme and in the 1967–68 season 202. By then the interested peasants had become too numerous to be assisted on a voluntary basis and a general manager was employed. In the first year of the scheme the profit of the members was much higher than that of other peasants. For whereas the average peasant family had a total agricultural income of some £50 in a year of average rainfall,[2] in 1964–65 the average peasant on the scheme made a profit of £170. But in the 1965–66 season each made a profit of only some £60, during the 1966–67 season of a mere £6, and during 1967–68 £37.[3] These exceptionally low returns were the result of successive drought seasons so that participants hardly regained the money they had invested in the land. Nevertheless, the crop failures caused great discouragement and even disillusionment.

Peasants who joined the African Farming Development company were expected to pay all expenses except administrative costs which were paid by donations from commerce and industry.[4] But just as credit schemes ran into difficulties so did the African Farming Development company. It closed down in 1969 when, after several successive drought years, its members owed it £40,000.

Help was also given to African peasants through the Natural Resources Board and European intensive conservation area committees.[5] From 1958 onwards the Natural Resources Board had encouraged purchase area peasants to establish agricultural committees which would perform functions similar to those of the intensive conservation area committees in European farming areas. By 1960 government agreed that proper intensive conservation area committees could be established in purchase areas, and by 1966 seventy-five such committees existed.[6] Intensive conservation

---

[1] The scheme is known as the 'Stanning Scheme', after the European farmer who initiated it.
[2] *The Rhodesia Herald*, 23.3.67.
[3] African Farming Development, 1968a
[4] Smith, 1969, p. 10.
[5] Intensive conservation area committees are formed by neighbouring farmers determined to conserve the soil in their area.
[6] Natural Resources Board, 1968.

area committees were often founded at the encouragement of neighbouring European farmers who willingly gave their advice,[1] and the twenty-fifth annual report of the Natural Resources Board praised such 'farmer to farmer' contact.[2] In 1968, 31 European intensive conservation area committees assisted Africans in neighbouring tribal trust lands.[3]

After the regimentation of agriculture in the preceding decade, such a variety of agricultural enterprises in African areas surprised both Europeans and Africans. The schemes initiated by enthusiastic Europeans outside the civil service, however, were able to reach only relatively small numbers of Africans. Government legislation was still required to channel efforts to improve the vast areas cultivated by peasants in tribal areas. Government decided that agricultural improvements in tribal trust lands should be brought about under the guidance of African chiefs.

(d) New Legislation: The Tribal Trust Land Act

The implementation of the Land Husbandry Act came to a standstill in 1962. In that year chiefs were for the first time allowed to allocate to their followers small fields in grazing areas. Chiefs made immediate use of this right and by the end of 1962 had allocated about 92,000 acres to some 20,000 followers. During 1963 they allocated about 84,000 more acres to a further 16,000 followers.[4] Several district commissioners expressed great concern at the reduction of grazing land.[5]

After these experiments, several Acts were passed in parliament. In 1967 the Tribal Trust Land Act became law. In contrast to the Land Husbandry Act it recognized the traditional tenurial system and returned to chiefs and other tribal leaders a large measure of control over the land. A deputy secretary for the Ministry of Internal Affairs stated that 'through the Tribal Trust Land Act government relinquishes its direct control over Tribal Trust land, restores traditional powers to traditional leaders and clothes them with legal authority'.[6]

The Act provided for the establishment of tribal land authorities,

---

[1] Holleman, 1969, p. 197.
[2] Natural Resources Board, 1966, p. 20.
[3] Personal communication by the Director of Lands, Salisbury, 26th June 1968, ref. G/207/8.
[4] S.I.A., 1963, p. 8.
[5] Ibid., p. 11.
[6] Howman, 1967, p. 15.

each consisting of the local chief and his advisers. A government circular stated that through these tribal land authorities 'we are seeking to build up a corporate body, not a one-man-show in the person of Chief or Headman'.[1]

The Tribal Trust Land Act laid down no definite rules concerning the composition of tribal land authorities, but expected that in each area local custom would decide who should serve on this body. Tribal land authorities had two important duties: to allocate land to the people and to see to soil conservation.

To assist tribal leaders in this task, chiefs were called for courses at agricultural training centres and taught how to face this new responsibility. The first course was given in September 1964. In particular the chiefs were told to consult the agricultural staff as to whether the land they wanted to allocate was suitable for ploughing, and not to allow any land to be ploughed before it was protected by contour ridges. Many chiefs accepted this advice and decided to employ peggers trained by agricultural civil servants, who would 'peg the fields' of new cultivators.[2] This was a revolutionary breakthrough after many years of opposition to modern farming techniques by tribal leaders. These peggers were especially successfully employed in the Victoria province.[3] In 1967 the Secretary for Internal Affairs reported that millions of acres of arable land had been protected by African village communities.[4]

A second channel for advice was opened to chiefs through conservation committees. Tribal land authorities were recommended to establish such committees to assist them to 'promote a greater consciousness by the people of the need for conservation', and 'to stimulate enthusiasm and joined action in the achievement of this purpose'.[5] The tribal land authorities were to decide who should serve on these committees. The first nine conservation committees were established that same year and associated with the Natural Resources Board.[6] By 1968 their number had increased to 23.

Though chiefs had for many years requested that they be allowed to allocate land to their followers, many soon realized

[1] Circular 1972, 1966, para. 3a.
[2] *Chiefs Conservation Conference*, Alvord Institute, 1965, JDJ/AVS/JB.
[3] S.I.A., 1969, p. 3.
[4] S.I.A., 1968, p. 2.
[5] Natural Resources Board, 1966, p. 19.
[6] Staunton, 1967, para. 14.

that they had been handed over 'a situation so complex and potentially explosive that the European authorities themselves had despaired of solving it'.[1] Consequently not all chiefs took a responsible attitude towards their land. Holleman reports 'exultant acts of deliberate disregard for the elementary lessons on soil conservation and wanton destruction of trees'.[2] The reaction of chiefs and people depended partly on the number of landless persons in a chiefdom, partly on the existence of boundary disputes between tribal groups and partly on the people's previous experience with government officials. In areas where land was very scarce and where cooperation between Africans and European civil servants had been strained, such destruction was frequent; it was less common in areas where land was more or less adequate and where officials had laid emphasis on good relationships with the people.

(e) Irrigation Schemes

While the Tribal Trust Land Act sought to regulate land use in African chiefdoms, the Tribal Trust Land (Control of Irrigation Schemes) Regulation Act of 1967[3] sought to regulate land and water use on African irrigation schemes.

Some African land has been irrigated in Rhodesia ever since 1931 when Alvord tried to relieve African food shortage in the Sabi valley during a year of severe drought. At first Africans were reluctant to settle on his scheme, though they were impressed by its yield of maize, beans and wheat, because their chief feared that should the scheme prosper Europeans might take the land from them. Yet when 1932 proved to be another drought year, people overcame their reluctance and settled on the irrigated land. In that year 230 irrigated acres were cultivated by African peasants, and by 1934, 513 acres.[4]

Interest in irrigation spread very slowly, and by 1965 only

---

[1] Holleman, 1969, p. 333.

[2] *Ibid.*, p. 335.

[3] From 1961 onwards all Rhodesian constitutions made provisions for African irrigation schemes. The 1961 constitution mentioned briefly the possibility of irrigated land in African areas (para. 47). The 1965 constitution gave more extended consideration to African irrigation. The 1969 constitution, taking into account the recommendation of the *Sadie Report* in 1967, which strongly recommended irrigation schemes in African areas (Sadie, 1967, 2.4.3. and 2.4.5.), treated extensively with African irrigation schemes (para. 43–44).

[4] Smith, 1966, p. 11.

some 5,700 irrigated acres were cultivated by some 1,700 Africans.[1]
By this time, however, a change had taken place in government
policy. The constant growth of the African population—the 1969
population census enumerated 4·8 million Africans, of whom
60 per cent were living in tribal trust lands[2]—and unemployment
in the cash economy[3] as a consequence of economic sanctions
following the unilateral declaration of independence of Rhodesia
from Great Britain, forced government to seek for some means of
settling heavy populations on comparatively small acreages.[4]
Consequently government spent some £800,000 annually on
African irrigation,[5] and irrigation schemes increased rapidly
both in acreage and in number. By 1968 there were fifty African
irrigation schemes in Rhodesia covering 9,300 acres,[6] and by
1969 there were sixty irrigation schemes covering 14,000 acres.[7]
These sixty schemes supported an African population of 70,000
people.[8] Adding to the irrigated land a half-acre plot for each
family's homestead, the population density on these schemes is
about 2,200 persons per square mile, a fantastically high population
density for Rhodesia.

Though irrigation schemes have increased in number, they
have not yet become popular with Africans,[9] and most of the
schemes have vacant plots. The reasons are various. Chief among
them are the lease conditions which lay many burdens on plotholders, but grant them few rights.

As soon as the land is irrigated, it is transferred from the control
of chiefs to the control of district commissioners, for agricultural

---

[1] *Ibid.*, p. 29.

[2] 1969 Census, Preliminary Results, Part IV, p. 1. By the end of that year
Africans were estimated to number more than 4·9 million. S.I.A., 1970, p. 15.

[3] Whereas in 1961 nearly 17 per cent of the African population was working
in the cash economy, by 1970 their ratio had fallen to 14 per cent. *The Rhodesia
Herald*, 16.7.71.

[4] The Ministry of Internal Affairs, quoted in *The Rhodesia Herald*, 25.4.69.
In 1971 the Deputy Secretary for Internal Affairs stated: 'Our policy is to place
as many people on as little land as possible where they can make a very good
living. Our average allocation is two acres.' *The Rhodesia Herald*, 14.7.71.

[5] *The Rhodesia Herald*, 25.4.69.

[6] *Ibid.*, 12.10.68.

[7] Many extensions of African irrigation schemes are planned. The Chisumbanje
scheme on the Sabi river alone is seen as the forerunner of a 120,000 acre
scheme on which Africans are expected to cultivate plots varying between 3
and 20 acres in size. *Sabi-Limpopo Authority*, 1970, p. 26.

[8] *The Rhodesia Herald*, 2.12.69.

[9] African suspicion of irrigation schemes was again recorded by the S.I.A. in
1970. S.I.A., 1970, p. 26.

supervision of irrigation schemes passed from the Ministry of Agriculture to the Ministry of Internal Affairs long before African agriculture itself was returned to these administrators.

Civil servants of the Ministry of Internal Affairs have great authority over Africans in irrigation schemes. In 1968 the Secretary of Internal Affairs reported that the Irrigation Act was 'designed to provide the district commissioners with the necessary legal power to ensure that all irrigation schemes are properly farmed by plotholders. The regulations also require all plotholders to enter into an agreement of lease and to pay a water rate which, after two years of occupation, will rise to a maximum of £14 per acre per annum for all-the-year-round irrigation. As a general rule each plotholder will be allocated an irrigation plot of two acres, as experience has shown that the average family cannot cope with a larger plot.'[1]

Two years later still greater powers were given to these civil servants, because in 1970 the Land Tenure (Suspension of Irrigation) Regulations was passed which enabled provincial commissioners at any time 'to order the immediate vacation of an irrigable area' or 'the suspension of the water to an irrigable area', if a breakdown of discipline or widespread resistance to the authority of the district commissioner occurred, or for 'any other reason which the provincial commissioner considers to be good and sufficient'.[2] As a consequence African plotholders felt very insecure on irrigation schemes.

Opposition to lease conditions has been strongest in areas with long established irrigation schemes where people had farmed irrigated land in the past without being burdened by the new regulations. On six irrigation schemes in the Sabi valley people refused to sign leases which would make them dependent on the instructions of the district commissioner. They claimed that their fathers had themselves built the irrigation channels with the help of Alvord in the 1930s, and that they would not live on their self-built schemes on sufferance.[3] As a consequence of their opposition the Ministry of Internal Affairs cut off the water supply.[4]

Apart from such opposition, difficulties arise from technical

[1] S.I.A., 1968, p. 5.
[2] Land Tenure (Suspension of Irrigation) Regulation, 1970, 3 (1).
[3] The Shield, 1969, pp. 13–14.
[4] The Rhodesia Herald, 26.9.68.

shortcomings of the schemes and wrong agricultural advice. In the
Beit Bridge area, for example, schemes experienced water shortage
when the sand extraction schemes in the Limpopo river failed to
pump up enough water.[1]

(f) Private European Enterprise in African Areas

A further attempt to increase the economic productivity from
African areas was made in 1968 when the Tribal Trust Land
Development Corporation Act was passed. This Act aimed at
developing tribal trust lands with European capital under European
management, but with African cooperation whenever possible.

The Act seems to be a result of the efforts of the Associated
Chambers of Commerce of Rhodesia to introduce private enterprise into African areas in order to stimulate production and so to
increase the internal market for consumer goods.[2] Though an
official of the Ministry of Internal Affairs saw a 'social snag' in
this plan,[3] the Associated Chamber of Commerce prepared a
large research programme.[4]

The Tribal Trust Land Development Corporation Act states
that the 'objects of the Corporation shall be to plan, promote,
assist and carry out in all spheres, for the benefit of the inhabitants
of the tribal trust land, the development in the tribal trust land of
its natural resources and of industries and any other undertaking'.[5]
To achieve this objective, the corporation is to exercise its powers
in implementing a project solely 'on its economic merits irrespective
of other considerations'.[6] Africans were allowed to become shareholders in the corporation and it was envisaged that those, who
at first would be tenants of the corporation, would in time become
shareholders. The corporation also aimed at bringing work into
African areas in order to stop the flow of African labour migrants
into towns.[7]

This Act, which won the approval of some industrialists,[8] was
soon severely criticized for exploiting African peasants and turning
them into 'helots' in the very areas which had been reserved for

[1] S.I.A., 1968, p. 5.
[2] The Rhodesia Herald, 5.7.69, 27.6.69.
[3] Ibid., 6.7.69.
[4] Ibid., 1.2.68., 27.4.69.
[5] Tribal Trust Land Development Corporation Act, para. 4.
[6] Ibid., para. 5.
[7] The Rhodesia Herald, 10.10.69.
[8] The Rhodesia Herald, 21.3.69.

their protection.[1] The corporation ignored criticisms and embarked on several projects, including three factories,[2] a tea estate, an irrigation project[3] and a large ranching enterprise. The latter would turn all the peasants of the tribal trust land into tenants and so prevent them from cultivating their own land.[4]

The Corporation was attacked from all sides. Europeans championing the cause of Africans, saw in it a forerunner of borderland industries according to the South African pattern. Other Europeans concerned about their economic leadership in Rhodesia, saw in it a threat to their own position.[5] In 1971 the chairman of the corporation had to reassure Europeans that all care was taken not to develop Africans in a way which could have harmful effects on Europeans.[6] Even civil servants seemed sceptical of the corporation's aims.[7] With so much opposition from most varied quarters, it seems doubtful whether private European enterprise will succeed in developing African areas.

(g) Current Legislation

The last Act passed in the 1960s which affects African agriculture, was the Land Tenure Act of 1969. It reinforced most of the previous legislation. It declared that in African areas African interests were to be dominant, and in European areas European interests. The Act reinforced the division of land between the races in Rhodesia, first legalized in the Land Apportionment Act of 1931, and made this division still more absolute. The 1969 constitution of Rhodesia fixed African land at 45·2 million acres, European land at 44·9 million acres, and left 6·4 million acres as national land.[8]

The Land Tenure Act also replaced the Tribal Trust Land Act[9] by incorporating its content. It stated that no African may reside in a tribal trust land without the permission of the tribal land authority,[10] and regulated for the establishment of tribal land

[1] *Ibid.*, 7.3.69.
[2] *The Rhodesia Herald*, 4.9.69., 21.1.70, 30.5.70, 17.9.70, 22.9.70.
[3] *The Rhodesia Herald*, 25.2.71.
[4] *Ibid.*, 2.7.69.
[5] *The Rhodesia Herald*, 25.6.70.
[6] Statement made by the chairman of the Corporation at the Chichester Club in Salisbury, 1971.
[7] *The Rhodesia Herald*, 8.1.70, 10.9.70.
[8] 1969 Constitution, para. 73.
[9] Land Tenure Act, para. 55.
[10] *Ibid.*, para. 39.

authorities.[1] It also made provision for the introduction of in-dividual land tenure in tribal trust areas if the peasants desired it.[2] The Land Tenure Act also incorporated the rulings of the Tribal Trust Land (Control of Irrigation Schemes) Regulation Act.[3] Finally it ruled that the African Development Fund become the new African Production and Marketing Development Fund. It regulated in detail how this fund is to be operated.[4]

The Land Tenure Act stands at the end of a decade in which many experiments were made in African agriculture and binds to-gether its most important trends. Whether this Act will lead to a new rigidity and prevent further experimentation remains yet to be seen.

CONCLUSION

In spite of the many experiments by a variety of interested Rhodesians to improve African agriculture, African peasants seem to fight a losing battle. In 1971 the chairman of the agri-cultural marketing authority declared that African agriculture made an ever smaller contribution towards the national economy. Whereas in 1954 African agricultural output was valued to be worth 45 per cent of European agricultural production, in 1969 it was valued at only 37 per cent of the European figure, and whereas in 1954 African peasants sold 30 per cent of their produce, in 1969 they sold only 19 per cent.[5]

Low output is the result of poor and still deteriorating lands. At the end of the rainy season in 1971 the agricultural editor of *The Rhodesia Herald* observed, 'At a time when the Rhodesian countryside should be covered with a carpet of luxuriant grazing to see the national herd through the approaching seven-month dry season, vast areas of tribal trust land present a picture of desolation, with hardly a blade of grass showing on veld grazed at the rate of one animal to two acres instead of one to 20 or more acres.'[6] Many cattle died of starvation, causing an annual loss of

[1] *Ibid.*, para. 47–51.
[2] *Ibid.*, para. 43–44.
[3] *Ibid.*, para. 45.
[4] *Ibid.*, para. 52.
[5] *The Sunday Mail*, 14.3.71.
[6] *The Rhodesia Herald*, 19.3.71. On August 10th, 1972, the same newspaper reported that over the past ten years 500,000 head of cattle had been lost because of poor grazing in the tribal areas, and that only 2 per cent of all grazing land was covered by veld management schemes.

millions of pounds to the Rhodesian economy. The Minister of Internal Affairs expressed the hope in parliament that African peasants had learned a lesson and would in the future voluntarily de-stock their herd.[1] In spite of the depressing evidence of deteriorating soils the Minister prophesied 'a prosperous and progressive future'[2] for Rhodesia's tribal areas.

But his was a lone voice of hope. The president of the African trade unions congress expressed an opinion shared by many Rhodesians who are concerned about African agriculture when he contended that 'the Government was not keen on developing agriculture in tribal areas. It looked upon them as reserve lands where the unemployed and retired Africans would return.' He claimed that the tribal trust lands had largely been allowed to deteriorate, and held the government and its agricultural policy responsible for low productivity of Rhodesia's peasant agriculture[3].

The case studies of various peasant communities presented in this book will examine the factors determining productivity. It is hoped that these studies will help towards a more objective evaluation of Rhodesia's peasant problems than is currently given by politicians.

---

[1] *The Rhodesia Herald*, 3.3.71.

[2] *Ibid.*, 18.3.71.

[3] *Ibid.*, 20.3.71. In July that year the prime minister himself admitted that the 'drought-stricken areas of Rhodesia's tribal trust lands were deteriorating into near desert conditions', though 'with the introduction of the Land Tenure Act, responsibility for the tribal trust lands had been placed squarely where it belonged—on the people, represented by the tribal land authorities.' *The Rhodesia Herald*, 8.7.71.

PART I

PEASANT COMMUNITIES IN THE TRIBAL AREAS OF KARANGALAND

CHAPTER 2

GOVERNMENT POLICY AND ADMINISTRATIVE CONTROL IN TRIBAL AREAS

(1) GOVERNMENT POLICY AND ITS EFFECT ON TRIBAL TRUST LAND COMMUNITIES

The previous chapter showed how since their first settlement in Rhodesia Europeans have tried to avoid living close to Africans, and how their wish for exclusive racial blocks of land was granted in 1931 when government passed the Land Apportionment Act. This chapter shows first the effects which this policy had on several communities in the centre of Karangaland, one of the most populous districts of Rhodesia, and then describes the administrative system through which African tribal areas are controlled.

(a) Land Alienation in Karangaland

Karangaland extends between the towns of Enkeldoorn and Gwelo in the north and the Lundi river in the south, and covers some 14,400 square miles, that is 10 per cent of the total land surface of Rhodesia.[1] In 1969 it was inhabited by some 1,072,000 Africans, or 22 per cent of the total indigenous population; by 25,830 Europeans, or 11 per cent of all Europeans in Rhodesia; and by 2,549, or 11 per cent of all Rhodesia's Asian and Coloured people.[2] Karangaland, therefore, is twice as densely populated by Africans as the rest of Rhodesia, and the ratio of Africans to Europeans, Asians and Coloureds is also twice as high.

Yet in spite of this high population density, much of the land has been alienated from the Karanga for European settlement. The extent of this alienation can be seen from the case histories of

---

[1] It extends into two administrative provinces, the Midlands and the Victoria provinces. Victoria is the province in which African peasant agriculture has progressed more than in any other region of Rhodesia.

[2] Calculated from the 1969 Census.

the tribal trust land communities studied in this book. The Shiri-Ngara tribal trust land consists of two chiefdoms, Shiri (Bird) and Ngara (Crocodile). At the turn of the century chief Ngara controlled a vast stretch of land, extending 55 miles to the north east of his present territory. He himself and many of his subjects lived outside their present tribal trust land boundaries in several large villages. They cultivated small plots of land and used the remaining land for hunting. When in 1902 the European government fixed the tribal boundaries, it set aside an area of some 255 square miles for chief Ngara and his people. The chief and many of his followers moved into this land. By 1914 chief Ngara ruled over 12,202 followers who lived inside his chiefdom, but 4,431 of his people still lived on European land. During the following decades most of these were moved into Ngara chiefdom so that in the late 1960s chief Ngara ruled over some 18,100 people. Ngara chiefdom, therefore, had a population density of 71 persons per square mile. This figure, however, overestimates the land at the people's disposal because 30 to 40 per cent of the chiefdom consists of rocky outcrops and swampy depressions and is therefore unsuitable for cultivation and grazing. Hence the effective population density is 108 persons per square mile. Never before in their history had the Ngara people been forced to live so densely together and to wrest a living from so little land. Their traditional farming techniques have proved quite inadequate to grow enough food for their subsistence needs.

Chief Shiri's chiefdom in the same tribal trust land is in a still greater plight. In the 1930s government moved a whole chiefdom, whose land had been declared European farm land, into Shiri's territory, and in 1956 government declared a piece of land adjoining Shiri chiefdom a purchase area and told the people who lived there to move elsewhere. Since they had not been offered a new home, most moved into Shiri chiefdom to live with their friends and relatives. Hence Shiri chiefdom had in the 1960s the high population density of 148 persons per square mile. Twenty per cent of the land, moreover, was wasteland so that the effective population density was 177 persons per square mile.

The Shiri-Ngara tribal trust land is surrounded by large European farms and ranches whose owners use only about 10 per cent of the land for crop production or grazing. The tribesmen, therefore, have the frustrating experience of seeing large areas of unused land in the European area which they are unable to use to grow food for their families. This frustration is aggravated by the knowledge that this land had once been theirs.

The second tribal trust land, Shoko, consists of several chiefdoms, one of which has two communities, Shoko Murewa and Shoko Museamwa. Shoko chiefdom suffered a similar loss of land as had the Shiri and Ngara chiefdoms. The ancestors of the Shoko people had been living on the land currently occupied by two mining towns, one commercial town and the interspersed European farm land. In 1905 only 3,272 of the Shoko people lived within their newly allocated tribal areas; over a thousand continued to live on land classified as European. When in the 1930s this land was sold to European farmers, the Africans were evicted. Many moved into the Shoko Museamwa community. In the 1960s Shoko tribal trust land had an overall population density of 67 persons per square mile. Yet little of the land was suitable for farming. Only 10 per cent of the land in the Shoko Murewa section can be cultivated, and only 24 per cent of the land in the Shoko Museamwa section. Part of the remaining land is used for grazing, but much has to be written off as wasteland because it consists of a large mountain range of bare rocks.

These two tribal trust lands are typical of the other tribal trust lands in Karangaland. Their loss of land shows that Karanga chiefdoms have suffered greatly from the official policy of separating African and European farming areas.

(b) The Ecological Environment of Peasant Communities

The effects of land alienation must also be evaluated against the ecological environment of peasant communities. Both tribal trust lands lie in a relatively low rainfall area: the Shiri-Ngara chiefdoms have an average annual rainfall of some 23 to 25 inches; rainfall in the Shoko Murewa area is slightly higher and in the Shoko Museamwa area slightly lower. According to the assessment of the officers who administered the Land Husbandry Act, peasants in these communities should have some eight acres of land to plough and some six head of cattle to graze on some 80 to 100 acres. Such large holdings, however, are seldom available. Because both tribal trust lands are subject to dry spells, they are classified as regions suitable only for grazing and drought resistant crops. Hence crop cultivation is hazardous and crop failure frequent. Moreover, the soils are often poor. The Shiri-Ngara tribal trust land has sandy soil and in the Shoko Murewa area the soil is very acid and poor; only the Shoko Museamwa people have a fertile black alkaline loam soil which, if rains are adequate, can produce a rich harvest.

The annual mean temperature in the Shiri-Ngara tribal trust land is just below 70 degrees Fahrenheit, and the annual mean temperature in Shoko just above 70 degrees. The climate in both areas is therefore healthy, but the people suffer from bilharzia contracted in the rivers and from various internal diseases. Many children suffer from malnutrition. Thus the people are physically weak and often cannot work long hours on a strenuous agricultural task.

The neighbours of the Ngara people are all European farmers, mostly Afrikaaners from South Africa, and few of them desire any contact with their African neighbours. The neighbours of the Shiri people are either European farmers or African peasant farmers in purchase areas. Neither group is in need of the staple crops grown by African peasant cultivators, and this deprives those who are able to produce a surplus of a local market. The nearest towns are some 70 miles distant from the tribal trust land.

The Shoko chiefdom is more favourably situated. Though also surrounded by European farms, it lies only 15 miles from the nearest town. This town is the provincial capital and therefore both the economic and political centre of the people. The town itself has a European population of 2,530 and an Asian and Coloured population of 350 persons. A separate township, which adjoins the European section, accommodates some 8,470 Africans.[1] These, as well as the Europeans, Asians and Coloureds, provide the people in the tribal trust land with a ready market for eggs, milk, fruit and vegetables. In the rural district around this provincial town live a further 1,650 Europeans. This larger non-African settlement in the immediate neighbourhood of Shoko chiefdom also provides the people with employment opportunities, and many peasants engage in part-time work on European farms while cultivating their own land. Several European farm owners have established personal ties with the tribal people and there is an exchange of services between Africans and Europeans, for unlike the European neighbours of the people in the Shiri-Ngara tribal trust land, who use most of their land for ranching, European farmers near Shoko chiefdom grow food crops and so need more farm labour.

[1] Calculated from the 1969 Census.

(c) Consequences of Reduced Living Space in Tribal Areas

The government policy of racial segregation of African and European farming communities in Rhodesia has reserved large tracts of land for white farmers and ranchers, only a small proportion of which is productively used. Great expansion and development of European owned land is therefore possible. But in the tribal areas the policy is causing economic hardships.

In recent years the effects of overpopulation in some tribal trust lands has caused concern to government. In an attempt to alleviate this problem, government has moved people from both the Shiri-Ngara and Shoko districts to new resettlement areas. In the mid-1960s, the Shiri-Ngara chiefdoms lost some 2,100 persons to Gokwe, a district along the northern boundary of Karangaland, and in 1956 the Shoko Museamwa community had whole villages resettled in Shangaan territory south of Karangaland.

Still greater numbers of tribesmen have tried to overcome rural poverty by temporary emigration to urban centres where they earn money to supplement their income from peasant agriculture. These labour trips temporarily break down the geographical barrier between Africans and Europeans. The extent and the effects of labour migration will be dealt with in the next chapter.

Population pressure in tribal trust lands also necessitated far-reaching changes in peasant agriculture, changes which could only be brought about by agricultural reforms initiated by government itself. These changes are also discussed in the next chapter. The aim of this chapter is merely to outline government policy and the bureaucratic system under which tribal trust lands are administered.

(2) ADMINISTRATIVE CONTROL IN TRIBAL TRUST LANDS

Tribal trust lands are administered both by traditional leaders and by civil servants. The former, always Africans, form part of the patriarchal system, the latter, predominantly European, form part of a bureaucracy. Only in the lower ranks of the civil service are Africans employed. Both patriarchal leaders and bureaucrats play an important role in the lives of Karanga peasants.

(a) Traditional Rulers

The largest local unit within which the lives of the Karanga revolve is the tribal trust land. Tribal trust lands are European creations and only occasionally have an African leader to whom all the people owe allegiance, for most tribal trust lands consist of several chiefdoms and each chiefdom has its own chief. At times neighbouring chiefdoms in the same tribal trust land are bound to each other by kinship ties. The rulers of the Shiri and Ngara chiefdoms, for example, regard each other as relatives since the first chief Shiri married two daughters of chief Ngara and so became his son-in-law. The relationship of son-in-law to father-in-law has been inherited by subsequent Shiri and Ngara chiefs and with it the subordination of the 'junior kinsman' to his 'senior'. Where such traditional alliances have been established, one chief becomes the 'great chief' in the tribal trust land and weighty matters are referred to him. As a result, the whole tribal trust land becomes a close-knit community.

For many people the tribal trust land is their social universe. This can be seen from a marriage analysis: of 700 marriages contracted by men in the Shiri-Ngara and Shoko tribal trust lands, 510 or 73 per cent of all husbands had found spouses in the same tribal trust land, 164 or 23 per cent in other Karanga areas, and only 26 or 4 per cent outside Karangaland.

The tribal trust land, then, is the largest social unit, but the chiefdom is the largest political unit which has a traditional leader. Chiefdoms are often divided into subchiefdoms. Chiefs and subchiefs must be officially recognized by the Rhodesian government, they must cooperate with civil servants and in return for their services they are paid a monthly salary. Most subchiefs tend to be classificatory brothers of the chief and candidates for the chieftainship when this position falls vacant. Some subchiefs are more distantly related, or they may not be related at all. For example, the stranger chief who in the 1930s was moved into Shiri chiefdom became a subchief under chief Shiri. In Ngara chiefdom, which has four subchiefdoms, one subchief is related to chief Ngara as his sister's son. This subchief Hove (Fish), is a progressive man and the community of Ngara chiefdom, analysed in this book, centres around subchief Hove's village.

In addition to these officially recognized tribal leaders there are men who are honoured as subchiefs by their own people but who lack government recognition. These leaders of large sections of a chiefdom often wield great influence. Shoko chiefdom is not officially divided into subchiefdoms, but the Museamwa community has chosen its own leader and acts as if it were a subchief-dom with some regional autonomy. Chief Shoko, who resides in the Murewa section of the chiefdom, does not recognize this bid for partial independence and intervenes at times when the Museamwa leader tries court cases or allocates land, for land allocation and the hearing of court cases are the two most important tasks of chiefs and subchiefs.

Village headmen occupy the lowest rank among traditional rulers. They tend to be leaders of kinship groups that form the largest section in any one village. It is said that in the past all village headmen were related to their chief or subchief, but today many headmen are unrelated to their chief because they have been moved into the area by European civil servants. Of the 31 village headmen in the Shoko Museamwa community, only 18 or 58 per cent are related to their leader, and of the 132 village headmen in Shiri chiefdom, only 45 or 34 per cent are related to their chief. In the past a man could only become a village headman if he was recognized as such by his chief. Today he needs in addition to the chief's recognition government approval. He has to carry out orders from civil servants and in return he received for many years a percentage of the tax he collected from his villagers.

Whereas in the past the village equalled an extended family, and the chiefdom was a village writ large, today a chiefdom is a territorial unit which includes many unrelated people. A government survey of 1956 showed that less than 40 per cent of all men in the Shoko Museamwa community and less than 10 per cent of all men in Shiri chiefdom were agnates of their chiefs, that is, related to them by blood in the male line.

The percentage of strangers in villages is lower than in chiefdoms. Of my own sample of 1,843 adults in 39 villages, 69 per cent were agnates of their village headmen, 22 per cent were in-laws, and only 9 per cent were strangers. Most of these strangers were personal friends of headmen who had been invited by them to live in the village. This shows that kinship still plays an important role in village composition, and that it is more frequent to find unrelated villages in a chiefdom than strangers in a village. This has important consequences for agricultural work units, many of which are still to a large extent made up of kinsmen.

Chiefs, subchiefs and village headmen continue to exert a great influence among their people. As guardians of the patriarchal system they value the traditional way of life and are often sceptical of innovations, especially since few of them have received much formal education.[1]

(b) Civil Servants

The administrative control of civil servants is superimposed on the traditional political structure. In many aspects of rural life, civil servants are more powerful than traditional rulers, and the outward sign of the chief's dependence on modern bureaucrats is the salaries which they draw from the administration.

The civil servants working in tribal trust lands belong to various government ministries, the most important of which is the Ministry of Internal Affairs. Rhodesia is divided into seven administrative provinces[2] whose senior administrators, the provincial commissioners, are directly responsible to the Secretary for Internal Affairs. Provinces are divided into districts, and local district commissioners form the backbone of rural administration. District commissioners are the direct government representatives to African peasants.

District commissioners are feared by Africans because of their great power. Though district commissioners spend most of their working hours with Africans in their offices or in the tribal trust lands, they remain remote authority figures, do not mix socially with the people, and generally insist on an elaborate etiquette on the part of Africans who come to them with their problems.[3]

Though the power of district commissioners is great, their personal influence is often small because district commissioners are frequently transferred from one district to another. Continuity of administration is provided by an African staff, the district commissioner's sergeants, corporals and messengers. These junior civil servants are mostly drawn from the local people and are familiar with the events of the district. District commissioners rely to a large extent on the advice of these assistants and peasants turn to them to intercede with the district commissioner when they need a permit or a certificate. With kinship ties to the people and ready access to the administrator, these junior civil servants can play an important role in local administration.

Apart from African messengers, corporals and sergeants, district commissioners are assisted by a staff of Europeans with

---

[1] For further information on chiefs see Weinrich, 1971, pp. 59–60.

[2] In 1974 an eighth province was created.

[3] For further information on district commissioners and other civil servants see Weinrich, 1973.

technical knowledge. Closest to district commissioners are primary development officers. These men are employed by the Ministry of Internal Affairs and are directly responsible to the district commissioner for the construction of roads and bridges, and for other development works.

Up to 1962, and again from 1969 onwards, district commissioners also controlled the work of technical officers responsible for African agriculture. Between 1962 and 1969 African agriculture was amalgamated with European agriculture and agricultural extension officers were responsible to the Ministry of Agriculture. Freed from the supervision of administrators, extension officers soon registered their first successes in peasant agriculture. It was during this time that most developments in African farming took place, and it was also during this time that most of the research published in this book was carried out. Most extension officers are Europeans, though in Karangaland some Africans have been appointed to this post.[1]

Extension officers live closer to the African people than do district commissioners. They occasionally mix with them at local beer drinks and some go out of their way to be accepted by them. As a result, extension officers have a more direct and intimate knowledge of peasant life than district commissioners, and peasants feel free to approach them for advice.

Every extension officer heads a team of junior African helpers, consisting of an extension supervisor and several extension assistants. These men have undergone several years of training in agriculture and advise peasants in their work with crops, cattle and soil conservation. When government policy places emphasis on mechanical soil conservation, virtually unqualified helpers, called peggers, may be employed for strictly circumscribed tasks. Peggers, for example, were employed in the Shiri-Ngara tribal trust land during the implementation of the Land Husbandry Act to supervise the construction of conservation works, and in the late 1960s peggers were employed by chief Shoko to peg contour ridges in the new fields he allocated in former grazing land.

The previous chapter repeatedly referred to successful agricultural schemes in the Victoria province which includes most of Karangaland. The success of agricultural ventures in this region is due to the work of the Alvord Institute at Makoholi where

[1] For further information on extension officers, see Weinrich, 1973, chapters 2–4.

indefatigable members of the extension staff are running courses for all who are engaged in peasant agriculture, for civil servants as well as for African peasants. When chiefs were given back the right to allocate land, the Alvord Institute ran the first courses for chiefs on soil conservation. Young farmers clubs received a vital stimulus through this Institute, and through the initiative of its staff the cattle fattening scheme spread rapidly throughout the province.

Even during the 1960s, however, African agricultural development suffered from a serious drawback. Though the technical assistance was given by extension officers, the financial administration of peasant agriculture remained with district commissioners. District commissioners controlled and still control the African Development Fund which is derived from levies made on all African cattle sales and major grain crops marketed through government controlled agencies, together with government subsidies. District commissioners channel this money into tribal trust land development and allocate it to projects which they judge to be most important. For many years cattle dipping has been subsidized from this fund. Also the work of primary development officers is financed by these levies. Moreover, district commissioners control the loans available to African peasants through the Agricultural Loan Fund and are responsible for the repayment of these loans. If the money set aside for peasant development had been controlled by the extension staff, progress might have been still greater and more coordinated.

The strict control over peasant agriculture by district commissioners may be one reason for the slow development. For district commissioners are administrators, and administrators are not necessarily suited to direct development plans.

With the return in 1969 of peasant agriculture to the Ministry of Internal Affairs, the district commissioners' tasks increased in complexity, and too many services depended on them to be handled efficiently. It may be suggested that bureaucracy itself, because it moves so slowly, is a major factor of non-development in African areas.

Apart from district commissioners' complex duties, these civil servants failed to win the people's confidence partly because they are representatives of a government with whom the people cannot easily identify, and partly because of the social distance the district commissioners interpose between themselves and the people.

Aloofness hinders communication, and though communication barriers are a problem in all bureaucracies, they are especially great in the tribal situation where the administrators belong to the race of a ruling minority which emphasizes its distance from the African people.

(c) Consequences of a Dual Authority Structure in Tribal Trust Lands

This outline of traditional patriarchal and modern bureaucratic control reveals few contacts between the two administrative systems. Traditional rulers have to be approved by government and have to carry out the orders of civil servants if they want to remain in office. But apart from a minimum conformity to the requirements of European civil servants, chiefs, subchiefs and village headmen remain very much a part of their own people. Few come forward of their own accord to implement new government policies: for example, no chief in the Shiri-Ngara and Shoko tribal trust lands formed a conservation committee, as government had recommended when it handed back to chiefs the power to allocate land. African chiefs are also socially separated from senior civil servants because of their race, and take it for granted that their values are not those of the Europeans. As guardians of the traditional way of life they are even less likely than some of their progressive subjects to venture the adoption of technological innovations and modern values.

Senior civil servants, for their part, are outsiders to peasant communities, and the higher their rank, the more remote they are from the people. They can give orders and advice, but they find it hard, if not impossible, to understand the motives and fears of peasants from a totally alien culture. If civil servants do not even make an attempt to understand, communication may be impossible. The ideal mediators in this situation should be the junior civil servants. Too little is known about the role they actually play and further research is urgently required to explore their function in promoting or blocking understanding and communication between African peasants and European civil servants.

Between 1962 and 1969 extension officers directly contacted African peasants. Since 1969, when district commissioners resumed control over development work, most plans have been channelled through tribal leaders. This has both advantages and disadvantages. Since chiefs are dependent on the administration for office, they can be put under pressure to cooperate. But since the sentiments of tribal leaders are much closer to those of their people than to those of European civil servants, the people's reluctance to accept modern farming techniques is shared by their chiefs. For example, the peasants' demand for more land rather than for modern farming techniques, seems meaningful to chiefs who, like their subjects, see the empty stretches of European owned land next to their over-crowded tribal trust lands; but to civil servants such demands are contrary to law, and therefore not even deserving of consideration.

Moreover, patriarchial and bureaucratic values clash in the persons of chiefs. For traditional rulers are closely enmeshed in a local power game and cannot act as impartially in their administrative duties as can civil servants. District commissioners have no kinsmen in the tribal trust lands who ask them for favours, and so find it hard to understand the pressures bearing down on African chiefs.

With these basic differences in outlook and approach, the dual administration of tribal areas becomes a handicap for development. Chiefs and people do not necessarily agree that what civil servants suggest is best, and they definitely do not always want to cooperate. This is shown by the lack of cooperation when government recommends, but does not enforce, certain administrative or agricultural practices.

CHAPTER 3

FORCED AND VOLUNTARY ADJUSTMENT TO LAND SHORTAGE IN TRIBAL AREAS

(I) LAND SHORTAGE AND THE DUAL ECONOMY

(a) *Population Increase*

Land shortage in tribal areas is not only due to land alienation to white settlers. It is also caused by a steady growth of the African population. This population growth would not have been as fast during the twentieth century as it has been, had Europeans not provided Africans with modern health services. In Shiri chiefdoms, for example, Catholic missionaries built a large hospital which in 1966–67 treated 4,113 inpatients and 7,944 outpatients. In Ngara chiefdom government runs one clinic, a second clinic is run by Catholic missionaries, and subchief Hove recently built his own small clinic in his subchiefdom. The people of Shoko chiefdom have easy access to a large Protestant hospital just outside their chiefdom. The health of all the tribesmen is therefore adequately looked after.

As a result of these medical services, the life expectancy of the people is rising, the death rate is declining and the infant mortality rate has fallen rapidly. But no drop has occurred in the birth rate. In 1967 the two tribal trust lands had a replacement rate of 2·3. This means that for every person then living there will be more than two in the next generation. Forty-three per cent of all the people were 15 years and younger. Through natural increase alone, therefore, the population of these tribal areas will double in twenty years time. This rapid population increase has even more serious consequences for the people than land alienation, for whereas land alienation to Europeans took place once and for all, population growth still continues and there are as yet no indications that it will abate.

This rapid population growth has had its effects on the economic and political life of the people. As the old men reserve to themselves the control over the little land available for cultivation, the young, who have just founded their own families, remain landless. But landless men have little status and no stake in the tribal system. They are therefore predisposed to leave their home areas to earn a living elsewhere.

The close relationship between age and the right to cultivate land is shown by the following figures. Whereas in the Shiri-Ngara and Shoko tribal trust lands, 47·1 per cent of all men are landless, only 5·5 per cent of the men aged 45 years and above have no land, but of the men who are 30 years and younger, 80·7 per cent are landless.[1] This means that the more energetic and enterprising men, who could effectively develop peasant agriculture, are forced to leave rural areas. Thus land shortage does not lead to the most capable men gaining control over the land. It rather brings about a concentration of land in the hands of an ageing peasantry whose interests lie in the past.

(b) Labour Migration

One attempt at overcoming land shortage is through labour migration. Almost all Africans in the Shiri-Ngara and Shoko tribal trust lands have worked for several years in European employment. Most of them found work in the towns, some in mines and a few on European farms. At any one time, some 43 per cent of all men and some 14 per cent of all women are absent from their villages; the men are away in search of work, and the women either accompany their husbands or, if they are still unmarried, seek work of their own. A husband, who has found a good job and accommodation, often takes his wife with him to town, and sometimes also his children.

Labour migration has great effects on the age-sex composition of villages. Very few men between the ages of 20 and 45 years are living with their families in the rural areas. Only a small proportion of them have taken their wives with them to towns; most leave their wives and children at home so that two to three times as many women as men in the 20 to 45 years age group live in villages. Migrants entrust the cultivation of their fields to their wives so that peasant agriculture draws its labour force predominantly from women and old men.

Some labour migrants continue to make short contributions to agriculture. Their contributions vary with the length of their labour trips. Of 1,538 labour trips to town by 902 men, 272 trips,

[1] See Appendix, Table 38.

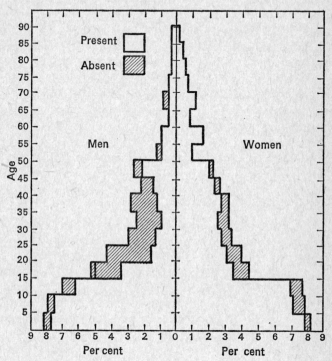

Fig. 1. Population pyramid of two tribal trust land populations

or 18 per cent, lasted only a few months. These trips were under-
taken after harvesting time, mainly from July to October, when
peasant cultivators found little work in their villages and went out
to earn money for their families. These trips neither handicap nor
help peasant agriculture, for these men are traditional in their
outlook and not interested in modern farming techniques; they
have no education and are only looking for unskilled jobs. Even
if they stayed at home, few of them would prepare their fields for
the next season.

More important for peasant farming is the absence of men who
plan labour trips lasting one to three years at a time. Of all trips,
696 or 45 per cent, last this length. These men generally plan their
absences from the village with their brothers so that when one
man goes to town, his brother stays at home to assist his wife on
the land. In return, the first migrant stays at home when his
brother seeks wage employment. In this way the extended families
of peasant cultivators are always supplied with both food and
money. These men, who work in both peasant agriculture and
industry, are the most typical representatives of Rhodesia's dual
economy and they constitute the largest section of all economically
active Karanga.

Of all labour trips 570, or 37 per cent, last four years or longer.
Many of these migrants have received several years of formal
education and succeeded in obtaining jobs which are well paid in
the context of the tribal economy. Only a few of them have land
in the rural areas and none contributes labour to peasant agriculture. Nevertheless, these men still visit their villages regularly and
often leave their wives in the country because they know that in
their old age they will have to leave the towns and settle in their
tribal trust lands. For this reason they send gifts in money and
kind to their kinsmen and so contribute to the upkeep of villagers.

Labour migration, then, plays a dual role in the rural economy:
it removes for shorter or longer periods large sections of the
people from the land and so relieves the land shortage and need for
food; it also injects money into the rural economy from the earnings of labour migrants with which additional food can be bought
as well as other consumer goods. Cash earnings from labour
migration provide most families with the necessary money to pay
taxes and school fees, for the average Karanga, who finds wage
employment with Europeans, sends some £20 a year to his
family in either cash or kind. Because of this cash income, peasants

expect little more from agriculture than to provide them with food.

Apart from its positive functions, however, labour migration has some serious negative effects on the rural economy: by withdrawing the most active and enterprising young men from their villages, it leaves peasant agriculture in the hands of the old and traditionally orientated tribesmen. Hence little progress, and only a very slow adoption of modern farming techniques, can be expected.

(c) Education, the Basis of a Successful Dual Economy

That labour migration makes a significant financial contribution to the rural economy of the Shiri-Ngara and Shoko tribal trust lands has become possible through the work of Christian missionaries. Missionaries of the various denominations aimed primarily at converting the Karanga to the Christian religion, but found that the most effective way of doing this was to teach them reading and writing, and to familiarize them in general with western culture. Hence most missions have laid great emphasis on education so that religious affiliation, education and success in the modern cash economy tends to be correlated.

Though African education is controlled by a government ministry which pays a large percentage of the teachers' salaries and supervises the curricula and teaching, all the schools in the Shiri-Ngara and Shoko tribal trust lands have been built by Christian missionaries and their people.

Education is unevenly distributed between men and women, young and old. Girls attend school less frequently than boys, and whereas 38 per cent of all men in the two tribal trust lands have attended school for six years or more, only 13 per cent of all the women have done so. People who attended school for less than five years are generally illiterate. They cannot read newspapers and booklets, and so cannot be reached by literature explaining better farming methods. Eight per cent of all men and 3 per cent of all women have received some secondary schooling. Some of these well-educated people still cultivate their fields, though often in addition to other work. Most of these are teachers who, because of their high status in the community and their ability to finance experiments, become innovators in peasant agriculture. Most of the educated people, however, leave the tribal trust lands and find permanent jobs in towns.

The more educated people are, the younger they tend to be,

and the younger a man is, the less likely he is to have a field of his own. Thus only 40 per cent of all men aged 15–19 have received less than six years schooling, against 91 per cent of all men aged 45 years and over; and as many as 13 per cent of the younger men received a secondary education while only 3 per cent of the older men did so. When, therefore, the young and strong people seek urban employment, the country loses also its most intelligent and best trained men and women and so remains with the residue of those who have failed to master the new skills offered by education.

The missionaries have become aware of this selective migration and the consequent deterioration of peasant agriculture. Different denominations have adopted different methods of improving rural living standards. Since in any one area of Karangaland one Christian denomination tends to be dominant, such different church policies can be demonstrated. In the sub-chiefdom of Hove, 93 per cent of all adults are Catholics and in Shiri chiefdom, 86 per cent. In the Shoko Murewa community 50 per cent of the people are members of the African Reformed church and in the Shoko Museamwa community 44 per cent of all adults are Seventh Day Adventists. The rest belong to other Christian denominations or are traditionalists.

Reformed missionaries show least interest in the economic welfare of their people, though they encourage them to thriftiness. Seventh Day Adventist pastors frequently stress in their sermons that material wealth is a sign of God's favour and an assurance of entrance into heaven. Hence many peasants in the Shoko Museamwa community work hard in their fields and the community as a whole has more master farmers than any of its neighbouring communities.

For a long time Catholic missionaries showed little interest in agriculture. A change occurred in the 1960s when a new generation of missionaries came to Rhodesia who, influenced by a new awareness in the Catholic church of social problems, thought that they had a social and economic, as well as a religious mission. When they saw that the soil was deteriorating and the people reaping constantly less from their land, they began actively to encourage modern farming techniques. They organized credit unions for adults and also youth clubs to teach boys and girls skills to improve their homes and the fields of their parents. In 1963 the Catholic missionaries in the Shiri-Ngara tribal trust land formulated the motto: 'Better fields, better homes, better hearts.'

From then onwards many missionaries cooperated with the government's extension staff.

(d) The Dual Economy in Tribal Trust Lands

Karanga peasant communities not only draw on agriculture at home and on wage employment in European areas, but some of their members combine both activities simultaneously, for paid employment is also available in tribal trust lands. The most widespread and most profitable rural occupation with a high income is that of teaching. African primary schools are scattered over all tribal trust lands and local teachers form the most affluent section of peasant communities since they earn salaries of some £250 a year. Some women also earn good salaries as nurses at hospitals or clinics, but far fewer nursing posts are available than teaching positions. Some men are employed as junior civil servants in the Ministry of Internal Affairs, and they too receive regular salaries, although these are only between £50 and £199 a year. In a budget study of 172 peasant cultivators in the Shiri-Ngara and Shoko tribal trust lands, 19 families, or 11 per cent of all peasant households, received regular salaries. White-collar workers, who belong to the most educated section of the rural population, make therefore a considerable financial contribution to the village economy.

Apart from white-collar workers, some Africans are self-employed, either as businessmen or as craftsmen. Craftsmen have little formal education. After completing a few years of primary schooling, they acquired their practical skills in building, carpentry, tailoring or blacksmith work at mission stations. Income from crafts is very sporadic. Once a year a builder may be asked to build a house for a teacher or a store for a businessman, and so earn some £40. Since opportunities to ply a craft in the rural areas are so few, many craftsmen alternate between self-employment and labour migration.

In addition to the new crafts learned at mission stations, some peasants still engage in the traditional crafts of mat making, basket making, and pottery. Income from these crafts seldom exceeds £8 a year. The average herbalist or diviner may earn some £10 to £30 annually. Of the 172 peasant cultivators in my sample, 12 or 7 per cent earned some money from their crafts. Income from crafts, therefore, contributes little to peasant earnings.

The following Table lists the occupations of men in my census of the Shiri-Ngara and Shoko tribal trust lands.

TABLE 3

Occupations of Men in Two Tribal Trust Lands (N=902)

Occupation	Frequency	Percentage
Peasant cultivators	420	46·6
Unskilled labourers	294	32·6
Skilled labourers and craftsmen	76	8·4
Business men	23	2·6
White-collar workers	89	9·8
Total	902	100·0

At the time of the census, all men classified as peasant cultivators were in their villages cultivating the land. Almost all unskilled labourers were away in European employment; only a few were employed at nearby missions. Had the census been taken a few months earlier or later, many men classified as peasant cultivators might have been absent in town, and many classified as unskilled labourers might have been at home cultivating their fields, for men in these two categories always alternate between urban employment and peasant agriculture. Skilled labourers and craftsmen are partly absent from, partly living in, their home villages. Most businessmen live in the tribal trust lands, and of the white-collar workers about two thirds live in their home areas, the rest in towns.[1] This occupational distribution shows that most men draw their income from both peasant agriculture and wage employment, and that the tribal trust land economy has indeed a dual base. Land shortage is the major reason for the peasants' engagement in the wider economy, and the education provided by missionaries helps capable Karanga to take advantage of new economic opportunities outside their tribal trust lands. Labour migration therefore can be seen as a partly voluntary adjustment to land shortage because government officials no longer force people to leave their tribal areas as they did in the past. The force which today drives men out of their villages is economic necessity.

[1] The budget census of 163 families on which the analysis of chapter 5 is based, includes 18 white-collar workers, or 11 per cent. This is slightly more than the percentage of white-collar workers in the larger census.

(2) LAND SHORTAGE AND ENFORCED AGRICULTURAL REFORM

(a) Centralization

As the African population grew and could obtain no new land outside the recently fixed tribal boundaries, shifting cultivation became impossible and the same lands had to be cultivated year after year without a fallow period. As a result soil fertility quickly declined and erosion set in. To stem soil deterioration, government decided to implement a 'centralization' policy which Alvord had first advocated in 1927. Centralization has been one of the few government policies which met with little opposition from African peasants because they immediately saw the advantages it brought them, and most cooperated willingly.

This centralization policy seldom caused difficulties and was especially smoothly implemented in Shiri chiefdom in the 1940s, where only 20 per cent of the land was unsuitable for agriculture, where rivers were flanked by good grazing land, and where whole blocks of arable land could be separated by lines of villages from grazing areas. In Ngara chiefdom, too, people cooperated. Though much of the land had very shallow top soil so that grazing land could not be confined to river beds but had to be placed wherever cultivation was impossible, sufficiently large arable blocks could still be set aside, and as in Shiri chiefdom, so here too, people could live in villages which were close both to their fields and to the grazing land.

As soon as the villages had been re-sited, people were encouraged to build square brick houses instead of their former round pole and mud huts. The villagers had already learned brick making when they had helped their missionaries to build schools, and in a short time these two chiefdoms became famous in Karangaland for their advanced housing.

In Shoko chiefdom the re-siting of villages caused some dissatisfaction because the people had already built good brick houses before the land was centralized. These had to be abandoned and new homesteads built at the boundaries between grazing and arable land. This rebuilding brought financial losses to progressive peasants, and few people constructed houses as solid as they had before out of fear that a new instruction of government to move their houses would cause them another financial loss. Hence many peasant families in Shoko chiefdom still live in the traditional round pole and mud huts and modern living quarters are rare.

Moreover, the mountainous character of Shoko chiefdom prevented the construction of many compact villages. Most villages straggle for miles along the foot of mountains, allowing the people to graze their cattle on the mountain slopes and to cultivate land wherever it is suitable for cultivation. Yet even in these sprawling villages, centralization has brought advantages to peasant families. Herding has been made easier and peasants live closer to their fields. The centralization policy, therefore, was implemented almost everywhere with the cooperation of the people.

(b) From the Land Husbandry Act to the Tribal Trust Land Act

Whereas the centralization policy was well received by peasant cultivators, the Land Husbandry Act often caused an uproar. Implementation of the Act, which was passed in 1951, started in the Ngara and Shiri chiefdoms only in 1956. That year government officials counted the people, their livestock, and the number and size of their fields. In 1959 the district commissioner, with the assistance of the agricultural staff, allocated the first fields in Ngara chiefdom. Within twelve months some 6,000 peasant cultivators received land holdings which were registered in the district commissioner's office.

At first land allocation in Ngara chiefdom proceeded smoothly, but soon opposition built up. By the time the civil servants reached the boundary between the Ngara and Shiri chiefdoms, people offered open opposition. Here the population density was much higher and peasants strongly objected to registered land holdings. They feared that a registration of all arable land would deprive their sons in perpetuity of the right to plough their own fields. The villagers, therefore, stoned cattle dip tanks and destroyed government property. To circumvent the enraged people the district commissioner and his agricultural staff went to the very south where chief Shiri lived and started allocating land around the chief's homestead. By 1961 the district commissioner had allocated land in only 35 out of 132 Shiri villages. In the rest of the chiefdom the civil servants merely indicated the boundaries between the arable and grazing land and between adjoining villages, and left the final allocation of fields to village headmen.

This decision pleased the relatives of traditional leaders but distressed the strangers, for wherever land was allocated by civil servants, all families received an equal share in the village land; where allocation was left to village headmen and chiefs, great inequalities resulted. For example, in one village in the south of Shiri chiefdom, married men had land holdings ranging between 23 acres and one acre before the Land Husbandry Act was implemented; after the implementation all married men had between seven and nine acres. Members of the chief's clan therefore, who had a stake in the tribal system, were more opposed to the government's control over the land than strangers.

In Shoko chiefdom the people, especially village headmen, cooperated in the implementation of the Act because their area suffers from frequent crop failure and people depend on government for regular famine relief. This different reaction in the three chiefdoms shows that certain local conditions, such as great population density, increase hostility to government policies, and that others, such as dependence on government, reduce potential opposition.

The Land Husbandry Act, which aimed at preserving the soil and fitting the population to the carrying capacity of the land, failed and was finally abandoned. One important consideration leading to the abandonment of the Act seems to have been government's need of the support of chiefs to combat African nationalism.[1] But by returning to chiefs the right to allocate land, government sacrificed agricultural efficiency for political expediency. The effect of this change soon proved disastrous in many tribal areas.

In 1963, section 22c of the Land Husbandry Act was amended and chiefs were allowed to allocate small fields to their followers in grazing areas. It was intended that these fields be cultivated for only one year and then be allowed to revert to grazing. Chiefs were told to decide which land an applicant should plough, and then to take him to the district commissioner, who in turn would consult the extension officer as to whether the land could be cultivated without causing erosion.

Chiefs Shiri and Ngara closely followed this instruction and little new land was opened up in grazing areas. Wherever land was opened up, the extension staff encouraged the new cultivators to experiment with Turkish tobacco since this could be sold for good prices and would enable them to buy more food than they could grow on the small acreage. Moreover, Turkish tobacco was

[1] See Weinrich, 1971, pp. 16–18, 20–22.

thought to improve the fertility of the grazing land and so to have good long-term effects.

In Shoko chiefdom civil servants allowed the chief to allocate land freely since they knew of the forthcoming Tribal Trust Land Act, which would return full control over land to African chiefs. Chief Shoko made extensive use of this new right and indiscriminately allocated land in grazing areas, even on steep slopes which were soon marred by erosion. People who received land, 'thanked' their chief through gifts of money, ranging between £2 and £5. Within half a year of the amendment of the Land Husbandry Act, 37 men in the Shoko Murewa community obtained new fields in grazing areas. The new fields were concentrated in eight out of 43 villages, and no land was given out in the grazing area where the chief herded his own cattle. In the Shoko Museamwa community the chief allocated 54 fields in the grazing areas of nine villages. In one of these villages, twelve men obtained land in the communal pasture. Twenty-two villages at first succeeded in retaining their grazing land untouched. This large-scale land allocation so drastically reduced the common pasture that in the ensuing drought year of 1964–65 the Shoko Museamwa people lost 101 cattle through starvation.

Indiscriminate land allocation affected the tribal trust land as well as nearby European farms. Fields in the middle of grazing land not only obliterated the advantages which centralization had brought, but also reduced the common pasture. Desperate herd boys often led their cattle into European farms. If they were caught, the herds were impounded until the owners paid a fine of 10/– for each beast. A peasant who complained to the district commissioner about this fine, was charged £1 for each of his cattle by the district commissioner who said that the cattle had not only trespassed into a European's estate, but they had also eaten his grass.

The effects of irresponsible land distribution were even worse in the tribal trust land, for the district commissioner's refusal to enforce the Land Husbandry Act, and finally the Act's repeal, made progressive peasant cultivators hesitant to invest money in the land. For example, when chief Shoko ordered one cultivator, whose land holding had been registered under the Land Husbandry Act, to hand over his field to a friend of the chief because it yielded good crops—the man had regularly used fertilizer on his land to build up its fertility—a leading master farmer in the Shoko

Museamwa community, who had just obtained a loan from the African Development Fund to sink a borehole and irrigate his land, changed his plan and built a grinding mill instead. He feared that if he irrigated his land and made high profits from vegetable growing, the chief would exchange his land for land of inferior quality. Many complaints reached the district commissioner, but the district commissioner never intervened. He backed the chief's right to allocate land.

Chief Shoko, therefore, who had more fully cooperated in the implementation of the Land Husbandry Act than other Karanga chiefs, was one of the first to abandon it, for his concern had not been to improve the land of his people, but to win government favour or to make money.

Enforced agricultural reforms seem a dubious method of improving peasant agriculture. Unless peasants see tangible benefits from reform measures, they are unlikely to adhere to them once strict government control is relaxed. The rapid abandonment of the Land Husbandry Act in Shoko chiefdom shows that traditional leaders may be a major handicap to improved peasant farming. Unless civil servants succeed in the most difficult task of really convincing patriarchal rulers of the necessity of modern farming techniques, these rulers' control over natural resources is bound to have negative effects on agriculture.

If peasant agriculture is to develop, both force and freedom are necessary. Basic conservation works must be enforced. One provincial commissioner realized this. When the people of his province refused to construct soil conservation works and their chiefs allowed them to plough land on slopes and in other hazardous environments, he stepped in and forbade ploughing in a whole chiefdom until all cultivators had protected their land. When the first rains fell and no fields were prepared, the people and their chief realized that the provincial commissioner would not give in. They therefore made a communal effort to construct the necessary contour ridges in order to get their fields ready for the late rains. That year their harvest was poor because of late ploughing, but most of the land is now protected and the basis is laid for improved peasant farming. In 1970 a chief of the area told the Rhodesian senate that 99 per cent of all peasant cultivators in his tribal trust land had protected their land with conservation works.[1] In the Shiri-Ngara tribal trust land, where no such

[1] *The Rhodesia Herald*, 24.6.70.

force was exerted, the Natural Resources Board reported in 1970 that 'a massive draft of extra staff, money and machinery' would be required if the area were to be 'rehabilitated'.[1]

(3) LAND SHORTAGE AND VOLUNTARY AGRICULTURAL REFORM

As soon as the responsibility for African agriculture was removed from the Ministry of Internal Affairs, many voluntary agricultural reform movements started in Karangaland. Members of the extension staff were no longer bound to enforce new government policies. Instead they were free to act as advisers to peasant cultivators. The response of the people to this new role of the extension staff varied between tribal trust lands. In the Shiri and Ngara chiefdoms, where people had opposed government policies for many years, distrust of civil servants was widespread and could only be overcome with the help of Catholic missionaries. In Shoko chiefdom, especially in the Shoko Museamwa community, people had seldom opposed government officials. When, therefore, extension staff offered advice, peasant cultivators accepted it readily.

(a) Response to Agricultural Development in the Shiri-Ngara Tribal Trust Land

Shiri chiefdom, with its high population density, has a long history of opposition to government policies. Though civil servants took great care in explaining new agricultural measures to the people and never exceeded their orders, peasants generally refused cooperation and ended unruly meetings with the refrain: 'Hatidi', 'We do not like what you tell us'. Ultimately, therefore, civil servants had to resort to force to make people cooperate.

In 1963 the atmosphere changed. Whereas in the past peasant leaders had used agricultural meetings to tell the extension staff that their advice was completely unsuitable for their communities because the people lacked both land and money, peasants now began to listen. This change came about through a more positive relationship between the agricultural staff and Catholic missionaries.

In Shiri chiefdom a missionary, concerned about the low productivity of the land, asked the leader of a Catholic association

[1] Ibid., 18.6.70.

to use his meetings with the people to arouse an interest in artificial fertilizer. To provide the peasants with the necessary money to purchase it, he founded a saving club which soon grew into a credit union. Peasant cultivators were asked to contribute at least three pennies a week to the common fund, and from this money loans were handed out to members to buy improved seed, fertilizer and basic agricultural equipment. The club purchased these items in bulk from wholesalers and so cut out the middleman. As the profits to club members grew, many peasants joined. Among the first members were teachers, and the home of an African headmaster served as the depot from which the fertilizer was distributed to peasant cultivators. From its beginning the saving club, and later the credit union, was run exclusively by Africans. The European missionary who started it remained in the background as a friendly adviser. Thus the credit union started as a self-help scheme and it has remained so ever since.

Progress was even greater in the Ngara chiefdom. Here a European extension officer took the initiative. In 1960 he laid out a fertilizer trial on a peasant's field, and the cultivator reaped 21 bags of maize from this one acre, while from each of his other acres he reaped only two bags. The people were amazed and subchief Hove asked for further information. The extension officer suggested that he form a 'progressive society' and that all development be channelled through it. The people agreed, elected a chairman and committee, and ordered £115 of fertilizer in the first year. In 1962, when 94 cultivators joined, five more groups were formed. That year these men bought £575 worth of fertilizer. Within a few years 10 per cent of all peasant cultivators in Hove subchiefdom became master farmers, though in the rest of the tribal trust land only 3 per cent of all peasant cultivators ever obtained this certificate. Hove subchiefdom has better land than the rest of the chiefdom.

But when this ground work had been laid, difficulties arose from senior civil servants. At the advice of their extension officer, the people agreed to form a cooperative society and applied for permission. At the time, however, government lacked personnel to supervise new societies and postponed permission so long that the people lost interest. At this critical point a missionary stepped in and sustained the people's confidence in their extension officer. In 1963 the extension officer finally succeeded and had the cooperative society established. Progress continued until 1968, when a new district commissioner renamed the 'progressive societies' in Hove subchiefdom 'community boards', that is, small committees out of which government hoped community development councils would develop. The people objected to the association of their societies with community development and dissolved them. As soon, therefore, as an administrator intervened, agricultural development came to a halt. This is one of many instances where bureaucracy had a crippling effect on agricultural development.

Hove subchiefdom developed its agricultural potential faster than others areas in Karangaland because of the close cooperation of one extension officer and Catholic missionaries. In 1965 a missionary started an agricultural training scheme for young people. He collected 35 boys and girls aged 12 to 25, into a 'Christian youth club' which he modelled on the young farmers clubs. Within a year he established 22 clubs with a total membership of 500 young people. The extension staff gave a garden to every club where the boys and girls could grow bananas, pawpaws, lemons and peaches. Through their constitution club members pledged themselves to plant fruit trees around their parents' home, to build a latrine, to fence their parents' property and to collect the refuse around their homes and make manure. During club sessions both boys and girls learned handicrafts, such as pottery, woodwork, leatherwork and sewing. They also engaged in recreational activities and studied some school subjects, especially religion, geography and biology. The main emphasis, however, remained on manual work. Every club was led by a teacher. Since most club members had left school and had failed to find employment, the Christian youth clubs trained them for productive work in their villages. In 1969, when extension staff was again placed under the control of district commissioners, the local district commissioner ordered that the Christian youth clubs be re-organized as young farmers clubs and brought in line with those controlled by civil servants. The people objected, the youth became apathetic, and the clubs slowly dissolved. Again, therefore, progress resulted from personal initiative, but bureaucratic control brought it to a halt.

These temporary agricultural developments in the Shiri-Ngara tribal trust land show that peasant communities are not inherently adverse to modern farming techniques. But for any reform programme to succeed, the peasant cultivators must have confidence in the people who propose it, they must be convinced that the goals they set out to achieve can be realized, and that their realization lies in their own hands. Regimentation, which brings self-help schemes into association with government plans, is likely to destroy them, for then they become enforced reforms and as liable to boycott as other government reform measures.

(b) Response to Agricultural Development in Shoko Chiefdom

Peasants in Shoko chiefdom relied less on outsiders for agricultural progress than people in the Shiri-Ngara tribal trust land, and obstacles to progress, too, arose mainly from within the communities. Peasant cultivators in the Shoko Museamwa community, who had fertile land on which investment showed a quick return, were especially interested in modern farming. Soon an agricultural elite evolved whose leader was the rival of the acting chief Shoko during an ongoing dispute for the chieftainship.

This leader was known as the most successful peasant cultivator in the whole tribal trust land, for he reaped on an average 20 bags of maize per acre in a region in which even European farmers reaped no more than 10 bags per acre. While still growing the local staple crops—in 1967 he went in for cotton growing—this man sold annually crops worth £200. He regularly visited the European extension officer and asked him for advice. On one occasion he doubted the officer's assessment of his soil and sent a soil sample to Salisbury for analysis, and for advice on the exact type and amount of fertilizer he needed.

This agricultural leader was surrounded by a group of friends who, like him, were all master farmers and village headmen. Hence they looked to him for both agricultural and political leadership. These men were the best master farmers in the area and friendly with the African extension assistant. They also asked their leader for advice, but not the European extension officer.

Each of these master farmers was surrounded by a group of eager cultivators who wanted to learn modern farming techniques, but who were reluctant to ask the extension staff. Since these men received their advice at second hand, it was less accurate than that of their leaders.

Below these friends of master farmers stood the ordinary peasant cultivators who were not interested in modern farming methods. Many of them were openly suspicious of any suggestions by civil servants, and even of suggestions by their successful neighbours.

This agricultural elite formed the most important channel through which modern farming techniques were spread in the Shoko Museamwa community. Through their initiative, 10 per cent, or 49 out of 513 cultivators obtained master farmer certificates, whereas in the rest of the tribal trust land only 3 per cent, or 105 out of 3,700 cultivators, became master farmers. Like the people in Hove subchiefdom, therefore, the people of the Shoko Museamwa community, who had better land than their neighbours, showed great interest in agriculture and accepted agricultural advice when it was offered. Through the support of the agricultural leadership, the extension assistants were well received by the people in Shoko Museamwa. Whenever agricultural meetings or training sessions for those who wanted to become master farmers were held, some of the leaders attended and extension assistants drew them into the discussion so that their formal teaching was backed up by the experience of successful local peasants.

In Hove subchiefdom agricultural development had received an impetus from a traditional leader. In Shoko chiefdom, however, progress was held back by the chief. In 1962 the agricultural leaders in the Shoko Museamwa community formed on their own initiative an 'agricultural committee' on which the most successful peasant cultivators served. When the chief heard of it, he looked at it with disfavour because he felt insecure and saw in any organized group a threat to his authority. After watching the committee for several months and observing its influence among peasant cultivators, he closed it down. Yet in 1964 the peasants of the Shoko Museamwa community revived their committee in the hope of turning it into a cooperative society. Once again, however, the chief intervened and made it clear that he would tolerate no organization in his chiefdom over which he had not full control. The people appealed to the district commissioner, but the district commissioner told them that they had to obey the orders of their chief. Thus it became exceedingly difficult to form formal associations in the area.

Yet the people of Shoko Museamwa were deeply interested in farming. To circumvent the order of their chief, they organized informal gatherings at irregular intervals at which successful peasant cultivators and their wives explained to each other farming methods which had proved successful. These *ad hoc* meetings were also attended by ordinary peasants. Several peasants experimented with the advice they received and more people used fertilizer, some went in for raising chickens on a larger scale and sold eggs in the nearby town, and some paid special attention to their livestock so that they could regularly sell milk in an African township. The chief disapproved of even these occasional meetings, but he did not forbid them outright.

This intransigence of the chief, who did not want to see agricultural progress in the Shoko Museamwa community, shows that patriarchal rule can be as great an obstacle to progress as bureaucracy. If the two combine, progress may be impossible. Had the district commissioner not backed the chief in his refusal to allow the agricultural committee from functioning, the Shoko Museamwa people would have established their own cooperative society and obtained through it many advantages for agricultural sales and purchases which these societies offer. Thus the clumsiness of the dual administration of the tribal trust land prevented a fast evolution for which the cultivators were prepared.

The history of voluntary agricultural reform in the two Karanga tribal trust lands shows that self-help schemes and peasant initiative, which are the only measures likely to have lasting results, can be severely hamstrung by the very institutions which government created to further progress; in the Hove subchiefdom bureaucratic delays almost prevented the establishment of a cooperative society, and the district commissioner's attempt to bring the 'progressive societies' and Christian youth clubs in line with government organization, led to their closure. In Shoko chiefdom, the chief blocked progress, and his opposition was backed by the district commissioner. These incidents indicate that in a country in which government closely controls peasant communities, agricultural reform measures are rarely able to succeed: if they are enforced or recommended by government, peasants tend to react with resentment or apathy, and if they are requested by peasants who want to help themselves independently of government supervision, administrators are likely to intervene. If peasant agriculture in tribal trust lands is to make any progress in Rhodesia, government should exert force to preserve the soil; orders to do so can be channelled through bureaucrats and chiefs. But then government should leave peasants free to use their own initiative and to cooperate with any agency in which the people trust so that real development can become possible.

CHAPTER 4

ECONOMIC RESOURCES OF PEASANT CULTIVATORS IN TRIBAL TRUST LANDS

(1) INTRODUCTION

The two previous chapters described the general picture of the Shiri-Ngara and Shoko tribal trust lands, and showed how government policy and a falling death rate have created an acute land shortage. These chapters also indicated the major attempts by the people and government to cope with land pressure and poverty in rural areas. This and the following chapter analyse the economic situation of the two tribal trust lands in greater detail.

It was pointed out in chapter 1 that for many years government has sponsored master farming training programmes to acquaint peasant cultivators with modern farming techniques. Just over 3 per cent of all peasant cultivators in the Shiri-Ngara and Shoko chiefdoms have become master farmers. Government, and many Europeans interested in African agriculture, wonder why after so many years so few Africans have joined the master farmer training scheme. The answer lies in a number of factors which enable some peasants to progress, and prevent others from adopting modern farming techniques. Financial resources and labour seem to be the most crucial variables.

(2) THE EFFECTS OF EDUCATION AND LABOUR MIGRATION

Table 4 sets out the agricultural incomes of master farmers and other peasant cultivators in the two tribal trust lands. Of the total sample census of 1,839 men and women, 575 were cultivators.[1] Of these 19 or 3·3 per cent were master farmers, 458 or 79·6 per cent other male peasant cultivators, and 98 or 17·1 per cent widows or other single women who cultivated their own fields.[2]

---

[1] 425 men were landless and so had to be excluded from this sub-sample, and so had 839 women who had no land rights in their own name.

[2] Hunt, in a survey of another tribal trust land, notes that 23 per cent of all land rights were held by women and a further 23 per cent by men exempt from paying tax because of old age or bodily infirmity. (Hunt, 1963, p. 108). This

The agricultural data presented in this and the following chapters are based on a sub-sample of this census: all 19 master farmers are included, and so are one in four of all other peasant cultivators, men as well as women.

TABLE 4

Agricultural Income of Master Farmers and
Other Peasant Cultivators (N=163)

Agricultural Income	Master Farmers		Other Peasant Cultivators	
	Frequency	Per cent	Frequency	Per cent
Below £25	1	5·3	95	66·0
£25–£49	3	15·8	34	23·3
£50–£74	5	26·3	7	4·9
£75–£99	5	26·3	4	2·9
£100 and over	5	26·3	4	2·9
Total	19	100·0	144	100·0

The number of master farmers is, admittedly, very small, yet the difference in income between master farmers and other peasant cultivators is so great that it does suggest a significant difference in agricultural performance between these two groups of cultivators. Whereas only 10·7 per cent of all ordinary peasant cultivators have an agricultural income of more than £50 a year, 78·9 per cent of all master farmers have such an income. Both social and economic differences seem responsible for this uneven success in agriculture.

TABLE 5

Education of Peasant Cultivators (N=575)

Education in Years	Master Farmers		Ordinary Peasant Cultivatorss		Total	
	Freq.	Per cent	Freq.	Per cent	Freq.	Per cent
0–5	10	52·6	384	69·1	394	68·5
6–8	6	31·6	137	24·6	143	24·9
9 and more	3	15·8	35	6·3	38	6·6
Total	19	100·0	556	100·0	575	100·0

indicates a very high percentage of people who cannot cultivate their land efficiently.

Higher education, if followed by abstention from labour migration, is beneficial to peasant agriculture. Table 5 shows that although most peasant cultivators have less than five years schooling, a much higher percentage of master farmers has received upper primary or even secondary education than ordinary peasant cultivators. If education is correlated with agricultural income, the positive effect of education becomes still clearer: of all ordinary peasant cultivators with less than five years schooling, 96·7 per cent obtained an income of less than £50 a year from agriculture, but among those ordinary peasant cultivators with six years of education or more, 53·7 per cent had an agricultural income of over £50. Among the less educated master farmers 30 per cent had an agricultural income of less than £50 a year, but among the better educated master farmers 88·9 per cent had an agricultural income of over £50. This shows a direct and positive effect of education on agriculture.

Almost all master farmers are permanent rural dwellers. None of them engages regularly in labour migration; only in a drought year may one or two try to earn money outside their tribal trust land. Thus master farmers are always present to work in their fields and they do not suffer from the acute labour shortage from which most other peasant cultivators suffer. Yet in spite of their rural residence, a significant proportion of master farmers earn money outside agriculture. The three master farmers with more than nine years education are teachers and live in their home villages. For them agriculture is a part-time occupation, but because they invest a portion of their regular salaries in agriculture, both to buy fertilizer and improved seed, and also, if need be, to hire additional labourers, their non-agricultural work has a positive effect on agriculture. Some other master farmers are trained craftsmen. These occasionally build a house or store, or make furniture on contract. Such work takes place during the agricultural off season and so does not withdraw labour from agriculture, yet it brings in additional money. Moreover, master farmers, because they are better educated than other peasant cultivators, can read booklets and pamphlets explaining modern farming techniques, and so can keep up with modern farming research.

Ordinary peasant cultivators lack most of these advantages. The substantial majority of widows increases their illiteracy rate. These women are generally old and very conservative. Many of the men in this group, especially the better educated, are absent from their villages so that their education has a negative effect on agriculture. Moreover, the money they earn in European employment is seldom invested in the land because the interests of the more educated men lie outside agriculture, and the less educated earn so little that they need the money for general family needs, like buying clothing and food. Hence investment in agriculture is low among ordinary peasant cultivators, labour is in short supply, and few dare to experiment with modern farming techniques, for to adopt new farming methods a man must take a personal interest in farming and have money at hand to invest in implements and in the land.

The ordinary peasant cultivator's shortage of money has negative effects on agriculture and reduces his potential output. Master farmers have enough money to buy the necessary farming implements, and these implements, in turn, enable them to cultivate their fields efficiently. Table 6 sets out a summary of the farming implements possessed by master farmers and other peasant cultivators.

TABLE 6

Agricultural Equipment of Peasant Cultivators (N=575)

Agricultural Equipment	Master Farmers		Other Peasant Cultivators	
	Freq.	Per cent	Freq.	Per cent
At least one plough	19	100·0	300	54·0
At least one item of transportation	15	78·9	78	14·0
At least one item of cultivation equipment	14	73·7	62	11·2
At least one larger productive capital investment	4	21·1	1	0·2

Ploughs are the most basic farming implement and all master farmers own at least one plough. But not all other peasant cultivators possess a plough. Widows especially often rely on their kinsmen to plough their land, or they still use a hoe to prepare their fields. Most ploughs are very simple and light and are seldom adequate for deep ploughing.[1] None of the peasant cultivators in the sample owned a tractor, but some progressive master farmers hired a tractor from nearby missions.

[1] The ordinary light plough used by Africans costs about £5.

The most common means of transport is the two-wheeled cart, which is essential for carrying manure to the field, harvesting and finally taking the produce to a market. A few people, two of the 19 master farmers and nine out of 556 ordinary peasant cultivators, owned a car or lorry. Bicycles have not been included in Table 6, though they too may occasionally be used to take a bag of maize to the market: 17 or 89·5 per cent of all master farmers have a bicycle, and so have 180 or 32·4 per cent of all other peasant cultivators.

Just as master farmers are more adequately provided with transport equipment than ordinary peasant cultivators, so they are better provided with various cultivation implements. Very few ordinary peasant cultivators own a planter, cultivator or harrow, whereas about three-quarters of all master farmers have one or more of these. Sixteen out of 19 master farmers own a cultivator, nine own a harrow and six a planter. Thus master farmers are able to cultivate their fields more speedily and thoroughly than other peasant cultivators, and this in turn effects the output of their fields.

Of great importance too, especially to their owners, are large-scale capital investments. Four of the 19 master farmers distinguished themselves from the rest: two of them sank their own boreholes, one built a dam. One of these owned irrigation equipment. Two of them, moreover, bought a grinding machine and one a shelling machine. These four men gained high returns from their capital investments. Of the other peasant cultivators only one man owned a grinding machine, and this was out of order at the time of the census. Since he had no money to repair it, he had no idea when it would be used again. Two of the master farmers and one of the other peasant cultivators also owned small stores which contributed to their income.

Master farmers not only own more agricultural equipment, they also enjoy a higher living standard than other peasant cultivators. Their higher living standard is reflected in their superior housing. Whereas only some 13 per cent of all ordinary peasant cultivators live in brick houses, some 53 per cent of all master farmers do so. Moreover, 6 or 31·6 per cent of all master farmers built latrines next to their living quarters, whereas less than one per cent of all other peasant cultivators did so.

This picture of the skills, financial resources and implements possessed by master farmers and other peasant cultivators shows

that master farmers have many advantages over their neighbours.

(3) OWNERSHIP OF CATTLE AND ACCESS TO LAND

Unlike ownership of modern farming equipment, which is due
to success in the modern cash economy, ownership of cattle
and access to land are only partly dependent on money. Cattle may
either be inherited or they may be purchased. Although master
farmers often buy cattle, few other peasant cultivators do so.
Most obtain them through a variety of kinship ties, often through
bridewealth paid for their daughters. Hence a man's standing in
the community determines the size of his herd. Chiefs have
always larger herds than commoners, and relatives of chiefs own
more cattle than ordinary villagers. For example, in the Shiri-
Ngara and Shoko tribal trust lands, the average chief owned over
20 head of cattle, his sons over 10, but commoners only an average
of some five, if they had any cattle at all. Table 7 sets out the
ownership of cattle among peasant cultivators.

TABLE 7

Cattle Ownership Among Peasant Cultivators (N=575)

Number of Cattle Owned	Master Farmers		Other Peasant Cultivators	
	Freq.	Per cent	Freq.	Per cent
Nil	—	—	172	30·9
1–3	—	—	128	23·1
4–6	2	10·5	141	25·4
7–9	5	26·3	65	11·7
10–19	8	42·1	43	7·7
20–29	3	15·8	3	0·5
30 and over	1	5·3	4	0·7
Total	19	100·0	556	100·0

This Table shows that almost a third of all ordinary peasant
cultivators possess no cattle at all. Many of these are widows,
but also a substantial number of family heads have no cattle.
If these want to plough their fields—and many of them possess a
plough—they must borrow a pair of oxen from their neighbours.

But cattle owners only hire out or lend cattle when they do not need them themselves. At the beginning of the ploughing season, therefore, those who have no cattle can only plough their fields when their neighbours have ploughed theirs so that families without cattle are forced to plant their crops late, and late planting reduces crop yield. Cultivators with few or no cattle also lack manure, and even if they were willing to manure their field, they could not do so. Most ordinary peasant cultivators, who own cattle, have one or two pairs of oxen.

Among master farmers relatively few men are related to chiefs, except in the Shoko Museamwa community and in Hove sub-chiefdom. Most master farmers have built up their herds through savings. Thus their attitude towards cattle is more commercialized than that of ordinary peasant cultivators who obtained their cattle through bridewealth payments or inherited them from their fathers. This is reflected in their readiness to sell cattle, which is analysed in the next chapter. Here it need only be stressed that all master farmers have enough cattle to plough their fields and enough manure to fertilize them. Master farmers view cattle in much the same light as other agricultural equipment and look at them as capital rather than as 'wealth' which is set aside for traditional purposes.

In the past, access to land was almost solely determined by kinship ties to traditional rulers. Since the implementation of the Land Husbandry Act, land holdings have become more equal, and only in areas in which the Act was not implemented, such as in Shiri chiefdom, are landholdings still uneven. In most areas of Karangaland widows were given two to three acres under the Land Husbandry Act, and heads of families between six and eight acres. Chiefs, who later allocated land in grazing areas, generally gave out some two to four acres to new cultivators. While the Land Husbandry Act was still enforced, successful peasant cultivators were encouraged to acquire land holdings of their less successful neighbours who decided to migrate permanently to urban areas. Several master farmers did so, especially in the Shoko Museamwa community, and this accounts for some larger holdings among master farmers. Table 8 sets out the land holdings of peasant cultivators.

TABLE 8

Land Holdings of Peasant Cultivators (N=575)

	Master Farmers		Other Peasant Cultivators	
Acres	Freq.	Per cent	Freq.	Per cent
1–3	—	—	209	37·6
4–6	7	36·8	266	47·8
7–9	9	47·4	75	13·5
10 and over	3	15·8	6	1·1
Total	19	100·0	556	100·0

This Table shows that even under a law to which all peasant cultivators were equally subject, master farmers were able to obtain larger fields than their neighbours. Hence in addition to better farming equipment and more cattle, master farmers also cultivate more land.

In addition to their fields, 8 or 42·1 per cent of all master farmers have planted gardens of about half an acre to grow vegetables, and so have 9 or 1·6 per cent of the other peasant cultivators. These gardens are generally situated near rivers in grazing areas and protected by high fences against cattle. They are worked in the dry season when little labour is required on other agricultural tasks. One master farmer, however, has irrigated a garden of three-quarters of an acre near his homestead on dry land and grows vegetables all the year round for sale. None of the ordinary peasant cultivators sells his vegetables.

Progressive peasant cultivators also distinguish themselves from their neighbours by growing cash crops rather than food for home consumption. The traditional food crops are millet and sorghum. Millet has always been used to prepare a stiff porridge which is served at all meals, and sorghum, which can also be used for porridge, has traditionally been grown for brewing beer. In recent years government has begun buying some sorghum for commercial beer brewing, and peasant cultivators can register as sorghum producers. Some peasant cultivators, especially master farmers, have done so.

During this century, maize has become a very important crop and has almost replaced millet as the staple food.[1] People value

[1] Maize was introduced into Central Africa by the Portuguese in the 17th century. Cf. Hellen, 1968, p. 84.

maize because it can be eaten green during the annual hunger months before the next harvest is brought in. Most Karanga also prefer maize to millet porridge. In addition, maize is a most suitable cash crop which can be sold through government agents. Maize, however, presents peasant cultivators with certain hazards. It needs better soil than millet and more rain, for it is far less drought resistant. Since the Shiri-Ngara and Shoko tribal trust lands lie in a region of marginal rainfall and, apart from the Shoko Museamwa community, have poor soil, the yields of maize fields are more unreliable than those of millet fields.

In addition to grains, the Karanga are used to growing ground-nuts and groundbeans. Groundnuts have become a cash crop with a ready market since government buys them for oil production. Groundnut crops are traditionally owned by women. Most groundnut fields are, therefore, exclusively cultivated by women, and women dispose of the money derived from the surplus sales of this crop.

Depending on soil conditions, a few other crops may be grown. In Hove subchiefdom, which has several vleis, people grow rice. A few peasant cultivators have also begun to grow small patches of tobacco in the sandy soils of the subchiefdom. In 1967, some progressive peasant cultivators in the Shoko Museamwa community took to cotton growing, for cotton does well on the fertile black basalt soil of the area. Six families, in which both husband and wife take an active part in agriculture, formed a 'cash crop farmers' club' in order to buy cotton seed, fertilizer and insecticides in bulk.[1] By 1970 the leading master farmer of the area had completely given up food crop production and had put all his acres to cotton. At the time of the agricultural census, however, no cotton had yet been planted.[2] Table 9 sets out the acreages under the various crops grown by 19 master farmers and 144 other peasant cultivators.

Table 9 shows that master farmers grow a higher percentage of both maize and groundnuts than other peasant cultivators. Other peasant cultivators, who are mainly concerned with growing their own food, sow a greater proportion of their land with the more drought resistant millet. This is especially true for the peasant

[1] This club was not closed by the chief.
[2] Both tobacco and cotton are new crops to Rhodesian Africans. In 1962 practically no Africans grew tobacco; by 1965 Africans produced close to half a million pounds. Between 1960 and 1965 the weight of African grown cotton increased more than ten times. Cf. Hunt, 1967.

TABLE 9

Crops Grown by Peasant Cultivators (N=163)

Crops	Master Farmers		Other Peasant Cultivators	
	Acres	Per cent	Acres	Per cent
Maize	72	40·7	250	31·4
Millet	49	27·7	266	33·4
Sorghum	11	6·2	57	7·1
Groundnuts	36	20·3	130	16·3
Groundbeans	9	5·1	82	10·3
Other Crops	—	—	12	1·5
Total	177	100·0	797	100·0

cultivators in the Shoko chiefdom where rainfall is lower than in the Shiri-Ngara tribal trust land. The other crops grown by ordinary peasant cultivators are mainly rice; some also cultivate small patches of sweet potatoes, and some mix sugar cane or pumpkins with grain crops. None of these crops are ever sold.

There is no great difference between master farmers and other peasant cultivators in the type and proportion of crops grown, though even the small difference indicates a greater orientation towards the market among the more progressive cultivators, for master farmers have planted 67 per cent of their land with potential cash crops, whereas their neighbours have done so on only 51 per cent of their land.

(4) LABOUR REQUIREMENTS AND LABOUR SUPPLY IN PEASANT AGRICULTURE

So far I have shown that master farmers have more land than other peasant cultivators and grow a greater proportion of cash crops. They have also more implements for cultivation and this should reduce their need for more labour due to slightly larger acreages.

African peasants often complain of labour shortage and state that this prevents them from cultivating their fields more intensely. A greater labour force should overcome this handicap and increase their agricultural output. Table 10 sets out the average household size of master farmers and other peasant cultivators in the two

4

tribal trust lands. A household is taken to consist of those men, women and children who eat together, share in the daily economic tasks of their family, and are subject to the supervision of the family head.

TABLE 10

Average Household Size Among
Peasant Cultivators (N=575)

Household Composition	Master Farmers	Other Peasant Cultivators
Men	1·8	1·1
Women	2·1	1·8
Children aged 7–14	2·9	1·4
Children aged 0–6	1·6	1·2
Total	8·4	5·5

This Table shows that master farmer households are larger than the households of other peasant cultivators. Some master farmers succeed in attracting kinsmen so that they have more labourers than other peasant cultivators. Of special importance is the larger number of men in master farmer families, which is due to the permanent rural residence of the master farmers themselves.

Peasant cultivators have three sources of labour: family labour, the traditional work parties, and hired labourers. Only 30 per cent of all ordinary peasant cultivators can rely exclusively on family labour; most have to call in work parties to help them in their fields. A few, especially master farmers, employ hired labourers and pay them in cash or kind. Master farmers are sceptical of the value of work parties since they are based on reciprocity and so make demands on their own labour force. They also demand more accurate work than most peasant cultivators are used to performing and so prefer family or hired labour.[1] Since their families are large, master farmers can rely to a large extent on family labour.

The labour force of master farmers consists, roughly, of one third of men, one third of women, and one third of children. Among ordinary peasant cultivators, women constitute 40 per cent of the labour force because men are frequently absent in urban employment.[2]

[1] See Appendix, Table 39 for further details on the composition of the labour force of master farmers and other peasant cultivators.
[2] For further details, see Appendix, Table 40.

In this analysis of agricultural labour, every working hour, whether contributed by a man, woman or a child, is taken as equivalent to any other working hour. This brings about some distortion of the amount of work done, yet any subdivision of work according to age and sex[1] seems arbitrary, because not only does the amount of work performed by any two individuals of the same age and sex category vary, but also their contribution to individual agricultural tasks. For example, a woman who weeds in a field for one hour, may work over a larger acreage than a man.

The labour input survey, on which this section is based, includes all 19 master farmers, and also 36, or one in four, of the 144 other peasant cultivators. It is therefore a much smaller sample than that of agricultural productivity and less reliable. The findings, however, have been compared with those of Johnson, who did a similar study in another Rhodesian tribal trust land, and who came to similar conclusions.[2] Diagrams 2a and b show the labour input by master farmers and other peasant cultivators throughout an agricultural year.[3]

The diagrams overleaf show that there are two periods in the agricultural cycle which make exceptionally great demands on labour. The first occurs in November, December and January, when the fields have to be ploughed, sowed or planted, and weeded. Labour shortage at this stage could be reduced if peasant cultivators had prepared their land during the off season, especially if they had winter-ploughed their fields after the harvest. Few peasant cultivators, however, do this. The second labour intensive period occurs in April–May when the harvest begins. At these times additional labour is required, work parties are called, and peasant cultivators, who have gone off to work in town, may return to help their families.

The overall pattern of labour input is similar between master

---

[1] See, for example, Collinson's analysis. He converted the work done by men, women, children and old men into 'Men Equivalent' (ME) units: he uses the following categories:

Age-group	10–14	15–19	20–50	over 50
Male (ME)	0·25	0·67	1·00	0·67
Female (ME)	0·25	0·50	0·67	0·50

(Quoted in Ruthenberg, 1968, p. 15).

[2] Cf. Johnson, 1964, b and d. The main difference between the two surveys is due to the higher rainfall in the area studied by Johnson and the consequent higher labour input for maize in that area. See also Appendix, Table 42.

[3] For a statistical breakdown of the labour input figures, see Appendix, Table 41.

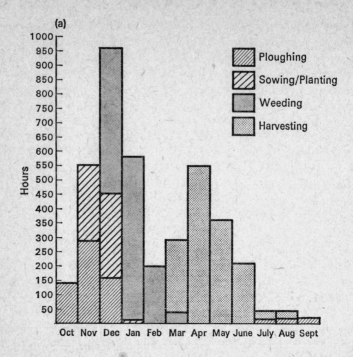

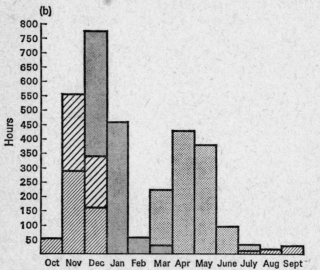

Fig. 2. Labour input on crops in tribal trust lands: (a) master farmers; (b) other peasant cultivators

farmers and other peasant cultivators since it is dictated by the seasons. A great difference, however, exists in the amount of labour master farmers and other peasant cultivators invest in any one agricultural activity. Earlier ploughing and more intensive weeding assure master farmers of better crops so that, when harvest time comes, they again spend more time in reaping their fields than ordinary peasant cultivators.

Early planting and weeding are the most critical activities determining agricultural output. It is here that the availability of labour and farming equipment become important. Ploughing has to be started as soon as the first rain falls. Yet at that time the oxen are in very poor condition because of the inadequate grazing during the preceding dry months. Hence, if the plough is not merely to scratch the surface of the soil, peasants must inspan four oxen before each plough.

The great demand on the limited supply of ploughs, oxen and manpower is specially critical for the families of ordinary peasant cultivators. Though women do plough, ploughing is heavy work and the Karanga prefer it to be done by men. In the ideal team, a man guides the plough and his wife or child the oxen. Many migrants try to come home in November to help their wives to prepare the fields or, of they cannot come home and if they have no relative in the village to help the family, they send some money to hire a ploughing team from a neighbour.

Shortage of oxen, ploughs and men is also overcome by pooling resources. One extended family in the Shiri chiefdom, for example, which consists of four households, possessed two ploughs and eight oxen. When the first rains fell, they arranged that every day of the week both ploughs, each spanned with four oxen, worked on the field of one household, so that each household got one or two ploughing days each week during the early rains.

Widows, who lack both ploughs and oxen, are often assisted by kinsmen. One old woman, for example, who was invited by a village headman, her classificatory sister's son, to look after his home during his wife's illness, had her field ploughed by him as long as she stayed at his village.

The special strain, which the ploughing season places on ordinary peasant families, is reflected in the number of work parties which are held to overcome labour shortage. Of all plough-ing done by ordinary peasant cultivators 13·5 per cent is in the form of work parties, though only 1·9 per cent of all ploughing done by master farmers is carried out by such groups. Master farmers are more inclined to hire a tractor for ploughing.[1] Tractors plough deep, and this has a good effect on plant growth.

All sowing and planting tends to be done by family members. Men plant much of the maize and sow most of the millet, while women plant most of the groundnuts and groundbeans. This division of labour during the planting and sowing season is related to the ownership of the grain and nut harvests. Groundnuts and groundbeans need careful planting and girls receive special instruction from their mothers. In families where men are absent as labour migrants, women and children take a leading part in planting maize and sowing millet. Millet is merely broadcast and so does not require special skills; maize is usually planted and all Karanga have learned this skill in their childhood.

Weeding is burdensome to all peasant families. Women and children are expected to do most of this work, for men shy away from it. Some men even go off to seek urban employment, and if their wives need additional help, they are encouraged to call in work parties. Almost 22 per cent of all weeding in the fields of ordinary peasant cultivators is done in work parties, and even over 14 per cent of all master farmers' fields are weeded by such groups.[2]

Harvesting again requires much labour, but it is also a more pleasant activity. The men, who left after the ploughing season for wage employment, return. Because harvesting can be spread over several months, the labourers work under less pressure than during the ploughing season. Moreover, the months of food shortage are over, much beer is brewed for the reapers, and people gather together in groups both for the pleasure of conviviality and for the satisfaction of working together. About 29 per cent of all harvesting by ordinary peasant cultivators is done by work parties, and even 17 per cent of all harvesting for master farmers.[3] Harvesting, therefore, is the time when work parties are held daily in the fields of all villages. Maize is the easiest crop to reap and it is mostly gathered in by small family groups. Millet and sorghum, however, are more laborious to harvest, and many people call in work parties for these crops. A typical work party to reap a millet crop was called by a village headman in Shiri chief-

[1] See Appendix, Table 39.
[2] See Appendix, Table 39.
[3] For a similar preference for communal work, see the writings of Forde and Douglas, 1967, p. 28, on tribes in the Congo.

dom. The people who participated did so because they were neighbours of the village headman; some came from his own, some from neighbouring villages. Most, but not all, could trace some kinship tie with him.

The headman's wife had brewed some pots of beer, and one was offered to the workers early in the morning before they started to reap. At that time only about a dozen men and women were present. They included 'the owner of the work party' and his wife, a neighbouring village headman, two teachers, an old man from the headman's own village, and some grown-up sisters' sons and classificatory grandchildren of the headman. Most of the women were the wives of these men. By lunchtime the party had increased to 16 men and 15 women, who sat down in the shade of a tree to eat their food and drink more beer.

During the morning, every member of the work party was expected to cut off the tops of millet with knives and to fill six baskets. These were then emptied into a cart which stood at the end of the field. At the cart stood a young relative of 'the owner of the work party' who counted the baskets and made sure that all did their required amount of work. Whenever the cart was filled, it was drawn by oxen to the granary. In the afternoon, every member of the work party was expected to fill another three baskets with millet. When all the work was completed, one or two more pots of beer were brought to the field by the headman's wife as a 'thank you' to the workers.

Groundnuts and groundbeans need careful handling at harvest time so that no beans and nuts are lost, and every field has to be gleaned twice. Since women are the owners of these crops, they call the necessary work parties in their own name. Many of these work parties are small family gatherings. A typical work party of this type was that of a widow who had already harvested her groundnuts and now wanted to prepare them for storage. The nuts had been taken from the field three weeks before the party was called and laid out for drying in long rows. That day the nuts were collected in big heaps and the people came to pluck them from the haulms. The workers sat in two groups. The group of young women consisting of the widow's daughter and her two daughters-in-law with their small children, sat around a pot of sweet beer which had been brewed the previous day. The second group, which sat around a pot of strong beer brewed four days earlier, included four old women: 'the owner of the work party', the wife of her village headman, her father's sister and an old woman distantly related to her father's sister. With the older women sat also three men: the widow's son, one of her sons-in-law and her husband's brother. In the late morning the son-in-law roasted some maize for the workers who then continued plucking the nuts until the afternoon when all went home for a late lunch.

Those who experiment with modern cash crops, such as tobacco and cotton, need additional labour. They have to spray the cotton during the growing season, and at harvesting time need special helpers to pick it. Hence most of them employ hired labourers. Progressive peasants also spend time applying fertilizer and manure to their fields. One master farmer employed an old man for three months to help him on his land. The most successful master farmers never call in work parties. In fact, work parties are a mark of the more tradition-orientated peasants.

In addition to labour in the fields, peasant families must herd their cattle. Herding duties are heaviest during the time when the crops grow and cattle have to be prevented from straying into the fields. Thus, though the average peasant family in the two tribal trust lands spends only over a thousand hours annually on herding, 83 per cent of this time has to be found between October and May when workers are urgently needed in the fields.[1] Traditionally, cattle were looked after by men and boys; today, however, 32·1 per cent of all herding time is provided by women because men are away in employment and children go to school. This withdraws important woman labour from weeding and harvesting.

Master farmers and other peasant cultivators spend about an equal amount of time on herding, because all the cattle of a village are herded in common. Every family who owns cattle, but irrespective of the number it owns, provides a cattle herder for a fixed number of days a month. Since more participants in a herding group reduce the number of herd days, people like to join large herding groups.

Once the crops are harvested, herding becomes easy, for the cattle are left free to roam in the harvested fields. Between July and September crops are threshed whenever they are needed. Some men, especially master farmers, winter-plough and cart manure to their fields, work on their contour ridges or carry out other maintenance work. Some peasants re-thatch their huts, but more go to seek work in town. Most leave necessary mainten-

[1] For detailed information on herding hours, see Appendix, Tables 43 and 52.

ance work until the early rains start, and then these tasks compete with ploughing. Few peasant families spend much time on repairing their agricultural equipment or preparing their fields. The average family devotes only some 315 hours a year to such work. Master farmers spend more time on such tasks than other peasant cultivators.

(5) CONCLUSION

The analysis of economic resources available to master farmers and other peasant cultivators shows that master farmers possess certain advantages over other peasants. They are better educated and, having given up urban employment in favour of agriculture, are always at home to supervise the work in their fields. Their non-agricultural earnings are sometimes substantial and can be used for investment. Hence they have better equipment than other peasant cultivators and so can cultivate their lands more efficiently. Master farmers also have larger herds and fields than their neighbours, mostly because of their ability to buy cattle and, under the Land Husbandry Act, to buy a 'right to cultivate'. Provided with better resources, they can grow crops for sale and even experiment with modern cash crops. Their larger labour force enables them to cultivate their lands more intensely and thus guarantees them larger yields per acre than ordinary peasant cultivators obtain.

In contrast to these factors which account for the success of master farmers, other factors account for the poverty of many peasant cultivators. With less education than master farmers, these men are more bound to traditional values. Fewer farming skills reduce their agricultural yields so that they turn to labour migration to earn additional money. Labour migration, however, has a regressive effect on peasant agriculture. It withdraws essential farm labour without compensating for this loss by high wage earnings. For most peasant cultivators have little education and so can only perform unskilled work. Their meagre incomes do not allow them to purchase modern agricultural equipment and hence much of their agricultural work has to be done by hand. Inadequate farming equipment and shortage of labour force peasant families to call in work parties, but work parties are seldom as efficient as family or hired labour. Moreover, since they require reciprocity, this again strains a peasant family's labour resources. Too few cattle for ploughing and too little manure for fertilizing the fields, which in any case are smaller than those of master farmers, further reduce output. Since the peasant cultivators' fields are cultivated more haphazardly and with less care than those of master farmers, their yields are lower. Most peasant cultivators find themselves caught up in this vicious circle of poverty and do not know how to break out of it. The odds are heavily weighed against them.

Master farmers and other peasant cultivators, then, differ in their agricultural success because they find themselves in different social and economic circumstances. Only if these circumstances are altered, can ordinary peasant cultivators hope to emulate their more successful neighbours.

CHAPTER 5

PRODUCTIVITY OF TRIBAL
TRUST LANDS

(1) INTRODUCTION

The agricultural income of peasant cultivators is mainly derived
from two sources, from the land and from cattle. Other agricultural
income, such as is raised by the sale of fruit, vegetables, eggs and
milk, is very low. As far as land and cattle are concerned, master
farmers have more of both than other peasant cultivators. Moreover, master farmers have a larger and more efficient labour
force than their neighbours, and for these reasons their agricultural
output is greater. With more crops than they need to feed their
families, master farmers can sell a significant portion of their
harvests and so earn money which can either be re-invested in
agriculture or used for other purposes.

Though agricultural skills vary between master farmers and
other peasant cultivators, all peasants face one problem in common:
drought. Drought threatens progressive and traditional cultivators
alike, and men who rely more on their fields than on wage employment suffer more seriously than their neighbours. Crop
failure increases the importance of cattle, for when no food is
available, peasants may sell their cattle to buy grain.

During the mid-1960s several drought years followed each
other and Rhodesian agriculture suffered great losses. While
European farmers were heavily subsidized by government,
African peasants were encouraged to sell their livestock. For those
who had no cattle, famine relief schemes were operated through
which people could work on public projects for food.

Drought is frequent in Karangaland. The agricultural staff in
the Shoko tribal trust land estimates that every fourth year is a
drought year. For this reason agricultural productivity in a
year of average rainfall[1] must be considered together with agricultural productivity in a drought year. During 1965–1966 all

---

[1] The phrase 'a year of average rainfall' is used in this book as referring to
those years in which rainfall is close to the statistical local average for an area.
Rainfall is measured at most mission stations and agricultural offices.

areas had about 25 inches of rain, and rain was always adequate for crop production. Hove subchiefdom had less than its annual average, but the rain was distributed in such a way that plant growth was not hindered. 1966–1967 was a drought year in all communities, most of which had just over 15 inches of rain.

(2) CROP PRODUCTION

The effects of adequate and inadequate rainfall in the Shiri-Ngara and Shoko tribal trust lands are set out in Tables 11 and 12.

Tables 11 and 12 show how great a difference rainfall makes on the harvests of peasant cultivators. Whereas master farmers reap in a season of average rainfall some 54 bags of various crops, in a drought season they reap only some 20 bags; and other peasant cultivators, who in a season of average rainfall reap some 15 bags, reap in a drought year only some nine bags. Master farmers, therefore, suffer a proportionately greater loss, and this is due to their greater emphasis on maize which suffers more from drought than millet. Yet even in a drought year master farmers reap more than other peasant cultivators do in a season of average rainfall. This is due to the more efficient way in which master farmers cultivate their fields.

Table 11 shows that of the two most important cash crops, maize and groundnuts, master farmers reap about twice as many bags per acre as do ordinary peasant cultivators. The yield of over nine bags of maize per acre compares evenly with the yield of maize on the fields of neighbouring European farmers who do not irrigate their land.

Thus higher crop output allows master farmers to sell a greater proportion of their produce than ordinary peasant cultivators. In a year of average rainfall, master farmers sell over half of their maize harvest and 46·6 per cent of their groundnut harvest. Their sales of sorghum, millet and groundbeans are small in comparison with these two important crops. All in all, master farmers sell 40·9 per cent of all their crops, and this is a high percentage for peasant cultivators. Ordinary peasant cultivators sell only 13·0 per cent of the crops. Maize, millet, sorghum and groundnuts are the crops most frequently sold. But apart from sorghum, which is, in any case, grown only in small quantities, sales represent only a low percentage of all crop yields.

In a drought year, all sales are drastically reduced. Some

TABLE 11

Productivity of Peasant Cultivators in a Season of Average Rainfall (1965–1966) (N=163)

Crop	Bags harvested				Bags per acre		Bags sold				Bags consumed or unaccounted for per household	
	MF No.	MF %	OPC No.	OPC %	MF	OPC	MF No.	MF %	OPC No.	OPC %	MF	OPC
Maize	663	64·7	947	43·1	9·2	3·9	332	50·1	131	13·5	17·4	5·7
Millet	230	22·5	718	32·7	4·7	2·7	26	11·3	69	9·6	11·1	4·5
Sorghum	25	2·4	148	6·7	2·3	2·6	11	44·0	47	31·8	0·7	0·7
Groundnuts	90	8·8	169	7·7	2·5	1·3	42	46·6	32	19·0	2·5	1·0
Groundbeans	16	1·6	172	7·8	1·8	2·1	8	50·0	6	3·5	0·4	1·1
Other Crops (mainly rice)	—	—	44	2·0	—	3·7	—	—	—	—	—	0·3
Total	1,024	100·0	2,198	100·0			419	40·9	285	13·0	32·1	13·3

MF = Master farmers
OPC = Other peasant cultivators

TABLE 12

Productivity of Peasant Cultivators in a Drought Year
(1966–1967) (N=163)

Crop	Bags harvested				Bags per acre		Bags sold				Bags consumed or unaccounted for per household	
	MF No.	MF %	OPC No.	OPC %	MF	OPC	MF No.	MF %	OPC No.	OPC %	MF	OPC
Maize	180	47·9	400	32·1	2·5	1·6	34	18·9	13	3·3	7·7	2·7
Millet	127	33·8	559	44·8	2·6	2·1	6	4·7	54	9·7	6·4	3·5
Sorghum	20	5·3	74	5·9	1·8	1·3	8	40·0	—	—	0·6	0·5
Groundnuts	33	8·8	65	5·2	0·9	0·5	5	15·2	—	—	1·5	0·5
Groundbeans	16	4·2	123	9·9	1·8	1·5	—	—	6	4·9	0·8	0·8
Other crops (mainly rice)	—	—	26	2·1	—	2·2	—	—	—	—	—	0·2
Total	376	100·0	1,247	100·0			53	14·1	73	5·9	17·0	8·2

MF = Master farmers
OPC = Other peasant cultivators

master farmers are still able to sell some maize, groundnuts and sorghum, but their sales amount to only 14·1 per cent of their total harvest. Hardly any ordinary peasant cultivator can sell in a drought year, and sales amount to only 5·9 per cent of their total harvest.

A provincial agricultural officer of Rhodesia estimated that an African peasant family needs a minimum of 60 bags of various crops as a bare minimum to see its members through a year, and that some 120 bags are required if the family is to meet all the normal requirements of everyday life, such as clothing, school fees and taxes.[1] Apart from master farmers in a year of average rainfall, none of the peasants in the Shiri-Ngara and Shoko tribal trust lands even approaches the minimum considered necessary by this agriculturalist.

Africans themselves estimate that a family needs a minimum of two bags of crops for each person in a household to provide adequate food throughout the year. Such an estimate, however, does not include any needs other than food. With an average family size of eight persons in master farmer households and five in the households of ordinary peasant cultivators, master farmers need at least 16 bags per family and other peasant cultivators at least ten. The last two columns in Tables 11 and 12 show that this bare minimum is mostly available to all peasant cultivators, and in a year of average rainfall master farmers still have a considerable surplus.

Yet such average figures conceal differences between master farmer families, as well as between the families of ordinary peasant cultivators. In the drought season of 1966–67, for example, ten of the 19 master farmer families bought additional food, and so did 106 out of 144 other peasant families. The others still had a surplus for sale. On the average, each of the ten master farmer families bought food to the value of £22, and each of the 106 ordinary peasant families to the value of £18. Even in a drought season, therefore, master farmers consumed much more food than their neighbours and bought enough additional food to maintain the living standards to which they had become accustomed.

---

[1] Plowes, 1963.

(3) CROP SALES

African peasants have three major markets on which to sell their surplus crops: the Grain Marketing Board and its agents, Christian missions and fellow Africans in tribal trust lands. The market which an individual producer chooses depends on the prices paid and on the amount he intends to sell.

Government has tried to regularize the sale of crops by annually fixing crop prices through the Government Gazette. These are the prices paid by the Grain Marketing Board, the official channel through which agricultural produce should be sold. Since the Grain Marketing Board, a statutory body, cannot establish branches in all African communities, it recognizes certain African store owners as its buying agents. These store owners are allowed to deduct handling charges for their services. In addition to these handling charges African producers have to pay a levy to the African Development Fund. This fund had been set up to provide money for basic developments, such as the construction and maintenance of roads and bridges in African rural areas. Johnson calculated that African peasants who sell their surplus through this channel are paid out 14s. 8d. for a bag of maize which was originally worth 29s. 7d.[1] Because of these heavy deductions, few peasant cultivators sell their crops through local store owners. Of the 704 bags of surplus crops sold by 163 peasant cultivators in this survey, 57·2 per cent of the sorghum, 35·6 per cent of the groundnuts, 8·6 per cent of the maize, 8·3 per cent of the ground-beans and 3·2 per cent of the millet were sold at local stores. Sorghum and groundnuts are, therefore, the only crops sold regularly through this channel because government pays a high price for them. The reason is that sorghum is needed by European commercial companies to brew African beer, and groundnuts are needed for oil production. Groundnuts, moreover, are usually sold by women in very small quantities at a time. The other crops, which fetch low prices, are sold in other markets.

Those peasant cultivators, who have joined a cooperative society, often sell their surplus in bulk to the Grain Marketing Board. In this way they save the handling charges, deducted by store owners, but they still have to pay the levy to the African Development Fund. Some 5 per cent of all surplus crops are sold in this way.

[1] Johnson, 1963c, pp. 3–4.

Progressive peasant cultivators who produce large surpluses prefer to sell their maize to Christian missions. One master farmer, for example, sold for several years in succession over 100 bags of maize to a Catholic mission at 30 shillings a bag. Mission stations, with their large boarding establishments, always need large amounts of maize. In directly selling their maize to the missionaries, African peasants cut out the middlemen so that both they and the missionaries make a profit. Missionaries pay African peasants between 10 shillings and £1 more than do government agents, and even so they obtain their maize cheaper than if they bought it through government recognized channels. In these transactions no levy for the African Development Fund is deducted. Such sales are legal if the mission station is situated in the same tribal trust land in which the producers live; if the mission lies outside the tribal trust land boundary, such sales are illegal. Yet whether legal or illegal, such sales are frequent, and 14·3 per cent of all surplus maize grown by peasant cultivators is sold directly to missionaries.

The third and most common market is to fellow peasants. Of all surplus millet produced 92·1 per cent is sold directly to the people, and so is 71·4 per cent of all maize, 66·7 per cent of all groundbeans, 60·0 per cent of all groundnuts and 21·4 per cent of all sorghum. Peasants who can withhold their maize for several months, can sell it at higher prices, often at £2 or more a bag, before the next harvest is reaped.

Thus prices vary not only between markets but also throughout the year. After the harvest prices are lowest, and only those peasants sell who are either in urgent need of cash or who want to sell their maize in bulk.

The practice of selling surpluses to neighbours means that peasant cultivators make only a minute contribution to the national cash economy. Produce sold within the community does not increase the community's wealth. A community which just manages to feed itself has no money to spare for local development and consequently tribal trust lands, just as individual peasant cultivators, are caught in a vicious circle of poverty from which they cannot extricate themselves.

Many peasants try to increase their income by brewing beer. If a bag of sorghum is used for beer brewing, it brings in four times as much money than if it is sold as grain. Many peasant families, therefore, prefer to invest the extra labour in beer brewing and so increase their income.[1]

The extensive sale of surplus crops within tribal trust lands has created fixed selling and buying patterns. Some subchiefdoms or neighbourhoods sell their surpluses of one crop to members of another subchiefdom or neighbourhood who lack this particular crop, and poorer communities depend on the surpluses of richer communities. Thus people from the Shoko Murewa community generally buy additional food from members of the Shoko Museamwa community. Most master farmers have a permanent clientele and trading patterns often cut across political allegiances. In Shoko chiefdom these trade links are among the few ties which hold together a chiefdom divided by constant faction fights.

Because of the various channels through which crops are sold and the great variations in price, it is unrealistic to adopt the prices fixed in the Government Gazette as a measure of the value of locally produced crops. I therefore recorded in every single transaction the amount sold and the price paid. From these figures I calculated the average local price for every crop in each season. It is these prices which are used in the following analysis.

In the 1965–66 season, when rain was adequate, the average master farmer harvested crops worth £104 and sold crops worth £56. Other peasant cultivators reaped in the year of the average rainfall crops worth £36, of which they sold crops to the value of £6.[2] In the drought year of 1966–67, the average master farmer family reaped crops worth £19, of which they sold crops worth £9. The other peasant cultivators reaped during that season crops worth £17 per family and sold crops to the value of £2.[3]

If income from crops is expressed in relation to the acreage on which it is produced, the more efficient methods of master farmers stand out clearly. In a year of average rainfall, master

[1] The recent establishment of beer halls by local councils in rural areas is a serious threat to this source of income since they divert profits from local peasants to European commercial companies and local authorities. Peasants, especially women, strongly object to council beer halls.

[2] A. F. Hunt, a Rhodesian agriculturalist, writes that the income of ordinary peasant cultivators from crops averages some £20 to £25 gross or £18 to £20 nett per annum, and that the income of master farmers is about four times as large. A. F. Hunt, 1966, p. 3. For similar data on peasant productivity see also Johnson, 1964d, pp. 102 and 104.

[3] Holleman writes that in an agriculturally poor season in another tribal trust land with a higher annual rainfall, the average income of master farmers was about £62, and that of other peasant cultivators about £17. Holleman, 1969, p. 59.

farmers reap £12 worth of crops per acre, but ordinary peasant cultivators only £6.14s.0d. This yield of £12 per acre is very high for peasant dry land cultivation and exceeds, as a later chapter will show, the output of peasant farmers in purchase areas. Master farmers in tribal trust lands, therefore, stand out as a most successful group among Rhodesian peasants.

Apart from crops, peasant cultivators raise some money through selling vegetables, fruit, milk and eggs. About half of all master farmers sell these items regularly either in the local provincial town or at nearby mission hospitals, but only 21 out of the 144 ordinary peasant cultivators gain money from this source. In 1965–66, the average master farmer, who sold such items, raised some £8; of the ordinary peasant cultivators, only ten gained more than £5 from these sales. If these incomes are averaged out among all peasant families, the contribution from this source is as low as £4 in master farmer families and £2 in the families of other peasant cultivators. In a drought year income from these sales falls to £2 per master farmer family and to a mere 2 shillings in the families of ordinary peasant cultivators.

In a year of average rainfall, therefore, income from the sale of crops, vegetables, fruit, milk and eggs, amounts to £60 in the families of master farmers and to £38 in the families of ordinary peasant cultivators. In a drought season such income falls to £21 a year for master farmer families and to £9 a year for the families of other peasant cultivators. These figures show that in a drought year peasant cultivators have hardly any money on hand from agriculture for regular expenses, however urgent these may be; and if purchases for additional food are taken into account, most family budgets show a deficit.

These considerations have not yet taken into account production costs. Apart from ordinary peasant cultivators, who in a drought year use their seed grain as food, production costs do not vary between drought years and years of average rainfall. The average master farmer family spends some £2 a year on seed, £4 on fertilizer, and £1 on labour, thus investing some £7 a year in the land. No depreciation costs of agricultural implements are included, nor the value of family labour, since such figures are too difficult to obtain for Karanga peasant communities.

Ordinary peasant cultivators spend less money. Only in a drought year do they buy seed for about £1 per family. Their average expenditure on fertilizer is as low as 10 shillings per family, since few of them ever buy fertilizer. But expenditure on labour is higher among them than among master farmers if the grain brewed into beer for work parties is taken into account. For whereas master farmers pay on the average £1 for labourers ordinary peasant cultivators pay about £2 per family on work parties. The total investment of ordinary peasant cultivators on crop production is, therefore, £2.10.0 in a year of average rainfall and £3.10.0 in a drought year.

These figures show that both groups of peasant cultivators invest little money in their land, though the investment of master farmers is twice as high as that of their neighbours. In 1964 only 94 out of 7,800, or 1·2 per cent, of all peasant cultivators in the Shoko-Ngara tribal trust land and only 40 out of 3,863, or 1·1 per cent, of all peasant cultivators in the Shoko tribal trust land used fertilizer. A local fertilizer company calculated that fertilizer worth £8.10.0 ought to be put on every acre planted with maize. Hence even those peasants who do use fertilizer, spread it far too thinly to derive maximum benefit from it.[1]

The possibilities of improvement open to peasant agriculture in tribal trust lands can be seen from the crop yields obtained by the most successful peasants. The best master farmer in the two tribal trust lands reaped on eight acres crops worth £325, and the best ordinary peasant cultivator reaped crops worth £125. If these record yields were attained by a large majority of all peasant cultivators, tribal trust lands would be much more prosperous than they are today. To achieve higher yields, peasant cultivators must be able to set aside money for improved seed and fertilizer. Even the slight investment of master farmers shows that with some fertilizer yields can be doubled.[2]

(4) ANIMAL HUSBANDRY

The Karanga say that the land is their life and that cattle are their wealth. I have shown that cattle are essential for peasant agriculture. Cattle are the only draught power available to most cultivators; they provide manure for the fields and meat for the

[1] For a similar lack of investment in crop production and consequent low output of peasants, see Dequin, 1969, p. 48, in his study of Malawi peasant agriculture.

[2] In the year of average rainfall master farmers reaped crops worth £104, but ordinary peasant cultivators reaped only £36 worth of crops. This difference is not solely due to better equipment and more adequate labour. The use of fertilizer has also contributed to it.

people. When cash is urgently required, especially when the crops fail, cattle can be sold to raise the necessary money to meet family needs. In addition to these economic services, cattle play an essential role in the social and religious life of the people. Hence cattle are very highly valued and the Karanga are most reluctant to sell them.

The people's reluctance to sell their cattle is not fully appreciated by civil servants. In 1970 the Secretary for Internal Affairs stated that Africans owned a record number of two million head of cattle, worth between £50 million and £60 million, and expressed the hope that this 'fantastic but latent potential of wealth' be exploited for the national economy.[1] The reason why members of the Ministry of Internal Affairs press Africans to sell their livestock is concern for the land. Land shortage, partly due to the alienation of African land to European farmers, partly due to a rapid increase in African cattle herds, has caused havoc to tribal trust land pastures. These pastures are now heavily overstocked, the soil is eroded, and the bush is encroaching so that village herds can no longer be adequately fed. Compulsory de-stocking under the Land Husbandry Act aimed at reclaiming the grazing land in the tribal areas, but it aroused violent opposition among cattle owners. In the Shiri-Ngara tribal trust land, which in 1958 had its cattle herd reduced by 60 per cent, peasants rioted. They stoned local dip tanks and burned the hide sheds.

When in the 1960s control over the natural resources of tribal trust lands was returned to chiefs, the temporary improvement achieved by the Land Husbandry Act was soon lost. Agricultural staff estimate that in the Shiri-Ngara tribal trust land, with its low and uncertain rainfall, one head of cattle needs 14 acres of grazing land to feed it throughout the year. In 1962 this tribal trust land had a cattle population of 15,800 and each beast had 5·6 acres for grazing. By 1967 the herd had increased to 29,755, leaving less than 3 acres for each beast. In the Shoko tribal trust land 8,400 head of cattle had in 1962 some ten acres each for grazing. By 1967 the herd had increased to 10,970. In addition the grazing land had been drastically reduced by chief Shoko's allocation of fields in the chiefdom's pastures. As a result the grazing land in both tribal trust lands has deteriorated.[2] In the

---

[1] *The Rhodesia Herald*, 9.7.1970.
[2] For detailed information on the condition of the grazing land in the two tribal trust lands, see Appendix, Table 44.

Shiri-Ngara tribal trust land broad gullies have formed in the
grazing land. Gullies have also ruined the grazing in the Shoko
Murewa community. But the Shoko Museamwa community
has been hit hardest. This area had always had better pastures
than the other communities since its grazing land consisted of
sweet annual grasses, whereas the other areas had mainly perennial
sour grasses. Hence the herd of the Shoko Museamwa community used to be well fed. When the chief allocated land in
the grazing area, pastures deteriorated rapidly. The cattle ate the
sweet grasses in the remaining land before they could seed. By
1966 the grazing land was covered with witch weed, a parasite
which grows on plants in poor soil. By 1970 grazing was confined
to the hills and all land which could possibly be ploughed was used
for crop production. During the drought of 1966–67, 101 head of
cattle, or 8 per cent of the total herd of the community, died.
Most peasants ate the meat of the carcasses, only a few were able
to sell some of it.

Recognizing the importance of cattle in peasant agriculture as
well as the shortage of grazing land, the agricultural staff tried to
improve the condition of the veld and the quality of the herds.
Veld improvements have almost everywhere failed, but attempts to
improve the quality of the cattle have partly succeeded.

In the Shiri-Ngara tribal trust land agricultural officers tried to
persuade cultivators to grow supplementary fodder on two of their
eight acres, but no peasant accepted this advice. In Shoko chiefdom
the agricultural staff tried to stop bush encroachment by encouraging peasants to cut down shrubs and trees in their grazing
lands, but cultivators refused the work for a communal goal. The
agriculturalists then advised the people to paddock their pastures
so that through rotational grazing parts could rest. One village
accepted this advice, but when a neighbouring village saw the
unused grazing land, it drove its herd into the resting paddock.
The villagers reacted by abandoning rotational grazing and drove
their neighbours' cattle out. Neither tribal trust land had by 1970
accepted extension advice on veld improvement, though in other
areas of Rhodesia rotational grazing has been successfully adopted.[1]

Advice on how to improve the quality of the herds has been
more readily accepted. Cattle dipping, which is compulsory, is
universally practised. The Shiri-Ngara tribal trust land has 16
cattle dips, the Shoko tribal trust land eight. Every week during

[1] Cf. Staunton, 1969.

the wet season and every fortnight during the dry season all cattle are driven to these dip tanks where they have to swim through a solution of arsenic to free them from ticks. In addition many cattle owners pick by hand any ticks they see on their livestock. Dipping protects the health of the cattle, but it greatly increases soil erosion, for the large cattle tracks, which converge on the dip tanks, are washed out by the rains and soon turn into gullies.

In the master farmer training sessions, members of the extension staff place special emphasis on animal husbandry. They teach that with improved livestock management a cow can calve every year, whereas at present the average cow in the two tribal trust lands has a calf only every three years, and few of these calves survive or grow into healthy stock. The reason is that peasant cultivators let the bulls run with the cows all the year round so that many calves are born in January and February, just before the dry season begins. Many calves, therefore, either die of starvation or, if they do survive, develop into inferior stock.

Master farmers greatly appreciate advice in animal husbandry. After one training session a progressive peasant commented: 'I am very pleased with this information. We are told to treat cows and oxen like human beings and to look after them when they are sick. Long ago we gave our cattle no shelter against the rain. Now we treat them as if they were our children.'

The most successful extension advice was the revolutionary suggestion that Africans stall-feed their cattle. Cattle fattening has a double advantage. Only old cattle are fattened for sale, that is, stock which is no longer useful for ploughing and which fetches very low prices when sold in its emaciated condition. Cattle fattening also reduces pressure on the communal pastures and makes a cattle owner independent of the grazing practices of his neighbours. This last point is of great importance since the Karanga are very reluctant to cooperate on communal projects.

After some initial resistance, cattle fattening became widely accepted and in 1970 a district commissioner in the Victoria province claimed that the Cold Storage Commission, a statutory body for the purchasing of cattle and beef, received enough stall-fed cattle from African peasants in the province to meet one twelfth of its annual requirements for the processing of beef. In 1967 the peasants of Shoko tribal trust land sold 85 fattened cattle to the Cold Storage Commission, or almost one per cent of their total herd. Peasants in the Shiri-Ngara tribal trust land sold that year to the Cold Storage Commission only 41 stall-fed cattle, or 0·2 per cent of their total herd.

Cattle fattening demands a small initial investment so that men who have a regular income, such as a teacher's salary, show more interest in the scheme than other peasant cultivators. One cattle owner fattened an old ox which, had he sold it immediately, would have brought him about £15. He bought one drum of molasses for £2, one bar of salt for £1 and one block of ruvenite for 15 shillings. He also employed a young man for the additional work involved, such as cutting grass, and paid him £1.5.0 a month. When he sold the ox to the Cold Storage Commission, he paid 13 shillings to transport the animal to the depot. His total outlay was thus about £6. He sold the ox for £53, making a profit of about £32.

Another man bought an ox for £19, fattened it, and sold it for £35. His expenditure amounted to £6 so that he made a profit of £9. A third man fattened four head of cattle and was paid out £170. Since his family provided all extra labour involved, his only expenses were the extra food he bought for the oxen.

In the Shoko Museamwa community, the most progressive master farmers formed in 1968 a 'cattle feeders' club' whose aim is to share their knowledge of cattle husbandry and to buy animal remedies in common so that they can increase their income from livestock.[1] Most members of the 'cattle feeders' club' are also members of the 'cash crop farmers' club'. This means that families with large incomes from crops also get the highest returns from their cattle.

(5) CATTLE SALES

Though the grazing areas of Karangaland are overstocked, individual peasant families have too few cattle to meet their agricultural needs. If a peasant decides to sell an ox, not only his own household, but also his extended family is affected by it since oxen are pooled during the ploughing season. If a peasant after much deliberation decides to sell a beast, he expects a certain minimum price below which he will not sell. This minimum price is often determined by a particular need. One man, for

[1] Like the 'cash crop farmers' club', the 'cattle feeders' club' was not stopped by the chief. Both seemed too unimportant to him.

example, whose daughter suffered from paralysis, decided to sell an ox to take her to Bulawayo for medical treatment. He expected to receive £25 but was offered only £15. He therefore refused to sell and let his daughter stay in the village without medical care.

In the past, especially during the compulsory destocking under the Land Husbandry Act, Africans experienced difficulties in selling their cattle. Government therefore instituted sponsored auction sales in tribal areas. The first auction sales were started in 1948, but only in the 1950s did they become widespread. By 1969 there were 122 sales pens in African areas[1] at which auction sales should take place every two months. Very often, however, sales are cancelled, sometimes because a disease has broken out in the area, and sometimes simply because too few cattle are on offer. In the Shiri-Ngara tribal trust land, for example, three successive sales were cancelled in 1963 because too few cattle were brought to the sales pen. On the fourth occasion, when 60 beasts were brought for sale, the auctioneer was inclined to cancel it again, but the agricultural staff urged him to proceed since the local grazing land was in very poor condition. If an auctioneer cancels a sale, he receives a flat minimum fee from government which may in fact be higher than his commission from a poor sale.

Auction sales are subject to heavy deductions. Ten per cent of the offered price is taken as a levy for the African Development Fund, $7\frac{1}{2}$ per cent is deducted as handling charges, and $1\frac{1}{2}$ per cent as a commission for the auctioneer. Because of these heavy deductions many peasants merely take their cattle to the auction to have them valued and then withdraw them to sell them to local butchers or to other buyers.[2] In the Shiri-Ngara tribal trust land, for example, only a small proportion of all cattle brought to the sales are actually sold. During the sale in March 1964 of 122 cattle brought for sale only 31 or 25·4 per cent were sold.[3] Of the total herd in this tribal trust land, 11 per cent annually change hands, yet only 5 per cent are sold at auction sales.

---

[1] S.I.A., 1970, pp. 18–19.

[2] Some Africans then take their cattle to a European farmer friend who sells their cattle for them at a sale for European owned cattle. In this way African peasants make a profit since no deductions are made for the African Development Fund and more buyers are present which pushes up the prices. Such sales are illegal, but not infrequent.

[3] See Appendix, Tables 45 and 46.

Auction sales are announced to cattle owners when they bring their cattle for dipping. The sales are attended by three groups of people: firstly, by the representative of the firm of auctioneers, the grader and civil servants of the Ministry of Internal Affairs; secondly, by African peasants who bring their cattle for sale; and thirdly, by buyers. These may occasionally include an African butcher from the tribal trust land, often some European farmers who buy up poor stock for fattening on their farms, and always a representative of the Cold Storage Commission. At times the representative of the Cold Storage Commission is the only buyer. Then only the guaranteed minimum prices are paid.

Minimum prices are taken from a table listing the current grade-price structure. Cattle are graded according to their quality and then weighed. The Cold Storage Commission is bound by a government contract to buy up all stock which does not sell and on the average the Commission buys some 90 per cent of all cattle at these sales. In order to keep cattle sales constant throughout the year, government orders that higher prices be paid at the end of the dry season when the quality of the cattle is poor, and lower prices at the end of the rainy season when the quality is better. Yet since cattle are most urgently needed during the first rains, need for draught animals prevents peasants from availing themselves of the higher prices.

The previous chapter showed that master farmers have more cattle than ordinary peasant cultivators and also indicated that master farmers take a more commercial attitude towards their livestock than their neighbours who are more bound by traditional values and who do not regard cattle as commercial assets but as extensions of the family and channels through which human relationships are established and maintained. With larger herds and a more thorough knowledge of good animal husbandry, master farmers make a larger profit from their cattle than other peasant cultivators. In 1965–66, when the rains were normal, master farmers had a cash income from the sale of cattle of about £15 per family. This means that almost all master farmers sold one beast that year. Ordinary peasant cultivators had an average cash income of only £4 that year from their livestock. This means that only one in four families sold a beast.[1] These figures show that master farmers make more than three times as much money from their cattle as do ordinary peasant cultivators. This

---

[1] For the average value of cattle see Appendix, Tables 45 and 46.

higher return is partly due to their interest in cattle fattening. In drought years cattle sales increase in importance, for when the crops fail many men sell cattle to buy food. Thus the average master farmer family sold cattle worth £25 in 1966–67, and the average family of ordinary peasant cultivators sold cattle worth £8. This means that most master farmer families sold one to two beasts each, and every second other peasant family sold one beast. Heavy sales of livestock by ordinary peasant cultivators in a drought year raise serious problems in the next ploughing season.

The low income of tribal trust land peasants from their livestock, especially the low income of ordinary peasant cultivators, seems to be due to the communal grazing arrangement. The average acre of grazing land produces two shillings worth of cash, when measured in term of sale of livestock. To this must be added draught power which cattle provide for their owners. Even so the return from grazing land is a tiny fraction of the cash value derived from arable land. It seems possible to increase return from grazing land by making individual peasants responsible for the land on which their own cattle graze. Such individual responsibility is likely to improve pastures, for a comparison with grazing land in purchase areas[1] shows that pastures which are individually owned are better cared for and less eroded than communal pastures.

(6) TOTAL INCOME OF PEASANT CULTIVATORS

This and the preceding chapter analysed the various sources of income on which peasant cultivators can draw. Table 13 overleaf summarizes these findings.

If the expenditure on seed, fertilizer and labour is subtracted from these total incomes, the average income of master farmers in a year of adequate rainfall is £128 and in a drought year some £54. The average income of other peasant cultivators in a year of adequate rainfall is some £60.10.0 and in a year of drought some £44.10.0. In a year of average rainfall, the total income of master farmers is about twice as large as that of their neighbours, but in a drought year this difference decreases. This narrowing difference between master farmers and other peasant cultivators

---

[1] See chapter 10.

TABLE 13

Average Incomes of Peasant Cultivators (N=163)

	Master Farmers				Other Peasant Cultivators			
	1965–66		1966–67		1965–66		1966–67	
Sources of Income	£	%	£	%	£	%	£	%
Crops	104	77·1	19	30·2	36	57·1	17	35·4
Cattle	15	11·1	25	39·7	4	6·4	8	16·7
Milk, eggs, fruit, vegetables	4	2·9	2	3·1	2	3·1	—	—
Salaries	11	8·2	12	19·1	10	15·9	9	18·7
Craft	1	0·7	2	3·1	1	1·6	1	2·1
Wages	—	—	3	4·8	10	15·9	13	27·1
Total	135	100·0	63	100·0	63	100·0	48	100·0

in a drought season is due to the heavy reliance of master farmers on agriculture.

In a year of average rainfall income from salaries, crafts, and from the wages of labour migrants, amounts to only £12 or 8·9 per cent of the total income of master farmers. In a drought year this non-agricultural income is not greatly increased since only a few master farmers leave for urban employment. That this income then amounts to 27 per cent of their total income is merely due to the reduced total earnings.

Among ordinary peasant cultivators the situation is quite different. Even in a year of average rainfall these families rely heavily on income from wages and salaries. Non-agricultural income then amounts to £21 or 33·4 per cent of their total earnings. Due to low sales of agricultural produce, wages and salaries provide the major part of money available to these peasant families. In a drought year this non-agricultural income is only slightly increased, for even if more men go to town in search of work, competition for jobs is high and many remain unemployed. Non-agricultural income then amounts to £23 or 47·9 per cent of the total income. In any year, therefore, ordinary peasant cultivators balance their budget to a large extent through a steady non-agricultural income.

(7) CONCLUSION

This and the last chapter showed that master farmers and ordinary peasant cultivators are not only differentiated by unequal earnings, but also by different modes of life. Although ordinary peasant cultivators spend half of their working life in European employment, they remain deeply rooted in the tribal system. Their very absences from the land force their families to rely heavily on the help of fellow villagers so that mutual obligations between kinsmen and neighbours knit local communities closely together. If these peasant cultivators invest little money in their land, they invest a great deal in social relationships. Many of them feel closely bound to their chiefs.

Such men, though by no means satisfied with their poverty, have no plans of permanently leaving their villages. They regard the tribal trust land as their home and merely hope that their children will have a better future. Hence they save money to send their children to school. Few ordinary peasant cultivators expect that the land will ever provide them or their children with more than food. In fact, most realize that in the very near future the land will no longer be able to feed them. Increasing landlessness among the younger men causes increasing insecurity and malaise.

Master farmers, though they spend almost all their time in the rural area, are far less integrated in the mutual system of indebtedness than are ordinary peasant cultivators. They are largely independent of their neighbours' help. They have no need to borrow cattle or farming implements; they have enough labour, and if they are short of workers can hire the men they need. Because of their investment in superior housing and agricultural equipment they can, if they wish, avail themselves of credit facilities offered by government or private companies. Hence master farmers are free from many of the limitations hindering ordinary peasant cultivators from moving into the cash economy.

Their self-sufficiency also frees master farmers from local opinion and enables them to experiment with modern farming techniques. Some desire still greater freedom and do all in their power to move out of the tribal system into a purchase area where neither kinsmen nor chiefs can hinder their economic progress, where they can re-invest their profits in land that is theirs, and where agriculture on a larger scale seems to promise them great wealth. Those master farmers who intend to stay permanently in the tribal trust lands are often teachers or close relatives of their chiefs. The desire of many master farmers to move out of the tribal areas makes them marginal to tribal agriculture, and the constant movement of the most capable men out of the tribal trust lands leaves these areas with those men who are least capable of developing them.

CHAPTER 6

PROFILES OF
PEASANT CULTIVATORS

(1) INTRODUCTION

The preceding chapters studied communities and groups of peasants in tribal trust lands rather than individuals. In this way certain characteristics of master farmers and other peasant cultivators could be isolated. Yet, as Blake writes, 'General Forms have their vitality in Particulars, and every Particular is a Man'.[1] This chapter, therefore, sets out in the form of case histories how individual master farmers and other peasant cultivators live, how they face their economic problems, and how they are caught up in, and even determined by, social and economic factors.

The case histories have been selected so as to represent a typical cross section of all peasant cultivators. Table 4 in chapter 4 sets out the agricultural incomes of master farmers and other peasant cultivators. The case histories have been selected with the help of this Table so that they include both successful and unsuccessful peasant cultivators in the proportion in which these occur in the wider population.[2]

The other characteristics of master farmers and ordinary peasant cultivators have also been checked. Table 5 in chapter 5, for example, sets out the education of peasant cultivators. The case histories have taken account of the educational levels achieved among African peasants. They have also taken into account the experience of labour migration of master farmers and other peasant cultivators; their implements have been compared with those possessed in the larger sample, and so have their agricultural practices, such as their use of work parties or hired and family labour. These case histories, therefore, are a fair cross section of peasant cultivators in tribal trust lands.

All the case histories presented in this book are ranked according

[1] Quoted in Turner, 1957, p. xvii.
[2] For the selection of the case histories from the wider sample see Appendix, Table 48.

to the agricultural success of the peasants. All the names are fictitious.

(2) PROFILES OF MASTER FARMERS

(a) *Thomas, the Agricultural Leader of the Shoko Museamwa Community*

Thomas is the son of an important village headman in the Shoko Museamwa community and claims that his father was a kind of subchief, though government had never officially recognized him as such. Born in 1922, Thomas went for seven years to a boarding school in Gwelo, a town some 110 miles distant from his village, for in his youth no village school offered more than three years' education. During his holidays he occasionally earned his school fees as a domestic servant, being paid 12s. 6d. a month.

In 1945 Thomas began his career as a labour migrant. At a nearby Christian mission he learned bricklaying and worked for the missionaries for two years at £2.5.0 a month. Later he worked for two years in Gwelo, earning a monthly wage of £5. By 1948 he had saved money for a plough and four head of cattle. He had also saved money for his bridewealth and married in the same year. By 1967 his wife had borne him three boys and four girls, all of whom went to school as soon as they were six years old.

In the early 1950s Thomas worked twice as a bricklayer during the agricultural off seasons, first at a rural development project, then in Salisbury. He earned £7 and £15 a month respectively. Yet in spite of his increasing wages, he saved very little. He only bought a harrow. The rest of the money he spent on himself and his family. By 1952 he had spent five years in European employment.

One day, while Thomas was ploughing his fields, an agricultural extension assistant commented on his inability to show much for his work for Europeans and suggested that he give up labour migration and concentrate on farming. Thomas carefully weighed the pros and cons and agreed. His first son was about a year old, his wife was expecting the second child, and he liked staying with his family. He also wanted more money. He therefore joined the local master farmer training sessions and in less than two years qualified as a master farmer.

Thomas was a determined man. He immediately put into practice what he learned and already his first harvest as a master farmer brought him a substantial surplus. With it he bought a cultivator. In 1954 he bought a cart, in 1960 a planter and a three section harrow, and in 1966 a water cart. That year he also erected a fence around his property. In 1967 he installed a grinding mill at his home and in 1969 he opened a grocery store. Within a few years, therefore, his agricultural surpluses allowed Thomas to buy adequate farming implements and to set up a mill and a store. But he never bought a second and better plough, for he preferred to hire a tractor from a nearby mission. The missionaries ploughed his land for £1.5.0 an acre. Thomas thought that land ploughed by tractor gave better yields than land shallowly ploughed by the light ploughs owned by Africans.

Thomas never invited work parties because he distrusted the accuracy of their work. As a Seventh Day Adventist he also objected to beer brewing. By 1967 several of his children and some relatives helped him on the land. He employed a man in his mill and left the store to his wife. He also used to hire labourers in his fields. By 1967 he had employed an elderly man for two years at a monthly wage of £2 and a herd boy at 10s. a month. During the weeding season he regularly employed casual labourers whom he paid in food. In the late 1960s, when Thomas went in for cotton growing, his expenditure on labour increased, but he still insisted on hired labourers and refused to call in work parties.

In addition to buying farming implements and investing money in buildings, Thomas invested money in his land. He bought large amounts of fertilizer, improved seed and whatever else the agricultural staff recommended to him. As soon as loans became available to peasant cultivators, Thomas applied for them and did so in every subsequent year in spite of his savings in the bank, for he enjoyed the visits of government officials who checked on his capital assets and declared him credit-worthy. Such visits increased his prestige in the eyes of his neighbours.

Thomas also founded several agricultural societies and became their chairman. He was therefore the undisputed leader in agriculture in the whole tribal trust land.

Thomas became the fifth master in his tribal trust land. His four predecessors, however, had left the area to take up purchase area farms. Thomas too was offered a farm, but he refused to accept it. He wanted to be an important man in his chiefdom rather than an ordinary peasant farmer in a purchase area. In 1965–66 he reaped crops worth £228.

5

Thomas' agricultural success is due to a variety of factors. As son of a local leader he inherited good land and a number of cattle from his father. His father had also sent him to a good school so that he had more education than other men of his age. These factors, as well as his intelligence and hard work, and his close cooperation with the agricultural staff, seem the reasons for his success.

Thomas opened his mill and store after a succession of drought years for he realized that in a region of marginal rainfall a man is unable to maintain a high living standard if he relies exclusively on agriculture. Just as economic considerations, therefore, induced him to give up labour migration in favour of agriculture, so economic considerations motivated him to invest his money in business. His ability to pay wage labourers enabled him to run such enterprises without endangering his agricultural activities.

(b) Timothy, the Enterprising Peasant

Unlike Thomas, Timothy could not rely on help from his father to set him off in agriculture. He was a stranger in Shiri chiefdom and inherited neither land nor cattle. Yet he gathered around him enough people, all strangers like himself, so that in the early 1950s he became a village headman.

Born in 1910, Timothy attended the local primary school for five years and then worked in several mining settlements some 30 to 50 miles from his village. From 1924 to 1925 he was employed as a cook for the workers in an asbestos mine, and from 1926 to 1930 he worked underground. In these years he earned about £1 a month. He saved some money and bought a plough. Then he went home and cultivated his fields.

In 1932 he sought work in a chrome mine, and in 1933 he was employed as a gardener in still another nearby mining settlement. From 1936 to 1938 he worked in a timber yard. In these years, too, Timothy earned only about £1 a month. In 1938, after seven years in European employment, he returned permanently to the rural area.

In 1935 Timothy married his first wife who bore him a daughter. He divorced her in 1938 and remarried. His second wife bore him two boys and two girls. In 1957 he divorced her too. In 1959 he married again, and this marriage still existed at the time of the survey. His third wife bore Timothy two boys and one girl so that by 1967 he had eight children.

After his uneventful and unsuccessful life as a labour migrant, Timothy took to farming. He began training as a master farmer and obtained his certificate in 1942. He became the first master farmer in Shiri chiefdom. He then joined a training course for builders and in 1946 obtained a builder's certificate. Timothy obtained this qualification at an opportune time, for the centralization policy had just been implemented in Shiri chiefdom and several people, especially teachers, wanted to live in brick houses. Timothy obtained several contracts and also built some local stores.

With money from his agricultural surplus and from his craft Timothy bought a plough, a harrow and a cultivator. In 1954 he bought a cart for £60 and in 1959 a sewing machine for his wife for £45. Next he purchased corrugated iron sheets for £27 to cover his three-roomed brick house, which he had built for his family, and then he bought fencing material for £50 to enclose his homestead and his fields. Later he bought two drums for £26 to fetch water from the river for his kitchen garden.

In 1960 Timothy decided to build a dam to irrigate a garden to grow vegetables for sale. At the recommendation of a missionary, he helped in 1962 to found a cooperative society of which he became the first chairman. Through this society he obtained in 1965 a loan of £85 for hiring machinery to construct the dam and to buy a pump. He signed a contract to repay the loan within nine years. With his savings he bought cement for £48 and aluminium sprays for £38. He then employed three labourers for £2.5.0 a month each. With their help he completed the dam in 1966.

In 1967 Timothy began irrigating a larger vegetable garden and sold £35 worth of vegetables to the nearby towns, mining settlements and to the mission hospital. He also used his dam as a fish pond. In 1966 he bought two pounds of fish for 12 shillings and by 1967 sold fish to the local people for 17 shillings.

In addition to farming, gardening and fish breeding, Timothy also raised rabbits. In 1964 he bought four rabbits, and when they had multiplied sold them at 15 shillings each to his neighbours. These various activities were suggested to Timothy by the agricultural staff with whom he closely cooperated. They were all connected with agriculture and integrated with each other. Thus kitchen refuse was used to feed the fish, and rabbit droppings were put into the vegetable garden.

Timothy was a good peasant cultivator. He was one of the first men in Shiri chiefdom who used fertilizer in his fields. In 1965–66 he reaped £87 worth of crops. Yet unlike Thomas, Timothy had not totally abandoned traditional agricultural practices. Whenever he was short of labour, he called in work parties. But he also hired labourers when he needed skilled or accurate assistance.

(c) *Titus, the Teacher*

Born in 1915 in the Shiri-Ngara tribal trust land as the second son of a village headman, Titus completed his primary education at a local mission station. As a youth he worked for one year in a hotel in a nearby mining town washing dishes. He earned 15 shillings a month, and then returned in 1931 to his parents.

In 1935 he was admitted to a teacher training college run by missionaries and qualified as one of the first teachers in his tribal trust land. During his college years he also received training as a builder. Though he obtained his diploma in 1937, he found employment as a teacher only in 1952. During the intervening years he worked as a builder and boarding master at a mission station where he was paid £2.10.0 a month. He married in 1940. By 1967 his wife had borne him seven children, three of whom found work in town or married, one of whom trained as a nurse at a government hospital in Salisbury, and three of whom were still in school. Their school fees amounted to just over £50 a year.

When Titus was appointed as teacher at a village school in 1952, he earned a salary of £10 a month. In 1954 he was transferred to a mission station where soon afterwards he became headmaster of the local primary school. By then his salary had risen to £29 a month. Ever since Titus has had sufficient money for a variety of purposes, and he invested it both in agricultural equipment and in his land.

Titus has been interested in farming since the 1940s. His occupations as boarding master and teacher, with their occasional transfers, forced him to live outside his father's village. In 1959 he registered as a master farmer trainee and obtained his certificate in 1961. When in 1962 the first cooperative society was formed in Shiri chiefdom, he became its treasurer and his home the depot from which fertilizer and seed were distributed to the members. Titus had used fertilizer on his fields since the early 1960s, and in 1965–66 reaped crops worth £84.

By the time Titus was over fifty years old, he was a well-established and highly respected man in his chiefdom. Through the combined income from teaching and farming he had about £400 a year at his disposal. Though he spent most of his time in the classroom, he also worked in his fields. He refused to call in work parties, since he thought that brewing beer would lower his prestige as a headmaster. His wife and children helped on the land, and together with them he was able to carry out most of the work.

Over the years Titus bought a wide range of equipment. First he purchased a plough for £5, a cultivator for £7.5.0, a rake for £5 and two wheelbarrows for £6 each. Later he bought a cart for £45. In 1966 he decided to drill a borehole to irrigate a vegetable garden. He applied for a loan, had the land surveyed and the borehole sunk to a depth of 125 feet. This cost him £177.10.0. He paid £85 in cash from his own savings and signed a contract to pay the rest in instalments of £10 a year.

Titus was the most educated of the master farmers. When the missionaries enlisted his help to found a cooperative society and to get the people interested in fertilizer, his standing in the community as a teacher and headmaster greatly contributed to the success of the cooperative society.

Thomas, Timothy and Titus had much in common. All were looked up to as leaders. All had an income apart from crops and so were able to make investments which other peasant cultivators could not make. All had large families and were able to pay hired labourers. They were intelligent men whose economic decisions always proved profitable.

(d) Tobias, the Husband of a Hard-working Wife

Tobias, son of a local village headman in Shoko chiefdom, was born in 1917. He attended school for only three years and then helped his father in the field. In 1943 he married, and by 1967 his wife had borne him two boys and two girls. Tobias' wife was more educated than he was and encouraged him to improve himself. At his wife's request, therefore, Tobias went back to school for two more years and then trained as a builder at a government training centre near Salisbury. This centre, Domboshawa, was started in 1920 by a district commissioner who wanted to improve African agriculture and simultaneously teach Africans a number of skills useful in their villages.[1] Tobias was interested in building, but not in agriculture. Yet without qualifying as a master farmer

[1] Cf. The Sunday Mail, 26.6.70.

he could not attend the training centre. In 1951, therefore, he qualified as a builder and in 1954 as a master farmer.

When Tobias returned to his village, he built a fine brick house for his family, but few of his neighbours needed his services. Since in Shoko chiefdom the centralization policy had been implemented after many people had already built brick houses and on re-siting the village had had to abandon them, they were not willing to invest more money in buildings. Not finding work as a builder, Tobias turned to the agricultural staff for help. For two years they employed him as a supernumerary demonstrator to teach local peasants better farming methods. At first Tobias was paid £1 a month, later £2.

Since Tobias took to farming by force of circumstances, he was not an enthusiastic master farmer. The same plough, which he had bought in 1945, he still used in 1967. In 1953 he bought a harrow and a cultivator. He never used fertilizer. His wife did most of the field work, and if he needed more workers than his family could provide, he called in work parties. Tobias, therefore, did not distinguish himself significantly from ordinary peasant cultivators. In 1965–66 he reaped crops worth £57.

Tobias, a man with little education, no urban experience and no real interest in agriculture, still lived a reasonably comfortable life. The few exertions he made, he made at the urgings of his wife. But for her determination to feed and clothe her children well, Tobias' income might have been much lower.

(e) Tony, the Former Labour Migrant

Unlike the other master farmers, Tony spent many years of his life as a labour migrant. Born in 1912 a son of a commoner in Hove subchiefdom, Tony went to school for four years and in 1927 began his career as a wage earner. For three years he worked in a chrome mine near his tribal trust land, and from 1931 to 1946 in a gold mine in the same settlement. His wages rose over the years from 15 shillings a month to £2.5.0. He saved some money to pay his father-in-law a bridewealth of £30 and six head of cattle. By 1967 his wife had borne him two boys and two girls.

From 1947 to 1948 Tony worked in Salisbury for a monthly wage of £3. He saved some money and retired to his village at the age of 37. He bought two head of cattle for £14.10.0, a plough for £5 and a wheelbarrow for another £5. The rest of his savings he invested over the years in fertilizer.

In 1951 Tony began training as a master farmer. He used cattle manure in his fields and even bought fertilizer from his savings, but in spite of his eagerness he obtained his master farmer's certificate only in 1960 because he did not understand what he was taught and implemented most advice wrongly. At one time he applied for a purchase area farm, but his application was turned down. In 1965–66, when another master farmer in his village reaped crops worth £105, he himself only reaped £38 worth of crops. Tony, therefore, lived hardly above subsistence level and distinguished himself in nothing from ordinary peasant cultivators, except in his eagerness for farming.

Like most master farmers, Tony joined local agricultural associations. As soon as the 'progressive society' was formed in Hove subchiefdom, he became a member, and when the co-operative society was founded he became its first secretary. Through it he obtained some loans for fertilizer, once his savings from wage employment were exhausted.

Tony's agricultural failure was due to a number of factors. First of all, he was short of labour. Whenever his family could not cope with the work, he invited work parties, but never hired labourers, partly because he had no money and partly because he was easily satisfied and did not make as great demands on the workers as other master farmers did. Secondly, he was short of cash. To earn some money he trained as a builder. He obtained his builder's certificate in 1957. He constructed a few houses in his subchiefdom, but never seemed able to set money aside to buy agricultural tools. His shortage of farming implements was one of his greatest handicaps, for whenever he wanted to cart manure to his field, he hired a lorry. Borrowing equipment of various kinds proved very expensive, and once he had paid for the loans, he had no money over to buy his own. Thirdly, Tony lacked education and, apparently, a keen intelligence. The agricultural staff wrote him off as a poor peasant cultivator and only gave him his master farmer's certificate because of his perseverance. But they did not allow him to buy a farm. It also seems that Tony could have invested his meagre financial resources more profitably by buying his own equipment rather than paying constantly for loans.

Tony talked more about the traditional values of Karanga society than any of the other master farmers. In spite of his use of fertilizer and his membership of modern agricultural associations, he was satisfied with a moderate income from the land. He had

more in common with Tobias than with Thomas, Timothy and
Titus.

(3) EVALUATION OF THE CASE HISTORIES

The major characteristics of these five master farmers are set
out in Table 14.

TABLE 14

Characteristics of Five Master Farmers

Name	Income from crops	Year of birth	Educ. in years	Labour migrat. in years	Non-agricultural skills	No. of farming imps.	Office in agric. assoc.
Thomas	£228	1922	7	5	bricklayer	7	chairman (twice)
Timothy	£ 87	1910	5	7	builder	8	chairman
Titus	£ 84	1915	10	1	teacher, builder	7	treasurer
Tobias	£ 57	1917	5	—	builder	3	—
Tony	£ 37	1912	4	20	builder	2	secretary

Table 14 shows that all master farmers are middle-aged or
old. Those with more education tend to be the more successful.
All can read and write, even Tony who attended school for only
four years, for his local cooperative society elected him as secretary.
Labour migration played a very minor role in the life of all master
farmers except in Tony's, and all have been permanent rural
residents for many years. Labour migration has been described as
non-progressive in peasant agriculture, and Tony's agricultural
failure supports this description.

It is of interest that none of these master farmers relied exclusively on his agricultural income. All learned a trade and one,
Titus, was a trained teacher as well as a builder. All, therefore,
except Tony, lived in superior houses, symbols of their aspiration
to be regarded as modern and progressive men. Yet no master
farmer received a regular income from his building skill. The only
regular sources of additional income were the teacher's salary,
Thomas' shop and mill, and Timothy's dam, and through them
these men could finance their farming enterprises. Those who had
no such extra income reaped only moderately good harvests.

All master farmers, except Tobias, took an active part in

voluntary agricultural associations. In fact, it can be said that cooperative societies and other agricultural clubs in tribal trust lands are mainly joined by master farmers, and most of them are committee members. Leadership positions of all kinds are coveted by Africans, and even men like Tony strive for them because of the prestige they bring in village life.

The case histories also show that aptitude in farming can be measured by the number of years it takes an individual to obtain his master farmer's certificate. Thomas, Timothy and Titus obtained their certificates in less than two years. Tobias took four years, although he lived at an agricultural training centre and so had many advantages over other trainees who lived in villages. Tony took nine years to obtain his certificate, and his slow acquisition of farming skills is reflected in his poor harvests.

In the larger sample of 19 master farmers, the average man took three to four years to obtain his certificate. Those who took longer did so because they lacked money to buy fertilizer and farming implements, or because they lacked labour to carry out the additional work which modern farming methods required. Long years of training, therefore, reflect slow progress in learning and in the adoption of new techniques. The frequent use of work parties in preference to family and hired labour is also an indication of traditionalism and lack of progress.

These case histories of individual master farmers, therefore, illustrate the findings of the two preceding chapters which showed that agricultural success is associated with education which, it is assumed, opens a man's mind to modern ideas, with adequate financial resources to buy necessary farming implements, and with a labour force motivated to work hard and conscientiously. Conversely, men with little education and an interest in the traditional values of society, men with little money and a labour force consisting to a larger extent of members of communal work parties, are unlikely to be successful in their farming. This last conclusion is also illustrated by the case histories of ordinary peasant cultivators.

(4) PROFILES OF ORDINARY PEASANT CULTIVATORS

(a) Pancratius, the Unsuccessful Master Farmer Trainee

Born in 1920 in the Shoko Murewa community Pancratius attended school for only three years. At the age of 21 he was employed as a 'spanner boy' in a workshop in Bulawayo. He stayed in this job for 11 years, earning first £2 a month, later £3.10.0, and finally £4.15.0. During these years Pancratius lived a thrifty life and saved much money in the bank. He married, and by 1967 his wife had given birth to eleven children for whom, in the 1960s, he paid about £50 school fees a year.

In 1952 Pancratius returned permanently to his village. While still in employment, his wife and children cultivated his fields, and he inspected his land and livestock during his holidays. He also sold regularly some cattle and added the proceeds from their sales to his bank account. On retirement he had a total of £300 at hand.

In 1955 Pancratius decided to open a mill and bought a grinding machine for £370. He paid £290 in cash and the rest in instalments. The machine, however, was faulty. By the time he had paid for it, it had broken down completely and he had no money to pay for repairs.

Between 1958 and 1961 Pancratius trained as a master farmer, but he obtained no certificate because he fell ill and gave up his training. He never fully recovered his strength. His failure to become a master farmer distressed him greatly, for he ardently desired to buy a purchase area farm.

Though Pancratius did not possess a master farmer's certificate, he was a reasonably good cultivator. In 1965–66 he reaped crops worth £67. He was, however, short of equipment. He possessed only a plough. Had he bought various implements rather than the ill-fated grinding mill, his agricultural output might have been higher. His large family partly made up for the lack of tools, and he never had to call in work parties.

His large family, however, was not only an asset, it was also a constant source of financial worry. Not only did school fees swallow up most of his income, but his many children had also to be fed and clothed. Consequently Pancratius could no longer set aside any money, as he had done while still a labour migrant. Having no money to spare, he could not buy fertilizer. He had no chance of taking out a loan.[1]

Circumstances, therefore, prevented Pancratius from improving his economic position. He had been better off while still in European employment. In spite of his good crop yields, he regarded himself, and was regarded by his neighbours, as poor since both he and his family went about in threadbare clothes.

[1] Until 1964 only master farmers could take out loans.

(b) Patrick, the Peasant Cultivator who Refused Master Farmer Training

Born in 1920 in Shoko chiefdom, Patrick went to school for only two years. He could therefore neither read nor write. From 1931 to 1941 he worked for a local European farmer as a cart driver and earned £1.10.0 a month. He saved the money for his bridewealth, and also bought some cattle for himself. He married in 1943 and gave his father-in-law £20 and six head of cattle. By 1967 his wife had borne him seven children, three of whom had married or found work in town.

Between 1942 and 1953 Patrick trained at a nearby mission as a builder and earned £5 a month. From 1953 to 1961 the mission employed him as a trained craftsman and paid him £8 a month. Patrick bought five head of cattle with some of his savings, the rest he invested in his children's education. Between 1963 and 1964 he worked as a painter in a sugar estate of the Rhodesian lowveld for £24 a month. In 1965 he returned home, and whenever he had an opportunity he worked at the local mission as a painter. For this work he received £2 a week. Most of this money Patrick spent on food and clothing, or he invested it in agriculture. In addition to this steady and significant income from wage labour, Patrick received £5 every month from his eldest son who held a well-paid job in Salisbury. With his wages and remittances Patrick bought two ploughs, a harrow, a cultivator, a planter and a cart. He had therefore adequate implements to farm well.

Patrick was a reasonably good cultivator. In 1965–66 he reaped crops worth £48. Unlike most ordinary peasant cultivators, he never called in work parties. If his family could not cope with the work, he hired men on a piecework basis and paid them in cash. But he never used fertilizer or improved seed. Nor did he ever show any interest in master farmer training. In fact Patrick distrusted the Rhodesian government, and was opposed to any cooperation with civil servants which was not absolutely necessary. In this he resembled most of his neighbours. To justify his objection to progressive farming methods, he pointed to a relative who held a master farmer's certificate but who reaped less than he did. Patrick claimed that after 30 years' work for Europeans he knew what they were like and that they could not be trusted.

(c) Paul, the Young Nationalist

Paul is one of the youngest of all peasant cultivators. Born in 1940 in Hove subchiefdom, he completed his full primary education and then went to Salisbury to work. From 1958 to 1965 he was seasonally employed in a tobacco warehouse where he earned £14 a month during the auction sales. This seasonal employment enabled him to return regularly to his village to cultivate his own fields. When Rhodesia declared itself unilaterally independent, and when economic sanctions were imposed on the country, Paul lost his job. By then, however, he had bought a plough for £4.16.0 and a wheelbarrow for £5.10.0. In 1966 he was on the look-out for a cart, and when a neighbour offered a secondhand cart for sale, Paul bought it for £22. To raise the money, he sold a cow.

Paul liked farming. He had an average income from crops of about £40 a year. But he greatly objected to modern farming methods. He never used fertilizer and refused to join any agricultural society. He was a nationalist since his youth and stated that since his ancestors had never heard about modern farming practices and yet lived good lives, there was no need for their descendants to follow European methods of farming. To raise the living standards of African peasants, Paul demanded a subdivision of European farms, not an intensification of farming practices in overcrowded tribal trust lands. Since master farmers had opted for intensified farming, Paul accused them of having 'soft hearts' and of being servile to government officials. Paul longed for an open confrontation between Africans and Europeans, and stated that if peasant cultivators stood together in their demand for more land, they could overcome white domination.

Paul, with his politically motivated emphasis on traditional values, invited about four work parties a year to help him in the field. He never paid hired labourers. In 1967 his family was still relatively small. He had married and had two small children. His mother-in-law lived with him, but she was too old to help in the fields. He also supported three half-sisters who helped on the land, but their support cost him more than their contribution of labour helped him. To meet his family needs, Paul received some assistance from his father's brother who supplied him with food, and some money from a younger brother who worked in Salisbury.

This enmeshment in social obligations shows that though a

young and educated man, Paul accepted his traditional kinship obligations. In fact, his readiness to give and receive help was the conscious action of a young man who, as a devoted nationalist, objected to the values of an alien culture. Since modern farming methods were encouraged by civil servants, opposition to them was widespread among those Karanga who were strongly imbued with African nationalism.

(d) Peter, the Eternal Migrant

Peter is perhaps the most typical of all ordinary peasant cultivators. Born in 1905 in Shiri chiefdom, he went to school for five years and then, in 1923, began his career as a labour migrant. For four years he worked in Gwelo as an unskilled labourer for £1 a month. Then he returned home and worked at a local mission station for six years, earning £1.10.0 a month. He married in 1933 and used his savings to pay his father-in-law a bridewealth of £6 and eleven head of cattle. By 1967 his wife had borne him three children, one of whom had married, one of whom worked in Salisbury, and the youngest of whom still attended school.

Soon after his marriage Peter found work in a timber yard in a nearby mining settlement. There he earned £2 a month. From 1936 to 1942 he went once more to Gwelo and found work in a factory, being first paid £3 a month and later £4.10.0. From Gwelo he went to a Catholic mission station in the lowveld where he was employed as a builder for £6.10.0 a month. At the recommendation of the missionary in charge of that station, another mission employed Peter to build a small house and a latrine for £13. In 1944 he returned home, but since his village was near an expanding mission station, he was soon able to combine farming with building. When the missionaries built a grinding mill and a clinic, Peter was employed as a builder for £6.10.0 a month. From 1945 to 1951 he worked as a boarding master at the mission school for £3 a month.

In 1951 Peter went to a mine, some 30 miles from his home area, and found work for half a year at a wage of £2.10.0 a month. With his savings he bought a plough, the only farming implement he ever possessed. He then returned home for six years. During these years he became village headman, for his elder brother, who had been in charge of the village up to then, was deposed by government for accusing a villager of witchcraft.

In 1957 Peter once more left the village and worked for two

years in a paper factory in Salisbury at a monthly wage of £5. Back
in his village, the mission employed him as an assistant builder for
£2.10.0 a month. By that time Peter intended to retire to farming
for he was getting old, but the drought of 1966–67 drove him
once again to town. He looked for work for over half a year, but
found none. He was 61 years old, unskilled or semi-skilled, and
no longer strong enough to compete with younger men for heavy
work. Moreover, during a beer drink in his village he had been
embroiled in a fight and lost one eye so that he was half blind. He
therefore returned home without any cash earnings, but with
the realization that his future income would have to come
exclusively from the land.

Peter was a very average peasant cultivator. In 1965–66 he
reaped crops worth £22. He never used fertilizer or improved
seed, nor did he invest his wage earnings in farming implements
other than a plough. His family was always small. But for his hard-
working wife he had no other helpers. Consequently he relied
heavily on work parties. Work parties always attracted him,
not only for the work they did but also for the good company
they provided and the beer, for Peter was a sociable man. He liked
to be with people and he liked a good drink. In fact, Peter liked
most things in his life. There was only one thing he did not like,
and that was the European government and the rural poverty for
which he held the government responsible.

(e) Women Cultivators

Chapter 4 showed that 17·1 per cent of all peasant cultivators are
women. Most of these are widows who cultivate two or three
acres of land to grow millet, perhaps some maize, and some
groundnuts to feed themselves and some children or grandchildren.
Most live in poverty, reaping crops worth £5 to £12. Some
widows are assisted by their married sons. The lives of these
single women are mostly uneventful. Only a few distinguish
themselves from the rest.

In the early 1960s the extension officer of Hove subchiefdom
tried to persuade peasant cultivators to grow Turkish tobacco,
but the peasants refused to experiment with it. They feared
failure, and any failure would endanger their family's food
supply. Finally some women came forward to pioneer tobacco
growing. These women had nothing to lose, and at best could hope
to make some money.

(i) *Patricia, the Successful Tobacco Grower*

Patricia was a relatively young woman. In 1954 she had left her husband whom she accused of ill treating her. By 1967 she had three illegitimate children, aged ten, seven and three. She lived with them at her father's home, but her father had already a large family and could ill afford to support his daughter and her children. When Patricia told the extension officer that she was willing to grow tobacco, she was given three-quarters of an acre in the grazing land of her village.

Patricia worked very hard with her two eldest children. She closely followed the instructions of the extension officer, bought seed for 9 shillings and later paid £1 for packing and transport costs. At harvest time she sold a bale of Turkish tobacco for £9, and later received a supplementary payment of £1.8.0. The European buyer was impressed with the quality of her tobacco and paid her a premium of £1. Patricia rejoiced. Having made a profit of about £10 she decided to grow another tobacco crop in 1967. The extension officer encouraged her and gave her a free bag of fertilizer.

Patricia used the money to buy food and clothing and to pay the school fees for her two elder children.

(ii) *Philippa, the Unsuccessful Tobacco Grower*

Patricia succeeded because she followed all the instructions of the extension officer to the letter and because she had enough labour to do all the necessary work in the field. Philippa failed because she fell ill.

Philippa was a married woman with small children. Her husband worked for years on a European farm for £2.10.0 a month and her family had no land in the village. She and her children were therefore undernourished and clothed in rags. None of the children went to school. Philippa's father gave a home to his daughter and her children, but he was poor himself.

When the extension officer asked for volunteers to grow tobacco, Philippa came forward. Her father gave her one acre of land and ploughed it for her. He also advanced her £2.10.0 to buy seed and insecticides, and to pay for the packing.

Philippa started off with eagerness, and like Patricia followed the instructions she received. Her younger sister helped her on the land. But then Philippa fell sick. Neither could she attend further instructions on tobacco growing, nor could she give the crop the care it needed. At harvesting time she reaped half a bale, which she sold for £1.9.0. Later she received a supplementary payment of 5s. 8d. Thus she did not even recover her expenses. Greatly disillusioned, she never again attempted tobacco growing.

(5) EVALUATION OF THE CASE HISTORIES

The major characteristics of the six ordinary peasant cultivators are set out in Table 15.

TABLE 15

Characteristics of Six Ordinary Peasant Cultivators

Name	Income from crops	Year of birth	Educ. in years	Labour migrat. in years	Non-agricul- tural skills	Number of farming implements
Pancratius	£67	1920	3	11	—	1
Patrick	£45	1922	2	30	builder	6
Paul	£40	1940	8	3	—	2
Peter	£22	1905	5	35	—	1
Patricia	£10	1932	3	—	—	—
Philippa	−15d.	1943	2	—	—	—

Table 15 shows that the age spread among ordinary peasant cultivators is much wider than among master farmers, that their educational level is lower, and that engagement in labour migration is more extensive. The three older men have long histories of labour migration, and two of them saved part of their wages. Only one of them, Patrick, was a trained builder, and it was only he who obtained a regular and significant non-agricultural income to finance his farming activities. Hence he was the only man with adequate farming implements. Pancratius' investment in a grinding mill proved a failure and he lost his earnings. Thus all the men, except Patrick, withdrew their own labour for many years from the land without acquiring capital to increase their agricultural production. Only master farmers could regularly draw on non-agricultural work to finance their farming.

Most of the ordinary peasant cultivators were averse to the adoption of modern farming methods. None of them bought fertilizer. Only Pancratius tried to become a master farmer and, although he failed, adopted some of the values generally shared by progressive peasant cultivators. The other men clearly expressed their opposition to master farmer training, and to the government which sponsored it. Even the young and relatively well-educated Paul looked to traditional rather than to modern values.

This emphasis on the Karanga way of life finds its clearest expression in the heavy reliance of ordinary peasant cultivators on work parties. Only the two most successful among them, Pancratius and Patrick, relied on family or hired labour. Work parties and mutual indebtedness, as has been pointed out earlier, integrate village communities. If ordinary peasant cultivators do not invest much money in agricultural equipment, they invest much time and even wealth in kinship obligations. It is through the system of mutual assistance that peasant cultivators can combine for many years a life of labour migration and agriculture. Should Paul, for example, who so generously supported his mother-in-law and half-sisters go back to town, his kinsmen will certainly help his wife and children.

Two other characteristics separate ordinary peasant cultivators from master farmers. They are seldom local leaders. Only Peter was a village headman. Nor did any of them belong to a voluntary agricultural association. Whereas master farmers, therefore, are prominent men in their villages and increase their leading positions by becoming committee members of voluntary associations, other peasant cultivators are predominantly ordinary commoners.

Much of what has been said of the men, holds true of women cultivators. They too have little education and no agricultural skills. Since they have never worked for money, they are even less open to modern farming practices. The case histories of Patricia and Philippa have been cited as exceptions. These women became innovators out of necessity: they had nothing to live on, and experimenting with tobacco could only contribute to, but not lower, their living standards. The case histories of these women, as well as the case history of Thomas, the most successful master farmer who went in for cotton growing, show that innovations are volunteered by two groups of persons: those who have nothing to lose but hope for some gain, and those who are financially so secure that they can risk an experiment with a new crop; for should they fail they have enough resources to cover up the failure. To the large majority of peasant cultivators, however, innovations seem dangerous.

Patricia's success and Philippa's failure are due to the amount of work they could put into their tobacco fields. Since communal work parties cannot be used for a new cash crop which needs very special handling, none of them could use this source of labour. Accidents, such as illness, were fatal. Illness not only ruined Philippa's year's work, it also prevented Pancratius from becoming a master farmer. The insecurity of the poor, therefore, who have nothing to fall back on, is a great handicap for their successful use of new opportunities. Real progress in peasant agriculture seems possible only to men who have a steady income to pay for their innovations.

None of the peasant cultivators, except Thomas, produced a significant surplus, yet most saved their wages to send their children to school. Paying school fees was practically the only investment peasant cultivators made. This reflects their evaluation of the future: they want their children to find well-paid wage or salary employment for which formal education is required, for they know that the land will no longer support their children.

The case histories of ordinary peasant cultivators add certain additional points to the analysis of the two preceding chapters. It is true that most of the peasant cultivators have little education, but men who engaged for 30 years in wage labour, often in towns, cannot be considered incapable of understanding modern ideas and techniques. In fact, if men who have worked with modern tools in factories and mines, and who have a closer experience of European society and its values than master farmers who spend most of their lives in their villages, refuse to accept modern farming methods, their refusal is not an indication of their inability to cope with modern farming techniques but a conscious rejection of them.

This unwillingness, rather than inability to use new techniques, is borne out by answers of a large number of peasant cultivators who were asked why they refused to undergo master farmer training. Some said they had tried but failed because they lacked capital or labour. Some just shrugged off the idea as fanciful. A greater number stressed that there was too little land available for profitable farming so that it was not worthwhile trying to gain a living from the land. But the great majority stressed that they objected on principle to modern farming techniques since these were introduced by European civil servants who tried to keep Africans bound to their tribal trust lands after they had taken away from them the land on which their ancestors had lived. Had there been no land alienation, so they claim, the traditional farming techniques of their ancestors would still be adequate. Though this reasoning is contradicted by the great natural population increase alone, through which permanent cultivation of all farming land in Rhodesia would be necessary, it is nevertheless widely accepted by rural Africans. African suspicion of the intentions of any government move to alter farming practices is one of the major obstacles in the development of peasant agriculture. Such suspicion is typical of all peasant societies and is not confined to Rhodesia. In Rhodesia it is merely aggravated by the political situation which precludes an identification of the peasantry with the ruling European minority.

PART II

INDIVIDUAL LAND TENURE

CHAPTER 7

GOVERNMENT POLICY AND PEASANT RESPONSE TO INDIVIDUAL LAND TENURE

(1) INTRODUCTION

Individual land tenure, which among some African tribes, such as the Chagga, evolved in response to land shortage, and in others, such as the Lala, in response to new opportunities to sell cash crops in open markets, was introduced into Rhodesian peasant communities by outsiders, and therefore brought about more far-reaching changes in peasant communities than it caused in other parts of Africa.

(2) GOVERNMENT POLICY TOWARDS AFRICAN LAND OWNERSHIP

The first African purchase areas were created in the early 1930s after the Land Apportionment Act had been passed which divided Rhodesia's land between Africans and Europeans. Purchase areas, therefore, were part of the overall plan to separate African and European farmers. The European concept of land ownership, which was to characterize African purchase areas, implies that land can be bought from the government and, once it has been purchased by an individual, can be sold to another person. Land, therefore, is seen as a marketable commodity just as are personal possessions, such as houses, cattle or cars.

This concept of land ownership is alien to traditional Karanga society. The Karanga never regarded land as a marketable commodity, but as God's gift to all men so that mankind could grow its food and be happy and increase in numbers. Hence, the more deeply the Karanga are bound to their traditional customs and values, the more consistently they reject any government suggestion that African land be individually owned.[1] Only

---

[1] Both the African Land Husbandry Act of 1951 and the Land Tenure Act of 1969 made provision for individual land tenure in tribal trust lands, but no chief has yet petitioned government to introduce private land ownership in his chiefdom.

peasants who are marginal to the tribal system have accepted the idea that land can be bought, and in accepting it they have moved out of their tribal environment.

In making provision for individual land tenure among Africans, European politicians were motivated by two ideas. Firstly, they wanted to prevent African farmers from opening up farms in predominantly European farming areas for in the early decades of the twentieth century some Africans had become wealthy, moved out of the tribal system, and bought farms on the same basis and in the same areas as Europeans. This ran contrary to the dominant ideology of racial segregation. Special tracts of land were therefore set aside where progressive African peasant farmers could buy their own farms. Wherever purchase areas were established, however, European economic interests came first, and no land was offered to African peasants which Europeans desired for farming or mining purposes. Secondly, there was also a real concern to assist progressive peasants. To establish economically viable farming communities, peasant farmers were forbidden to divide their farms into sub-economic units. Since European politicians believed that only on privately owned farms would the land be used to its best advantage, they made provision to allow for an eventual emergence of individual land tenure in tribal areas.

Government showed a further willingness to draw African peasant farmers into the cash economy when in the early 1960s it classed purchase areas with European farming areas and separated their administration from that of the tribal trust lands. Only in 1971, when ideological considerations outran concern for African economic development were plans discussed to separate the administration of African and European farming areas and to reunite purchase areas with tribal trust lands. One reason seems to be that by that time some purchase areas had become highly productive[1] and European farmers feared competition from African farmers.[2]

[1] On April 21st, 1971, *The Rhodesia Herald* reported that in one purchase area, Gota, some farm owners expected to reap crops worth £10,000. Their farms average 350 acres of which 280 are arable. Cotton is their greatest cash earner. Many of them employ about 150 cotton pickers at harvesting time.

[2] To reassure European farmers that the Tribal Trust Land Development Company would not turn African peasants into competitors of European farmers, its chairman declared in 1970 that under the Company's auspices Africans would only be allowed to grow those crops which were not produced in sufficient quantity by European farmers in order to avoid a saturation of the market. *The Rhodesia Herald*, 24.9.70.

Though some purchase areas in the higher rainfall regions developed into prosperous farming communities, the majority of purchase areas did not develop their full potential, and some seemed quite unsuitable for intensive cultivation. In 1970 the chairman of the Agricultural Land Settlement Board declared that many African-owned farms in purchase areas had been created in the past 40 years without regard to the requirement that each should have an assessed minimum annual nett income potential of £300. As a result most of them were sub-economic.[1] The two purchase areas selected for this study fall into this broad category.

The purchase areas of Guruuswa and Mutadza lie in the centre of Karangaland and are typical of most other purchase areas in the region. They lie at an altitude of 4,300 and 4,400 feet, have an annual mean temperature of 70 to 80 degrees Fahrenheit, and have an average rainfall of 20 to 30 inches. Like the two tribal trust lands of Shiri-Ngara and Shoko, they belong to natural regions three and four and are therefore not suitable for intensive cultivation. They have been chosen because they share the same ecological environment with each other and with the two tribal trust lands so that differences in agricultural productivity in these communities cannot be attributed to ecological factors. These four communities, therefore, two tribal trust lands and two purchase areas, provide an ideal test situation in which the importance of various sociological factors on peasant productivity can be examined.

Each of the two purchase areas is situated next to a tribal trust land, each shares a common boundary with another purchase area, and each lies adjacent to European farms. Like most purchase areas in Rhodesia, they form a transition zone between tribal communities and European farms. Both purchase areas are connected by dirt roads to tarred roads which link these farming communities to mining settlements which provide ready markets for surplus crops. From these mining settlements peasant farmers can reach all districts of Rhodesia by road, and buses connect them with all the major towns of Rhodesia. This good system of communication is of great advantage to both purchase areas.

Like many other purchase areas, Guruuswa and Mutadza were in the past inhabited by African peasant cultivators who owed allegiance to chiefs in the adjoining tribal trust lands. When

[1] *The Rhodesia Herald*, 3.9.70.

government decided to divide the land into purchase area farms, these peasant cultivators were evicted. Most of them moved into the adjoining tribal trust lands to live under the chiefs they knew. Mutadza purchase area was surveyed in the late 1940s and Guruuswa in 1954. When Mutadza purchase area was opened to peasant farmers in 1950, many of the peasant cultivators who had been evicted some years previously were given farms to reduce the overcrowding they had caused in the tribal trust land. This meant, however, that very few of them had any special knowledge of modern farming techniques. Of 60 peasant farmers in Mutadza in 1967, 48 or 78·3 per cent came from the adjoining tribal trust land, and only 18 or 30·0 per cent were master farmers. At that time a master farmer's qualification was not yet required of applicants for farms.

Mutadza purchase area was originally designed for 81 peasant farmers. On 21 farms, however, asbestos was discovered and this land was not allocated to African farmers. It is still held in reserve for European mining, and at present peasant farmers use this land as a communal pasture. In 1967 Mutadza had a total population of 706 men, women and children.

The opening up of Mutadza purchase area shows that European interests determined which land was offered to Africans. This land, since it had already been occupied by peasant cultivators, was no new grant of land to African peasants. It now became a buffer zone between African and European farming areas. It was settled by men who would never compete with European farmers for markets, and those tracts of land in which asbestos was discovered, were withheld from African ownership.

The Guruuswa purchase area was opened to prospective farmers in 1957. By that time all applicants had to have a master farmer's certificate[1] as well as £300 in cash or kind. Consequently, although the evacuation of peasant cultivators from this area had caused even more serious overcrowding in the adjacent tribal trust land than had occurred when peasant cultivators were evicted from Mutadza—for Guruuswa covers 66 square miles, but Mutadza only 38 square miles—only 34 or 23·6 per cent of all new farm owners came from the adjoining tribal area. Guruuswa peasant farmers, therefore, were chosen for their ability to farm

[1] Both purchase areas lie in the Victoria province. In 1969, 59·4 per cent of all peasant farmers in this province possessed a master farmer's certificate. Report of the Secretary for Agriculture, 1969, pp. 62–63.

well, not in order to relieve population pressure in an adjoining chiefdom. By 1967 Guruuswa had a population of 1,590 men, women and children who lived on 144 farms and 4 crown lands. Twenty farms had not yet been fully surveyed and were expected to be offered for sale in the near future.

(3) GOVERNMENT CONTROL OF PURCHASE AREAS

(a) Government Requirements of Farm Owners

As African interest in freehold titles to land increased, government laid down ever stricter requirements for applicants. Until 1952 only some agricultural knowledge was required. In 1953 the master farmer's certificate became a prerequisite. By 1957 applicants had to possess in addition capital assets in cash or kind to the value of £300. By the early 1960s a points system was introduced by which a certain number of points were given for capital equipment, agricultural experience, proved character of the applicant—a point most difficult to establish—and his statement of the use to which he intended to put his farm. By then, capital and farming experience were considered more important than a master farmer's certificate. Every candidate was personally interviewed, and on the basis of the interview each applicant was awarded a number of points. When a new area was opened to prospective peasant farmers, men with the highest number of points were given the first choice of a farm.

These ever stricter requirements of prospective farm owners assured that more recent purchase areas would have more skilled peasant farmers than the older purchase areas. This stricter selection procedure is reflected in the higher agricultural output of more recent purchase areas.

The more stringent requirements became, the longer men had to wait until they could obtain a farm. Of the 60 peasant farmers in Mutadza, 31 or 51·7 per cent waited less than a year to obtain a farm; of the 144 Guruuswa farmers none waited less than a year; 45 or 31·2 per cent waited five to nine years.[1]

Under current practice, once a man has chosen a farm, he can lease it for two years during which time he has to cooperate with the agricultural staff and prove his suitability as a peasant farmer. If he satisfies his supervisors, he can enter an agreement of

[1] For a detailed breakdown of the number of years applicants waited in Guruuswa and Mutadza to occupy their farms, see Appendix, Table 48.

purchase and pay annual instalments towards the purchase price. Title deeds are registered in a Deeds Registry. The minimum period for obtaining title is seven years after entering the agreement of purchase; the maximum, twenty years. The agreement of purchase states that the peasant farmer must use good farming methods and personally occupy his farm. Once he has registered his title deeds, he can use his land at his own discretion, subject only to the regulations of the Natural Resources Board to which all Rhodesian farmers are subject. By 1967, 16 of the 18 master farmers of the Mutadza purchase area had obtained their title deeds; 42 of the 48 other peasant farmers had paid the full price of their farms, but none of these had seen it worthwhile to pay the stamp duty to obtain their title deeds. In Guruuswa, which was settled seven years later than Mutadza, no farm owner had obtained title deeds by 1967.

Peasant farmers who do not comply with the terms of their lease agreement or agreement of purchase can be evicted from their farms. Government has appointed land inspectors whose duty it is to visit farms to see that conditions of lease are observed, and to take action when natural resources are endangered. These inspectors have also the right to evict 'squatters' from farms, that is, persons who in the eyes of government officials have no right to live on farms.[1]

In Guruuswa only one farm owner has ever been evicted by the land inspector. This man had been a leading nationalist in the late 1950s and shortly after entering a lease agreement for his farm was imprisoned for his political activities. Being unable during his imprisonment personally to occupy his farm, his lease agreement was cancelled.

In Mutadza six farm owners were evicted in 1967 for unsatisfactory farming practices. The agricultural staff had sent negative reports about each of these men to the Land Inspectorate and had stressed that soil erosion was widespread on their farms. The district commissioner had also reported that all of them were seriously in arrears in paying their annual instalments.

One of these men had been absent from his farm for five months when he was served with the eviction order. He had not ploughed his land during the preceding season and possessed no cattle.

---

[1] Strict control over residents in purchase areas keeps the population density in the communities constant. In both Guruuswa and Mutadza there are only 22 persons per square mile.

Each of the other five had during the preceding season reaped crops worth £20 to £30. The evicted peasant farmers appealed in vain to the Land Board to have their eviction orders withdrawn. They were told that if they did not vacate the farms, they would be arrested.

Most of them tried to find new homes for their families. Within a few months three of the evicted peasant farmers had left the purchase area: one had gone back to the tribal trust land from which he had come; one had gone to find work in Salisbury; and the neighbours did not know the whereabouts of the third. The other three families stayed on in Mutadza purchase area: one man lived with his family on the farm of his son-in-law while he negotiated with his former chief for a piece of land on which to settle; another stayed with an unrelated farm owner while he also tried to find a place in a tribal trust land. The third lived on his brother-in-law's farm and, in spite of his wife's pleading, did nothing to prepare for his family's future.

The histories of these two purchase areas show that during the early years government control is strict in these farming settlements. Selection procedures favour men interested in agriculture and capable of developing the land. Those who proved grossly inefficient were evicted before they became owners of their land. These early apprentice years of prospective farm owners aim at creating an economically viable community of peasant farmers.

(b) Administration of Purchase Areas

Though purchase area farmers are selected by government, and though their farming methods are initially supervised, they are from the moment they come into a purchase area relatively free to determine the administration of their community. No chief has authority over them. Civil servants of the Ministry of Internal Affairs and Agriculture show a lively interest in purchase areas, but do not intervene more than they do in European farming areas. The district commissioner, for example, may attend meetings in the purchase area if he is invited by the peasant farmers, and if the purchase area has a local government council, he is its ex-officio president.

The Ministry of Agriculture is represented in purchase areas through a non-resident extension officer and several resident extension assistants. Normally there is one extension assistant to every fifty peasant farmers. In 1967, there was one extension assistant in Mutadza and three in Guruuswa purchase area. The agricultural staff is influential because their reports on the peasant farmers' progress determine whether peasants will be allowed to take out title deed to their farms.

All the civil servants, however, are mainly advisers, and the administration of the purchase areas lies in the hands of local farmers. In some instances it takes a few years before the administration reaches its final form, for new settlers have some freedom to devise their own system of administration. In Guruuswa peasant farmers formed a society called *Mushandira Pamwe*, 'the group which works together'. They elected a chairman, vice-chairman and a secretary and resolved to assist each other in cases of sickness, death, or any other misfortune. *Mushandira Pamwe*, therefore, was a mutual aid society. When shortly after its foundation the huts of a peasant farmer burned down, all the people contributed labour or bricks to rebuild them.

This society also met to discuss local customs, for although 98·5 per cent of all Guruuswa farm owners were Karanga, some came from areas where different local customs were observed. One custom in particular concerned the community. The Karanga observe a weekly day of rest in honour of *Mwari*, their high god. This day is called *chisi*. In some areas people rest on Thursdays, in others on Fridays. The Guruuswa farmers decided to observe *chisi* on Thursdays so that this day could become the day on which public meetings and social gatherings could be held.

The *Mushandira Pamwe* society soon became a link between the extension staff and the peasant farmers, and whenever the extension assistants wanted the farmers to come together for agricultural instructions, the chairman of the society called for a formal meeting. After a year, in 1958, the extension assistants suggested that the peasant farmers join the national African Farmers' Union through which most purchase areas in Rhodesia are organized. This union is administered by a council, consisting of six members who are chairmen of the six branches into which Rhodesia's purchase areas are divided. Every branch has its own committee consisting of members elected by 'divisions', that is, by local purchase areas or sections of purchase areas. Each division is administered by its own committee, a committee similar to that of the *Mushandira Pamwe* society.

When the Guruuswa farmers heard of this union, they sent delegates to a well-established purchase area to learn the scope and function of the African Farmers' Union. Their report was favourably received and Guruuswa joined the union. Local farm owners now subscribe to the union's newspaper, *Murimi*, 'Farmer' and so are kept informed of agricultural problems and developments. They also pay the annual subscription fee of ten shillings to the union. From this ten shillings sixpence is retained for local use, one shilling is sent to the local branch and the rest is forwarded to the national head office. The use to which this money is put is regularly examined at meetings and members demand an exact account of their contributions. This gives them a strong sense of belonging and control over the various union officials at division, branch and national level.

As soon as the committee had been established in Guruuswa, the district commissioner invited the peasant farmers to suggest how their allocation of the African Development Fund should be spent. Until 1967 purchase areas received £12 annually for every occupied farm so that Guruuswa farmers could plan an annual budget of over £1,500. The farmers usually requested that the money be spent on road maintenance, dam repairs, the purchase of heavy machinery, such as a tractor, or the construction of a community hall. Once they asked that the money be spent to fence in their individual farms.

Discussions on spending the money of the African Development Fund soon became the most important function of the African Farmers' Union committee. None of the farm owners had ever possessed so large a sum of money and to decide its use fascinated them. When, therefore, in the mid-1960s, the African Farmers' Union asked its members to discuss whether they wanted to continue paying levies into the African Development Fund and so be entitled to this revenue, or to be exempt from the levy, opinions were strongly divided. Those peasant farmers who regularly sold large surpluses, pressed for the abolition of the levy, the less successful peasant farmers urged its continuance. After several hot debates a vote was taken and 42 farm owners voted in favour of the levy, 21 voted for its abolition. Guruuswa farmers notified the head office of their decision, but the majority of purchase area farmers in Rhodesia thought differently. In 1967, therefore, purchase area farmers were exempt from paying the levy and since that date no more public money has been available to the Guruuswa community for communal services. Roads have since fallen into disrepair and transportation of crops has become difficult.

In 1960 the farm owners of Guruuswa formed a cooperative society, and by 1967 out of 144 farm owners 107 had joined. Most farm owners welcomed the cooperative society because of the loans it made available to them. Since they had full control over this society and understood its administration—membership of the African Farmers' Union had familiarized them with committee procedures and bureaucratic administration—they felt no hostility towards it as did many tribal trust land peasant cultivators.

Peasant farmers who joined the cooperative society had to pay a five-shilling membership fee and take out a £2 share dividend which was to be refunded to them when they left the society. This share dividend helped to pay for the running costs of the local branch. These regulations are laid down by the cooperative movement of which local cooperative societies form a part. Officers of the movement occasionally visit local branches.

Members who want to take out a loan, need the recommendation of the committee of the cooperative society that they are efficient farmers. Before giving its recommendation, committee members consult the extension assistant and check whether the farmers have enough cattle so that, in case of crop failure, they can sell a beast to repay the loan. The committee in Guruuswa has been conscientious in checking the credit-worthiness of applicants, because if peasant farmers are negligent in repaying their loans, the cooperative movement requires repayment of the debt from the local cooperative society.

In 1962, forty Guruuswa farmers signed a petition to form an intensive conservation area committee. These committees are sponsored by the Natural Resources Board and aim at helping farmers to improve their land. The Natural Resources Board's sixth annual conference for purchase areas reported in 1967 that the Board was running many short courses which taught African farmers soil conservation and gave advice on rural development. It also recorded that during the preceding twelve months 320 Africans, members of intensive conservation area committees, had attended such courses.[1]

The proposal to form an intensive conservation area committee in Guruuswa did not meet with universal approval. Peasant farmers in the eastern section, whose land is of poor quality, were in favour of the committee because they hoped for assistance to improve their land, but peasant farmers in the western part were

[1] Natural Resources Board, 1967, p. 8.

opposed to it. They feared that an intensive conservation area committee would force negligent farmers to mend gullies on their farms and generally interfere in their farming. This difference of opinion caused a split in the purchase area. In 1964 the eastern section formed its own intensive conservation area committee, and in 1966 the purchase area split into two divisions, each section establishing its own committee of the African Farmers' Union. This split did not heal tensions between the peasant farmers and members of each division jealously watched the agricultural developments in the neighbouring section.

Mutadza peasant farmers developed their purchase area differently. They joined the African Farmers' Union and even formed a cooperative society, but by 1967 only 19 out of 60 farm owners had joined it. Most farmers preferred to sell their produce through private channels and do without loans. The Mutadza cooperative society, therefore, never flourished. Mutadza peasant farmers never established an intensive conservation area committee.

In 1956 the people of Mutadza purchase area formed a local government council, and this council aroused more enthusiasm than any agricultural society. The reason was that there were no Christian missions nearby, and consequently the children of the farm owners had no access to a school. The peasant farmers set up their own council because councils are statutory bodies which can draw on government grants to subsidize community projects. With the help of public grants, they built up their own primary school, and by the mid-1960s even planned to open a secondary school. By then, however, government had embarked on a community development campaign and urged all peasant communities to establish their own councils. Mutadza peasants, who in the past had been strong supporters of African nationalism and never willingly cooperated with government officials, then realized that their council conformed with the new government policy. This disturbed them and they looked for reasons to close their council. At one council meeting in 1967, at which the district commissioner as ex-officio president presided, their lack of co-operation became so clear that the district commissioner threatened to close their council. The people encouraged him to do so and the council was closed.[1] Government, thereupon, closed the council school. Some peasant farmers tried in vain to get their

[1] See Weinrich, 1971, pp. 201–203.

purchase area incorporated into a council area of a neighbouring community of peasant farmers so that government grants could again flow into their community, but the farmers of the successful purchase area did not want to be burdened with the Mutadza people.

The different administrative bodies in the Guruuswa and Mutadza purchase areas show that peasant farmers are to a considerable extent free to run their own communities as they wish. Guruuswa farm owners formed several committees through which they hoped to gain advantages for their farms. In Mutadza purchase area the most vital organization, until 1967, was the council whose prime aim was not agricultural but educational. This shows a different attitude of the peasant farmers in the two communities towards agriculture.

This different attitude towards agriculture is also clearly revealed in the communities' relationships with the extension assistants who are there to advise them on modern farming methods. Extension assistants, because they are very young, often find it difficult to win the confidence of farm owners, and old men often feel ambivalent towards highly educated young people. This is especially true for Mutadza where farm owners show little interest in modern farming techniques and are highly suspicious of young men in government employment. Extension assistants posted to Mutadza purchase area therefore, often ask for transfers to areas where their extension advice is more readily accepted.

In Guruuswa, on the other hand, farm owners are eager to learn from the extension assistants of the most recent agricultural research findings. They trust especially one extension assistant who has been in the area since its conversion into farms. He married the daughter of one farm owner and so became the 'son-in-law' of the community. He often visits the farm owners in their homesteads and receives them into his house as friends. When his superiors wanted to transfer him to another area, the farm owners sent a delegation to the regional office, pleading to be allowed to retain their 'son-in-law'.

(4) PEASANT RESPONSE TO LOCAL AUTONOMY

Because of the knowledge that they will one day own their own farms, and because of the relative freedom to administer their own areas, peasant farmers feel more secure than any other group of rural Africans. In the more progressive purchase areas, such as Guruuswa, this security has given rise to a number of agricultural societies, but it has also contributed to a carefree and uncooperative attitude in non-progressive purchase areas, such as Mutadza.

The freedom with which peasant farmers run their own communities is reflected both in the type of leaders they elect to their committees and councils, and also in the type of voluntary associations they form.

(a) New Leaders

In Guruuswa the African Farmers' Union committee and in Mutadza the council were the most important administrative bodies in 1967. The persons who were elected to leadership positions in these two communities differed greatly in character. In Guruuswa the first chairman of the African Farmers' Union committee held his office for ten years. He was born in the area of an African mother, but had a European father who abandoned him. When Guruuswa was declared a purchase area, he registered with the district commissioner as an 'African' and gave up his coloured status, for only Africans are allowed to buy purchase area farms.

This man was well accepted by his African neighbours who gave him the honorary clan name 'Nkosi', an Ndebele word for 'chief'. He was a skilled herbalist and completely identified himself with the African people. Civil servants esteemed him highly for his progressive attitude towards farming. The district commissioner summed up the Europeans' evaluation of the man in the words: 'He has a drop of white blood in his veins. This makes him superior to all his neighbours.' Because of his acceptance by both Africans and Europeans, this chairman was a suitable mediator between peasant farmers and civil servants.

The secretary of the Guruuswa committee was a retired civil servant who for 32 years had been in government employment. Son of a chief, imposing of stature, well educated and fluent in both the English and African languages, he was at first admired by his African neighbours and the Europeans trusted him. Through his personal initiative the cooperative society and the intensive conservation area committee were established. In 1964 he was honoured in Salisbury by the governor of Rhodesia with a certificate and medal for loyal service. But unlike his chairman, this secretary was not loyal to his fellow Africans. When his neighbours found out that he informed on them to the police, they began avoiding him. In 1963 he was not re-elected to the African Farmers' Union committee, and in 1967 he relinquished his farm and settled with his father in a tribal trust land.

Guruuswa farm owners expect their leaders to be good farmers. Of the 16 committee members on the purchase area in 1967, six had harvested in the preceding year crops worth more than £400, four crops worth more than £300, four crops worth more than £200, and only two crops worth just below £200. The average farm income from agriculture in that purchase area was around £200 in that season. This shows that community leadership in Guruuswa coincides with agricultural leadership.

Mutadza farm owners did not look for agricultural excellence in their leaders but for 'ability to speak up before Europeans'. Until 1967, councillors played a greater role in the community than members of the African Farmers' Union committee. Of the eight councillors, only one reaped in 1966 crops worth more than £400, two had an agricultural income of just over £200, one of over £100, and four reaped crops well below £100. The two councillors with the lowest agricultural income—they reaped crops worth £27 and £23 respectively—were evicted in 1967 for poor farming practices.

The last chairman of Mutadza council was an elderly, hardly literate, but ambitious man. European civil servants considered him incompetent though his farming income was average; his people suspected him of subservience to the district commissioner. He was proud of his chairmanship and determined to retain it. He therefore cooperated with the district commissioner as far as he felt he had to cooperate, and he also tried to win popular support. This he did by brewing beer for his neighbours whenever council elections drew near. He believed that political leadership and economic success were not exclusively due to a man's abilities. In one of his meditative moods he said: 'Life is strange. One's actions do not matter. One's motives do not count. Nothing, in fact, matters in life. One gets hit and hit again. Anything can happen, for we cannot control our future. All we can do is to surrender and live for the present moment.'

The secretary of Mutadza council, an aggressive young man, was the son of a farm owner. He cooperated with neither the district commissioner nor with his chairman. At a beer drink he once burst out: 'I always clash with the district commissioner because I am no "yes-man" like our chairman. If I do not see the reason why something should be done, I won't do it.' Since the chairman was unable to read, he depended entirely on his secretary. Occasionally the secretary informed the chairman of the content of government correspondence by sending a message through a school child, at times he invented a different content if this was to his own advantage.

The ordinary councillors too did not cooperate with each other. When one councillor, who was particularly interested in the school, ordered certain items without consulting his fellow councillors, he was forced to pay for them personally. Disunity among the leaders lowered the efficiency of administration, and the purchase area of Mutadza was run as unsatisfactorily as many of its individual farms.

(b) New Voluntary Associations

Apart from formal agricultural societies, a variety of informal clubs have sprung up in the two purchase areas. But whereas Guruuswa farmers formed a number of competitive farming clubs, people in Mutadza purchase area formed mainly saving clubs. A typical informal club in Guruuswa is called 'Who is the Champion?' It was founded at the home of the most successful farmer who had started his own irrigation scheme. His friends elected him as chairman and appointed as treasurer a peasant farmer who regularly sold eggs in a nearby mining settlement and seemed capable of handling money.

This club includes both men and women. Every club member has to pay an annual fee of 5 shillings with which a prize is bought for the most successful farmer of the year. At the beginning of each season, the members decide which crops are to be grown under competition, and during harvesting time the crops are displayed in the homestead of the competitors. No club member sells or eats any part of his harvest before he has invited his competitors to a party at his home to inspect the crops. When the harvests of all club members have been inspected, a final feast is held at the home of the winner who, together with his wife or wives, is then presented with the prize and declared the 'Champion of the Year'. Together with his family, he then explains to his neighbours what he has done to achieve his success.

These competitive clubs aim primarily at increasing agricultural production. No such clubs were ever formed in Mutadza

purchase area. Even in Guruuswa more farm owners are interested in these clubs than actually join. Some peasant farmers
stand aloof because they lack labour to work their farms more
intensively, some because the soil of their farms is poor, and others
simply because they fear a possible witchcraft accusation should
they be too successful. These competitive clubs are a sign of the
importance which peasant farmers in Guruuswa attach to agricultural achievement.

The saving clubs in Mutadza purchase area have another aim.
Most of them take the form of 'beer parties'. A group of farm
owners, of women or even of teenagers, club together and make
fixed contributions either in money, grain or food towards a party.
At the party itself, club members may eat and drink without
paying, but other guests must pay for their food and drink. The
money raised belongs to the 'owner of the party'. Beer parties
circulate among club members so that each in turn receives some
cash. Cash profits vary between £5 and £7 per party. In contrast
to agricultural competitive clubs, such saving clubs have little
effect on agricultural production, for most of the money is used
for clothing and school fees and hardly any is invested in the land.
Saving clubs are rather a device to make money since money
from agriculture is insufficient to meet family needs. Whereas the
competitive clubs in Guruuswa indicate agricultural success, the
saving clubs of Mutadza indicate agricultural failure.

The different adaptation of peasants in purchase areas is not
only reflected in the choice of their leaders and in their interest
in agricultural associations of various types, but also in their
attitudes towards routine meetings organized by the agricultural
staff. In Guruuswa such meetings are turned into social events
which capture the imagination of the people. For example, when
the extension assistants wanted to show peasant farmers the
advantages of fertilizer, the possibility of cotton growing, and the
profits they could make from stall feeding their cattle, they
selected 16 of the most progressive farmers to use part of their
land or some of their beasts for the experiments. Most of these
men were committee members of the African Farmers' Union, a
sign that Guruuswa farmers had elected committee members for
their advanced farming methods. The peasant farmers who participated in the fertilizer trials were advised to grow half an acre of
crops with fertilizer and half an acre without. Before harvesting
time demonstration lessons were held at these plots at which all

farm owners participated. Such demonstration lessons were always followed by feasting and drinking so that only wealthy farmers could volunteer for such experiments. Those, who had joined a competitive farming club, were assisted by club members. In this way a farming elite evolved in Guruuswa.

In Mutadza purchase area demonstration lessons met with little response. Farm owners merely attended for fear of being evicted from their farms should they show an open lack of interest in farming. No farm owner at whose field the demonstration was held gave a feast to his neighbours. In fact, neighbours looked askance at those peasant farmers who openly cooperated with the extension staff.

The different agricultural skills of peasant farmers in Mutadza and Guruuswa are publicly acclaimed at annual regional 'Green Shows'. At these shows peasant farmers from neighbouring purchase areas exhibit their best crops and cattle, and senior members of the Ministry of Agriculture award prizes. In 1967, most exhibitors from Guruuswa purchase area, but only one from Mutadza, received such a prize.

(5) CONCLUSION

In the Introduction to this book it has been hypothesized that self-administration, because it gives people a sense of security, is likely to encourage progress. The analysis of the Mutadza and Guruuswa communities showed that freedom to choose their own administrators is not sufficient in itself to encourage peasant farmers to develop an interest in farming. The choice of community leaders in Mutadza proves that elected leaders indeed represent popular opinion, but that if popular opinion is indifferent to farming success, freedom from government supervision and security of tenure do not automatically produce good peasant farmers.

On the other hand, where a community is interested in farming, such freedom greatly stimulates resourcefulness. The many competitive associations in Guruuswa and the eagerness with which farm owners participate in agricultural meetings, show how progressive farmers spontaneously avail themselves of those opportunities which seem likely to increase their farm income. Freedom from control, therefore, is a contributing factor to agricultural progress, but in itself it is insufficient to bring it about.

The question of whether individual land tenure is more conducive to high output than traditional Karanga land tenure, an
assumption made by some legislators, will be more fully discussed
in the last chapter.

CHAPTER 8

THE INTERNAL TRANSFORMATION
OF PEASANT COMMUNITIES

(1) INTRODUCTION

Since purchase areas are created by government in response to its policy of separate development and settled by men selected by civil servants, peasant farmers have to create new social ties among themselves because no kinship bonds exist between them. Though peasant farmers are free to administer their own communities, they are not free to select their neighbours. Moreover, the size of farms and the desire of people to live on their own property, prevent the creation of villages. Geographical distance between homesteads is reinforced by the absence of kinship ties, and both affect the interaction of farm families.

This chapter analyses the layout of purchase areas, the household composition of farms and family relationships, and the social ties of people in these farming communities with each other and with outsiders. Since social relationships determine the labour problems of peasant farmers, they greatly influence the productivity of purchase area farms.

(2) THE LAYOUT OF PURCHASE AREAS

When government surveyors plan a purchase area, they place at regular intervals between farms tracts of crown land, designed to become community centres. Here schools, stores and mills, depots for cooperative societies and community halls, as well as the homes of junior government servants, may be erected. These crown lands are the focal points of local neighbourhoods. They are always situated at major roads and so can always be reached by car. Guruuswa has four such tracts of crown land. Two of these have become business centres where stores have been built. On three Christian missionaries have erected primary schools, on three dip tanks have been constructed, and on one the farmers have built a community hall and a depot for their cooperative society. Mutadza purchase area has two tracts of crown land. On one stands their school, on another the house of their extension assistant and a dip tank. There is not a single store in Mutadza purchase area.

Apart from these social centres, all the land of purchase areas is divided into farms, most of which are some 200 acres in size. Many farms can be reached by car, but others only on foot or by bicycle. Peasant farmers on these remote farms must carry their crops to the nearest road before they can load them on trucks to transport them to a market. Since this is very burdensome, most prefer farms along the roads. Yet in spite of this inconvenience, no farm owner in either Guruuswa or Mutadza has tried to persuade his neighbours to join with him in building a road to their homesteads.

The land of both Guruuswa and Mutadza purchase areas is undulating country. Most Guruuswa farmers have built their homesteads on little hills overlooking their land. These homesteads can be seen from afar, especially since 119 out of the 144 farm owners have planted fruit trees around their homes and 85 have planted gum trees. These trees act as windbreaks. The fruit trees, moreover, provide the farming families with fruit for household requirements and even for sale, and the gum trees are used for fencing and building. Some Guruuswa farmers have used gum trees to paddock their grazing land. Three farm owners have sunk boreholes near their homesteads and one has built his own dam. Next to their living quarters 112 Guruuswa farmers established their own gardens. Most Guruuswa farmers cultivate their fields near the foot of the hills on which their homesteads are built.

Mutadza peasant farmers planned their farms differently. They prepared their fields in the vleis, the most low-lying parts of their farms, which required less labour to clear than the higher, well-wooded parts. As a result the fields are often waterlogged and productivity is low. To reduce the walking distance they built their homesteads next to their fields. Only two Mutadza families planted fruit trees near their homes and none planted gum trees. In 1967 only two grew their own vegetables. In previous years more Mutadza families had vegetable gardens, but they had established them along river banks where they caused soil erosion. When the land inspector ordered them to abandon these gardens, they did not start new ones.

One master farmer in Mutadza sank his own borehole and two built their own dams, for in contrast to Guruuswa, Mutadza purchase area has few streams. Apart from privately owned water sources, Mutadza peasants rely on one river and four government sunk boreholes. Of these four boreholes, two are centrally situated and give adequate water; but one lies in a corner of the purchase area where only a few families live and the pump of the fourth has broken down and not been repaired. Many women spend several hours each day fetching water for household requirements.

Farm owners in both Guruuswa and Mutadza lay great emphasis on their homes, and many invest much money in housing, though the agricultural staff advise them to use their scarce capital more profitably in land. Whereas in tribal trust lands most peasants live in round huts of pole and mud or of sun-burned bricks, a third of all purchase area farmers live in rectangular brick houses with several rooms.

Most farmsteads, especially those of polygamists, look like small villages. In the centre stands the brick house of the owner, and around it the huts of his wives and children, as well as the granaries, latrines, sheds and pigsties. Mutadza families pay still greater attention to their homes than Guruuswa families because they often came to their farms in order to retire there, not to make much money. In contrast to Mutadza farmers, Guruuswa farmers frequently build strong cattle byres of stone or wood, with separate divisions for calves and adult stock; and many put up sheds to protect their farming implements against the rain.

All the farms are separated from each other by wire fences. They are to a large extent self-contained social units. The walking distance between homesteads is about a quarter of an hour so that neighbours live in relative isolation from each other and visit each other only on special occasions.

(3) SOCIAL TIES IN PURCHASE AREAS

(a) Ties Between Homesteads

Since homesteads are far apart and since each family has much work to do in its own fields, cooperation between neighbours is much less than in villages and geographical distance gives rise to social cleavages. The split of Guruuswa purchase area into two divisions was discussed in the preceding chapter. The main road which runs from the north to the south through this purchase area, divides it into an eastern and a western section, and few social ties cross this boundary. Mutadza purchase area, though much smaller than Guruuswa, is likewise divided into two sections. A dyke of asbestos-bearing hills runs diagonally across the purchase area, and peasant farmers on either side avoid each other. They have created local stereotypes that families on the other side of the dyke are more quarrelsome and more given to drink than they are themselves so that social contact would be undesirable.

In addition to this community cleavage, neighbouring farmers are mostly strangers to each other. Guruuswa farmers come from eleven different tribal trust lands, and Mutadza farmers from seven. Since few relatives ever obtain farms in the same purchase area, families from the same tribal trust land feel closer to each other than they would have done in their home area, and in situations where in the past they would have asked kinsmen for assistance they now call on people from their own tribal trust land. To create new kinship ties, farm owners try to marry into each other's families. In marrying the daughters of their neighbours, they not only win allies in the community, but they also open up the prospect of one day inheriting a second farm.

(b) The Composition of Farm Families

The relative isolation of homesteads and the inability to call on neighbours for help, as well as the larger acreages of cultivable land at the disposal of farming families, present farm owners with the serious problem of labour shortage. To find additional workers, farm owners try to marry additional wives, to attract single kinsmen from the tribal trust lands or even towns, and to hire wage labourers. In Guruuswa, 37 per cent of all farm owners are polygamists and in Mutadza 43 per cent. Though most polygamists have only two or three wives, some have five, six or even seven. Because according to government regulation no farm may contain a second complete family consisting of father, mother and children, farm owners try to attract their unmarried or divorced adult sons and daughters with their children. Mutadza farmers have also successfully retained a larger number of brothers and sisters for seven Mutadza farm owners have already died, and when their sons took over their farms they persuaded their brothers and sisters to stay with them. A few parents and grandparents of farm owners are also resident on the farms, but these do not contribute much labour; at most they look after the young children and so free their mothers for farm work. About 2 per cent of all persons living on farms are unrelated to the farm owners. They are hired labourers who stay with their employers the whole year round. Due to these efforts to attract helpers, the average head of a farm family looks after about eleven dependants. The number of dependants is especially large in Mutadza purchase area, where farm owners are older and where polygamy is more widespread. Of all farm owners in Guruuswa 24·3 per cent are 60 years and older, and so are 31·7 per cent of all farm owners in Mutadza.[1] Of all Guruuswa farmers 37·1 per cent are polygamists and so are 43·2 per cent of all Mutadza farmers. Table 16 sets out the number of dependants of purchase area farmers.

TABLE 16

Number of Dependants of Purchase Area Farmers (N=204)

Number of Dependants	Guruuswa		Mutadza	
	Frequency	Per cent	Frequency	Per cent
1–4	2	1·5	2	3·3
5–9	73	50·7	24	40·0
10–14	50	34·9	20	33·3
15–19	9	6·1	7	11·7
20 and over	10	6·8	7	11·7
Total	144	100·0	60	100·0

(c) Farm Owners and Their Sons

Of all persons in the two purchase areas 53·8 per cent are sons and daughters of farm owners. Most of them are teenagers or young adults. There are relatively few children on the farms in relation to the women, for the fertility of women married to farm owners is much lower than is the fertility of women married in tribal trust lands. This may partly be due to the higher polygamy rate, partly to the fact that purchase area populations are ageing.[2]

The old age of farm owners, though it has enabled them to attract a number of kinsmen, is also creating problems in the

---

[1] For detailed data on the age of farm owners, see Appendix, Table 49.

[2] The fertility rate of women in the two purchase areas is 1·6, indicating that there will be only three persons in the next generation for every two persons now living. In tribal trust lands the population doubles in one generation.

families, both between fathers and sons and between fathers and daughters. Many of the old peasant farmers try to rule their dependants as tribal elders ruled their followers in the past. Their control over the land and farming capital gives them a financial power which none of their dependants can question. This power, however, calls forth resentment in their sons. Those sons who are really interested in farming, would like to have a greater say in the running of the farms. In fact, some would like to take over the management of the farms when their fathers become too old to direct the farm work efficiently. Yet farm owners do not think of handing over their farms to their sons before they die. In 1970 *The Rhodesia Herald* reported that 'a serious problem is the tendency of older farmers to cling to the management instead of passing it on to their sons. They obviously find it difficult to break with tradition.'[1] Yet no break with tradition would be involved in this, since land ownership is new in Karanga society. Since government forbids the subdivision of farms, peasant farmers can make a will, leaving their property to any person they choose. Farm owners generally leave their land to their eldest son, and even if they make no will, this son will claim the farm as his inheritance.

Many sons stay with their fathers and work hard for them, but as many leave the farms for wage employment in towns or, if they are slightly older and want to marry, try to find land for their own families in tribal trust lands. The fact that their sons leave the farms deprives the farm owners of the most efficient section of their labour force. Sons who work in towns seldom send remittances to their fathers, and those who live in tribal trust lands have themselves no money to spare.

Tensions between fathers and sons develop also from another source. The high polygamy rate of farm owners and their full control over money for bridewealth, results in a high bachelor rate among their sons. Whereas in tribal trust lands only 37 per cent of all men over 15 years of age are unmarried, in the two purchase areas this percentage is as high as 58.

In spite of these tensions, farm owners are greatly attached to their sons and do all they can to help them to become successful in their lives. This is most clearly shown in the great amount of money they invest in their children's education. Fifteen randomly selected peasant farmers with children of school age were asked about the school fees they paid for their children in 1967. Three

[1] *The Rhodesia Herald*, 21.5.70.

stated that they had paid over £100 that year, the highest amount being £160; six had paid between £50 and £90; and six less than £50, the lowest amount paid being £5. Four of these fifteen farmers had children in secondary school and one of them had five sons and daughters in boarding schools.

The high emphasis placed by farm owners on their children's education is evident from Tables 17 and 18. Table 17 shows that about 14 per cent of all sons are studying, and most of them are in boarding school. This is only slightly less than the percentage of men absent as labour migrants. Most of those classified as skilled and unskilled labourers are employed in towns, and so are a few of the white-collar workers. The other men are all rural residents.

TABLE 17

Occupation of Men in Two Purchase Areas (N=574)

Occupation	Frequency	Per cent
Farm owners	204	35·5
Farm assistants	146	25·4
Students	81	14·1
White-collar workers	37	6·5
Assistants to store owners	7	1·3
Skilled labourers	12	2·0
Unskilled labourers	87	15·2
Total	574	100·0

TABLE 18

Educational Achievement of Farm Owners and
Other Men in Two Purchase Areas (N=574)

Education in years	Farm Owners		Other Men	
	Frequency	Per cent	Frequency	Per cent
0–2	94	46·1	14	3·8
3–5	83	40·7	84	22·7
6–8	20	9·8	189	51·1
9 and over	7	3·4	83	22·4
Total	204	100·0	370	100·0

Table 18 shows that whereas peasant farmers are predominantly illiterate—only in Guruuswa do seven of the 144 farm owners possess secondary education, two because they had been extension assistants before they went to their farms and five because they had been teachers—other men, mainly their sons, have been to school for several years. Of these 51·1 per cent have attended upper primary school and 22·4 per cent secondary school. This high education among the non-farming population in purchase areas indicates a social distance between them and the old farmers. At one meeting of an African Farmers' Union committee in Guruuswa a farm owner cried out: 'I know that we are jealous of our children because our children are more educated than we are, and I also know that our children are jealous of us because we control the money. Nevertheless, they ought to help us and warn us of the tricks of the white men. After all, it is we who educated them.'

The sons of farm owners are all Christians, though about 8 per cent of their fathers still follow the traditional Karanga religion. This percentage of traditional believers in purchase areas is smaller than in tribal trust lands, yet the number of diviners in purchase areas is disproportionately large. In Mutadza two out of 60 farm owners and in Guruuswa 15 out of 144 are diviners. Because the diviners now living in these purchase areas could acquire money in the past through their craft, few of them ever engaged in labour migration. Hence they could concentrate on farming all their lives and had better opportunities than their neighbours to qualify as master farmers. Because the two purchase areas have so many diviners, magical beliefs are widespread. One third of all peasant farmers have had their homesteads magically protected against witches, and many believe that agricultural success is due to *divisi*, a charm, rather than to modern farming practices. Since some of the best farmers in Guruuswa are diviners, this belief is strengthened by their success. Extension assistants, and even the farm owners' own sons who no longer believe in *divisi*, find it impossible to wean the older men from this belief. Many sons are friends of extension assistants and show an interest in modern farming practices. But the old men argue that the young are unfamiliar with the wisdom of their own culture. Different religious beliefs, therefore, cause a further division between some fathers and sons.

Fathers and sons in purchase areas, then, often differ in their outlook on life. The young and well-educated men are inclined towards a modern approach to farming. Yet they are dependent on their fathers to set them up in life and, apart from the farm owners' eldest sons, most of the sons have little stake in the land and are forced to look for security in European employment or in tribal trust lands.

The farm owners, on the other hand, are usually old and illiterate, and many—in fact many more than the 8 per cent of religious traditionalists—adhere to traditional beliefs which are not conducive to modern farming. They control the money of their families, yet depend on their sons for help in the fields and for advice in their dealings with government officials. While they are proud of their educated sons, they nevertheless feel inferior to them. These tensions between fathers and sons are acutely felt in most families and give rise to a constant emigration of youths from their fathers' farms.

(d) Farm Owners and their Wives and Daughters

Not only the relationship between fathers and sons is strained in purchase areas, but also the relationship between husbands and wives and fathers and daughters is tension ridden. Since a prime concern of farm owners is to control a large labour force, they are opposed to any of their dependants joining non-agricultural voluntary associations, such as are organized by Christian missionaries and wives of the school teachers. They see in these clubs a threat to their economic well-being and fear that if their wives and daughters participate in them, they will become too independent. Wives and daughters resent this strict control, for they see what advantages women in tribal trust lands derive from voluntary associations.

Since women in purchase areas are mainly appreciated for their work, they realize that if they want to be respected, they must excel in farm labour. Some of them have responded to this opportunity, and wives who with their husbands joined the 'Who is Champion?' club, do receive respect. Agricultural leadership, however, is almost only possible for them if their husbands cannot take full charge of the farm. One woman, for example, whose husband suffers from a chronic illness, not only runs the farm but also takes an active part in agricultural demonstration lessons. When at one public meeting she showed how cattle are inoculated and de-horned, the extension assistant praised her for her first-class work, stressing that she surpassed in her skill the men of her neighbourhood. Thereupon the other women cheered her and subsequently honoured her whenever they met her.

Many husbands, who recognize their wives' important contribution to farm work, consult them before making major decisions. Such consultation is especially frequent in monogamous families. Polygamists consult at the most their first wives; their junior wives have little say in the running of the farm. But even if farm owners consult their wives, they expect them always to concur with their opinion, and most wives do so to reduce clashes in the family.

A large number of dependants not only contribute to a large labour force, but also require more money to feed and clothe them. In poor purchase areas, like Mutadza, this can lead to an independent search by women to earn cash. For example, 18 women on the 60 Mutadza farms, all of them either wives, sisters or daughters of peasant farmers, engage in prostitution to earn money to clothe themselves and their children, and to obtain money for their children's school fees, because the farm owners do not adequately provide for them. In most instances this gives rise to further conflicts in the family.

Because peasant farmers make a concerted effort to prevent the emancipation of their women, mothers often assist their daughters to marry out of the purchase area. Whereas farm owners try to marry their daughters to their neighbours, mothers help their daughters to marry into tribal trust lands. Girls too prefer to marry peasant cultivators rather than farm owners, because though peasant cultivators are poorer, work in a village is less hard than on a farm. Hence not only young men but also young women try to leave the purchase areas.

(e) The Population Structure in Purchase Areas

This movement of young people out of purchase areas, and the endeavour of older men to attract relatives and to marry additional wives, gives rise to a peculiar population structure in purchase areas. Most of the men aged 45 to 75 are the farm owners who control the lives of the people in purchase areas. Some of their wives are as old as they are, but some are still young, even in their teens. A middle-aged male population is missing, but not primarily because of a high rate of labour migration, as is the case in tribal trust lands, but because the married children of farm owners may not stay with their parents and few young men are farm

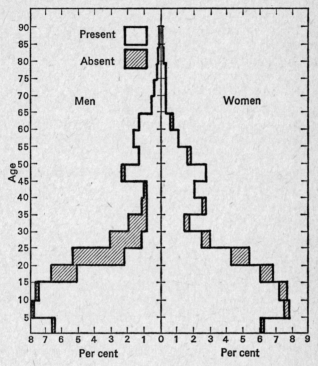

Fig. 3. Population pyramid of two purchase area populations

owners. In addition a great number of teenagers are in boarding schools. The number of small children in the two purchase areas is steadily declining. This population pyramid only shows a shrinking of the youngest age group. But if the population pyramids of Guruuswa and Mutadza were given separately, a shrinking of the 5 to 10 year age group would already be visible in Mutadza which was settled seven years earlier than Guruuswa. This means that as soon as peasant farmers settle in a purchase area, the number of births experienced by their wives becomes less than it had been in the tribal trust lands. A change in this population structure will only come about when the farm owners who opened up the land die, and their sons take over the farms.

(4) RELATIONS OF PEASANT FARMERS WITH 'OUTSIDERS'

Apart from kinsmen and fellow farmers, farm owners have to deal with two other groups of people, the non-farming residents in their own purchase areas and neighbours in tribal trust lands.

(a) Non-Farming Residents in Purchase Areas

Non-farming residents in purchase areas are mainly junior government employees, teachers and storekeepers. They account for some 3 to 4 per cent of all the people and always live together on crown lands.

Teachers and extension assistants are better educated than most of the peasant farmers and are therefore highly regarded by them. Teachers meet the farm owners at regular parent-teacher meetings and often peasant farmers consult them in matters which are not related to schools. They, therefore, fill positions of trust in their communities. The Mutadza headmaster, for example, was asked by the people regularly to collect their mail from the nearest post office.

But although teachers may be trusted, their frequent transfers prevent them from establishing close ties with the farm owners, and since the interests of teachers and farmers differ, teachers often form a group apart. In Guruuswa, for example, which has three primary schools with eleven teachers—five married men, four single men and two women teachers—their number is large enough to develop their own social life and to meet together to discuss their professional interests. In Mutadza purchase area the farmers employed six teachers in their council school, five men and one woman. These too cultivated close ties among themselves, were friendly to the peasant farmers, but did not mix too intimately with them. The fact that social clubs for women, organized by the women teachers or teachers' wives, were always opposed by farm owners, encouraged the teachers to keep to themselves. Only the five Guruuswa farm owners who had themselves been teachers before they took up their farms, are accepted in the social circle of teachers.

Extension assistants, who are fewer in number than teachers, cannot form an ingroup. They have closer ties with the peasant farmers than teachers because of their work, but except for the one extension assistant who became the 'son-in-law' of the Guruuswa farmers, extension assistants also look to other white-collar workers for companionship. The farm owners, for their part, though they look up to these men and often hope that their sons will one day become teachers and extension assistants, regard them as servants of the community who are paid for their work.

Businessmen are welcomed in purchase areas because both Guruuswa, but especially Mutadza, are inadequately served by stores. In 1967 Guruuswa had two business centres. One was started in the early 1960s by an African businessman from Umtali. He opened a grocery store which he left in the care of his daughter and son-in-law; a butchery which he entrusted to his brother-in-law; and a mill in which he employed his brother's son. In addition he employed a tailor from the adjoining tribal trust land to make shirts and dresses for the people. He himself does not live in the area. His enterprise is a family concern. Like many Africans he does not make a great profit from the stores and the mill, but they help him to support his large family.

The second business centre in Guruuswa was opened in 1964 near a primary school. An extension assistant from a tribal trust land thought of retiring from government service, but before doing so wanted to secure himself another source of income. He therefore opened a grocery store in Guruuswa and placed it in the hands of his unmarried sister. Later he opened a coffee house next to it and employed a girl to serve the guests. In 1965 the son of a farm owner opened a third grocery store in Guruuswa, just next to that of the extension assistant. He later built a butchery in the same place. He opened this butchery with a minimum of capital because he bought oxen from the peasant farmers on credit, then peddled their meat around nearby mining compounds, and only after he had sold the meat did he pay the farm owners. This enabled the farm owners to sell their cattle at higher prices than they would have obtained at auction sales, and the businessman had a new source of income.

These two business centres in Guruuswa do not adequately provide the peasant farmers with their requirements. Some buy their goods in the stores of the nearby tribal trust land, others go at regular intervals to local towns to buy goods in bulk.

If Guruuswa has few stores, Mutadza has none. To cater for the people's needs, a nearby European farmer opened a store on his ranch which he placed in the charge of an astute African from Malawi. When his storekeeper died, he employed the son of a Mutadza farm owner. This man, however, ran the store at a loss; he alienated the customers by raising prices and by impolite service, and he also helped himself and his family to the goods they needed. When the European owner became aware of the full extent of the mismanagement, he dismissed the man and closed the store. Since then peasant farmers in Mutadza have to buy their goods either in the stores of a nearby purchase area or in the adjacent tribal trust land. In 1966 a Mutadza farm owner opened his own mill.

At almost all stores peasant farmers can obtain goods on credit. Their indebtedness binds them to the businessmen, for since stores are few, no peasant farmer can neglect his debts and yet continue to obtain goods locally. Businessmen, therefore, have succeeded in making themselves indispensible to the farm owners. Yet because they themselves do not generally live in the purchase areas, peasant farmers have to deal with their employees, and these employees have relatively low status in African communities. Though the storekeepers live with teachers and extension assistants on crown lands, they feel more at ease when mixing with the farming population.

Teachers, extension assistants and businessmen with their employees, then, are appreciated by the peasant farmers for the services they render, and teachers, extension assistants and businessmen are pleased to find employment in purchase areas. Theirs is a symbiotic relationship which has advantages for both groups.

(b) Relation of Farm Owners with Tribal Trust Land Peasant Cultivators

Purchase area farmers are also bound by many ties to tribal trust lands. Most maintain close contacts with the tribal trust lands from which they came and in which their relatives still live. They sometimes visit their old villages, but more often receive visits from their kinsmen on their farms. The exodus of their sons and daughters to tribal trust lands further strengthens these ties. At one public meeting, at which the question was discussed whether a businessmen from a tribal trust land should be allowed to open his store in the area, one peasant farmer, brushing aside the concern of his neighbours who wanted to reserve for their own children the possibility of opening stores among them, stated: 'The tribal trust land is our mother. It is the place we came from. How can we refuse a man from home to open a store for us?'

The exodus of children, especially of daughters, gives rise to many new bonds between peasant farmers and peasant cultivators. Since farm owners cannot find sufficient additional wives for themselves in the purchase area, they have to marry wives from adjacent tribal trust lands. Peasant cultivators in tribal trust lands are keen to marry their daughters to farm owners because they expect not only a high bridewealth from a rich son-in-law but they also hope that he will provide them with food should their own harvest fail. Moreover, since the daughters of peasant cultivators have no direct experience of the hard life on farms, few object to marrying a rich polygamist.

Not only kinship ties but also economic ties bind tribal trust lands and purchase areas together. Purchase area farmers generally produce more food than they need, and peasant cultivators in tribal areas often produce less. Hence many farm owners sell a great part of their surplus crops directly to peasant cultivators in neighbouring tribal areas. This direct transaction, though illegal since purchase areas are administered together with European farming areas, cuts out the middleman and until 1967 avoided the African Development Fund levy. Both Guruuswa and Mutadza farm owners have established permanent trading links with villagers in the adjoining tribal trust lands. Some farmers cart their crops on lorries to the more distant parts of these tribal areas, while farmers living along the border wait for peasant cultivators to come and buy crops directly on their farms.

Economic links extend beyond trading. Purchase area farmers who are chronically short of labour, are often assisted on their land by people from the nearby tribal trust land. Some pay them in crops, others reward them through beer parties. It is understood that farm owners do not have to reciprocate and attend the beer parties of peasant cultivators. Farm owners who are short of herd boys, also obtain help from peasant cultivators. Some farm owners reward their herd boys by paying their school fees in the succeeding year, some pay their fathers in cash and give to the boys secondhand clothing.

Farm owners also assist their tribal neighbours with cattle. If a peasant cultivator is short of draught animals during the ploughing season, a purchase area farmer may lend him his and in turn receive from him free labour later on in the season. Occasionally farm owners allow peasant cultivators to graze their cattle on their farms if their land is understocked.

These many ties between tribal trust lands and purchase areas unite peasant farmers and peasant cultivators and make them interdependent. When a farm owner was asked whether he thought tribal trust land peasants liked purchase area farmers, he answered: 'I do not know, and I do not care. All I know is that they make us rich, and therefore we like them.'

(5) THE POSITION OF PURCHASE AREAS IN THE DUAL ECONOMY OF RHODESIA

Whereas peasant cultivators in tribal trust lands participate in the dual economy of Rhodesia by dividing their time between European employment and agriculture, peasant farmers in purchase areas do not combine farming with other economic activities. Their sons, who seek urban employment, keep their earnings to themselves, and locally employed white-collar workers and storekeepers are seldom related to the farmers. Farm owners, therefore, depend even more exclusively on agriculture than do master farmers in tribal trust lands. Farming has become a full-time and specialized occupation for them, and every service they require they obtain from other specialists.

Their ability to pay for specialist services shows that they possess some wealth. Their superior housing, too, indicates that they have more money at their disposal than their neighbours in tribal areas. The fact also, that purchase areas have been classified together with European farming areas, indicates that administrators regard peasant farmers as part of Rhodesia's cash economy. The peasant farmers' participation in the money sector is directly based on their sales of surplus crops.

Yet although many purchase area farmers share economic characteristics with European farmers in Rhodesia, some look more like tribal peasant cultivators. Their harvests are as low as those of their tribal neighbours and hardly cover their subsistence needs.

The relation of purchase areas to Rhodesia's dual economy can therefore be seen under a dual aspect. On the one hand, some farmers employ farm labour from tribal areas and most sell surpluses to the wider Rhodesian society, thus acting as cash croppers; others are still subsistence cultivators. Hence, although hardly any farm owner simultaneously participates in wage employment and cash production, individual farms in the same community belong to either the cash or the subsistence sector of the country's economy.

Labour migration, which in tribal areas binds town and country together, plays no important role in purchase areas. These peasant farming communities are used to a strict division of labour. They hire the services of the specialists they need, and do not depend on the skills of returning migrants. Nor do these communities depend on labour migration to drain off their surplus population, since all people who are not needed emigrate permanently.

Purchase areas, then, stand in a very different relationship to the European controlled sector of Rhodesia's economy from that of tribal trust lands. Peasant farmers are independent of Europeans for obtaining money. At most they look to them as a market for their crops, but these can almost always be sold locally to their tribal neighbours. Consequently farm owners feel secure and self-sufficient. They are the most settled and contented section of Rhodesia's peasant population.

CHAPTER 9

ECONOMIC RESOURCES OF PEASANT
FARMERS IN PURCHASE AREAS

(1) INTRODUCTION

The previous chapters showed that the more carefully peasant
farmers are selected by government officials, the more interested
they are in agriculture and the more readily they cooperate
with the agricultural staff. Since peasant farmers are allowed great
freedom to administer their local communities, their interest or lack
of interest in agriculture can be seen by their participation in both
formal and informal organizations.

In these communities, where people are rich enough to purchase
necessary farming equipment and to pay for essential services,
their general attitude towards farming is more important than
slight differences in education and access to natural resources.
Table 19 sets out the agricultural income of farm owners in
Guruuswa and Mutadza purchase areas.

My census of agricultural productivity, as well as my census of
labour input in purchase areas, includes every second farm in
Guruuswa that is, 72 out of 144 farms, and every farm in Mutadza,
that is 18 farms owned by master farmers and 42 farms owned by
men who possess no master farmer's certificate.

Table 19 shows that there is a significant difference in the
annual income of farm owners in Guruuswa and Mutadza, and
a smaller difference between master farmers and other peasant
farmers in Mutadza purchase area. Whereas only one family, or
1·4 per cent of all farm owners in Guruuswa, has an annual
income of below £100, 7 or 38·8 per cent of all master farmers in
Mutadza and exactly 50 per cent of all other farm owners in
Mutadza purchase area earn so small an income; and whereas
13 or about 18 per cent of all Guruuswa farmers have an income
of over £400, none of the Mutadza farmers earns as much. Because
of these significant differences in income between the three
groups of farm owners, the subsequent analysis of farming
activities is based on these categories: Guruuswa farm owners,

TABLE 19

Agricultural Income of Peasant Farmers in Purchase Areas (N=132)

Agricultural Income	Guruuswa Freq.	Guruuswa Per cent	Mutadza Master Farmer Freq.	Mutadza Master Farmer Per cent	O. Peasant Farmer Freq.	O. Peasant Farmer Per cent
Below £50	1	1·4	3	16·6	8	19·1
£50– £99	—	—	4	22·2	13	30·9
£100–£149	3	4·2	4	22·2	10	23·8
£150–£199	14	19·4	1	5·6	5	11·9
£200–£249	16	22·2	1	5·6	3	7·1
£250–£299	9	12·5	4	22·2	2	4·8
£300–£349	13	18·0	—	—	1	2·4
£350–£399	3	4·2	1	5·6	—	—
£400–£449	8	11·1	—	—	—	—
£450–£499	1	1·4	—	—	—	—
£500–£549	3	4·2	—	—	—	—
£1,000 plus	1	1·4	—	—	—	—
Total	72	100·0	18	100·0	42	100·0

master farmers in Mutadza, and other peasant farmers in Mutadza.

Peasant farmers in purchase areas possess all the basic farming equipment. All have at least one plough, all have a cultivator, all Guruuswa farm owners own a harrow and so do four, or 22·2 per cent of all master farmers in Mutadza. Two thirds of all Guruuswa peasant farmers also possess a planter, and so do just over a third of all Mutadza farm owners. Most peasant farmers are also well provided with transport. All Guruuswa farmers and over two thirds of all Mutadza farmers possess a cart, the rest own wheel barrows. Eleven Guruuswa farmers and two Mutadza farm owners possess a car or lorry. All Guruuswa farmers have a bicycle, and two-thirds of all Mutadza farmers possess a bicycle as well. One master farmer in Mutadza possesses a motor cycle.

Three Guruuswa farm owners and one master farmer in Mutadza have sunk their own boreholes and own a pump, one Guruuswa farmer and two master farmers in Mutadza possess a grinding machine, and one Guruuswa farmer owns a shelling machine. No ordinary peasant farmer in Mutadza possesses any of these items. Although, therefore, all peasant farmers possess the basic farming equipment, only the better farmers have invested money in more expensive, but highly productive, machinery.

The differences in the ownership of equipment between Guruuswa and Mutadza farm owners are to a large extent due to the more stringent requirements from applicants for farms in Guruuswa, since by the time this purchase area was opened, candidates had to possess at least £300 in cash or equipment.

No farm owner possesses a tractor, but the African Farmers' Union committee of Guruuswa once purchased a tractor through the African Development Fund. Maintenance problems and competition for first service among farm owners, however, caused difficulties and after two years the tractor was sold.

(2) RESOURCES IN LIVESTOCK AND LAND

The differential income of master farmers and ordinary peasant cultivators in tribal trust lands is to a large extent due to the bigger fields and larger herds of master farmers. In purchase areas, too, some relation exists between the size of herds and farms and total annual income, but this relation seems to be coincidental rather than the reason for larger or smaller farm income.

TABLE 20

Cattle Ownership in Two Purchase Areas (N=204)[1]

Number of Cattle Owned	Guruuswa		Mutadza Master Farmers		O. Peasant Farmers	
	Freq.	Per cent	Freq.	Per cent	Freq.	Per cent
Below 10	2	1·5	2	11·2	8	19·0
10–19	74	51·5	4	22·2	23	54·8
20–29	57	39·4	6	33·3	8	19·0
30–39	9	6·1	6	33·3	2	4·8
40 and over	2	1·5	—	—	1	2·4
Total	144	100·0	18	100·0	42	100·0

Table 20 shows that the majority of farm owners possess between ten and twenty head of cattle, and some have significantly more. The average Guruuswa farmer owns 20, the average master farmer in Mutadza 18, and the other peasant farmers in Mutadza own about 16 head of cattle. All peasant farmers have enough

[1] Johnson found that in a purchase area in the north of Rhodesia the average herd size was 16 head of cattle, the same as on most Mutadza homesteads. Johnson, 1964a, p. 9.

oxen to plough their fields, and many have more so that they can hire some to their neighbours in adjoining tribal trust lands.

Larger cattle herds also provide peasant farmers with adequate manure; all they require is labour to cart it to their fields. Thus neither shortage of ploughs nor shortage of oxen, the most serious handicaps which face peasant cultivators, exist in purchase areas.

Purchase area herds tend to be adjusted to the farm size. Local extension officers estimate that in both purchase areas 10 to 15 acres of land are necessary to graze one head of cattle throughout the year, and this amount of grazing is available on most farms. The size of most herds indicates that farm owners have built up their herds to the maximum carrying capacity of their land. Since farm owners are not competing with each other for grazing, and since each has a stake in the good condition of his own pasture, farm owners seldom over-stock their farms.

In addition to cattle, most farms have some small stock. About a third of all peasant farmers keep some goats which are used for meat as well as for ritual purposes. Goats are seldom sold. Sheep, which fetch good prices in the Rhodesian market, are mainly kept for sale. Practically every homestead in Guruuswa has its flock of sheep, but only every second homestead in Mutadza keeps sheep. Because Guruuswa farmers are more orientated towards the cash economy than Mutadza farmers, they pay attention to marketing facilities for small stock.

Whereas the differences in herd size of Guruuswa and Mutadza peasant farmers is slight, the difference between the size of their farms is somewhat greater.

TABLE 21

Size of Purchase Area Farms (N=204)

	Guruuswa		Mutadza Master Farmers		O. Peasant Farmers	
Acres	Freq.	Per cent	Freq.	Per cent	Freq.	Per cent
100–149	4	2·8	—	—	9	21·4
150–199	55	38·2	14	77·9	26	61·9
200–249	73	50·7	2	11·1	7	16·7
250–299	11	7·6	1	5·5	—	—
300 and over	1	0·7	1	5·5	—	—
Total	144	100·0	18	100·0	42	100·0

Table 21 shows that most farms in Guruuswa are over 200 acres, whereas most farms in Mutadza purchase area are below 200 acres. In Mutadza, furthermore, master farmers tend to have larger farms than their neighbours. Guruuswa farmers plough on the average 23 acres, Mutadza farmers only about 17. The smaller acreage of cultivated land in Mutadza is not due to the unsuitability of more land for ploughing. In fact, in both purchase areas more land is cultivable than is at present put under the plough. Shortage of labour and lack of capital to engage in large-scale farming, rather than shortage of land, are the major handicaps of local peasant farmers. Since in a year of average rainfall crops are the main source of income of peasant farmers, income is roughly related to the size of the cultivated land.

Yet if no farm owner in either Guruuswa or Mutadza has attempted large scale farming, neither has any farmer reverted to shifting cultivation. Such a regression to traditional farming patterns too has been prevented by labour shortage. For land which is cultivated by machines must be properly cleared lest ploughshares break, contour ridges must be constructed, and these necessary improvements make shifting cultivation uneconomic.

Peasant farmers grow the same crops as peasant cultivators in tribal areas, and cash crops play a very minor role. A few Mutadza farm owners grow tobacco and one once attempted cotton, but none of them have been very successful. Some Guruuswa

TABLE 22

Crops Grown by Purchase Area Farmers (N=132)

	Guruuswa		Mutadza Master Farmers		O. Peasant Farmers	
Acres	Acres	Per cent	Acres	Per cent	Acres	Per cent
Maize	528	31·6	117	38·1	236	33·9
Millet	653	39·1	89	29·0	247	35·4
Sorghum	139	8·3	31	10·1	85	12·2
Groundnuts	286	17·1	66	21·5	125	17·9
Groundbeans	51	3·1	1	0·3	4	0·5
Other crops	14	0·8	3	1·0	1	0·1
Total	1,671	100·0	307	100·0	698	100·0

farmers grow rice and sweet potatoes. It is surprising that farm owners grow such a relatively low percentage of maize since master farmers in tribal trust lands plant a greater percentage of their land with this crop than do peasant farmers.

Like their tribal neighbours, peasant farmers also grow some sugar cane, pumpkins and melons in their maize and groundnut fields. The only difference between tribal and purchase area peasants is that the latter cultivate larger acreages of each crop than do the former. Labour requirements, though greater in purchase areas than in tribal trust lands, are therefore of an identical nature and farm owners require no special skills from their labourers.

(3) LABOUR REQUIREMENTS AND LABOUR SUPPLY IN PURCHASE AREAS

The previous chapter outlined the residential pattern of purchase areas and indicated the labour difficulties which farm owners encounter due to the isolation of their homesteads. Many peasant farmers married additional wives or tried to attract kinsmen to increase their labour force. Though Mutadza farmers have a higher polygamy rate than Guruuswa farmers, Guruuswa farmers have nevertheless been able to build up a slightly larger labour force. The average farm owner in Guruuswa has about 9, the average farm owner in Mutadza about 8 workers.[1] Guruuswa farmers have slightly more men working on their farms than

TABLE 23

Average Household Size in Two Purchase Areas (N=204)

Household Composition	Guruuswa Number	Mutadza Number
Men	3·3	2·5
Women	2·8	3·3
Children aged 7–14	2·6	2·3
Children aged 0–6	1·4	1·8
Total	10·1	9·9

Mutadza farmers, yet in spite of the larger number of men,

[1] Children below the age of six make no contribution to agriculture.

women contribute the largest number of working hours. Whereas in Mutadza, just as among master farmers in tribal trust lands, men, women and children each contribute about a third of all agricultural labour, in Guruuswa women contribute over 46 per cent of all working hours, men over 27 per cent, and children almost 27 per cent.[1] Women in Guruuswa are therefore the hardest working group of people in the two communities.[2]

The division of labour between men, women and children in purchase areas is similar to the division of labour in tribal trust lands. Ploughing is most often done by men. The men lead the plough and children guide the oxen. Women seldom assist since there is a tendency in purchase areas to leave livestock in the care of men. In sowing and planting, men, women and children help together. Women do most of the weeding and harvesting, and in Guruuswa they work longer hours at these tasks than men and children together.

The ploughing and planting season is the most critical time in purchase areas; not because, as in tribal trust lands, ploughs and oxen are in short supply, but because of labour shortage. During these months the working days are longer than at any other time of the year. In Guruuswa, for example, peasant farmers go to their fields at 4 a.m. and plough until 11 a.m. After a rest to avoid the heat—for the ploughing season coincides with the hottest time of the year—they resume their work from 2 p.m. to 6 p.m. when it is getting dark. One farmer stated that his crop failure in a year of average rainfall was due to labour shortage during ploughing and planting time.

In Guruuswa purchase area 81·2 per cent of all work in the fields is done by family members, 10·6 per cent by work parties, and 8·2 per cent by hired labourers. Among master farmers in Mutadza purchase area, only 65·2 per cent of the work in the fields is done by family members, and among unqualified farm owners as little as 57·7 per cent. Hired labourers do not constitute more than 0·3 per cent in the labour force of Mutadza farmers, but

---

[1] For further details see Appendix, Table 50.
[2] Their hard work has earned these women considerable wealth in livestock. Women in Guruuswa possess more property in their own right than women in any other rural communities studied in this book. Of the wives of 144 farm owners, women on 62 farms possessed cattle, women on 61 farms possessed sheep, women on 32 farms possessed goats and women on 9 farms possessed pigs. Some of these women possessed more than 10 animals. Women derive prestige from such personally owned livestock.

instead work parties where beer is provided account for 40 per cent of all farm labour. Guruuswa peasant farmers employ hired labourers at ploughing, weeding and harvesting time, and work parties are hardly more important in Guruuswa than hired labourers, for although slightly more working hours are contributed by members of work parties, hired labourers who receive wages work harder and so get more work done than members of work parties.

Hired labourers are mainly employed by monogamists and seldom stay with their employers all the year round. Polygamists rely almost entirely on family labour.

Work parties become important when family labour is insufficient and peasant farmers do not possess enough money to hire labourers. Work parties increase in importance as farm productivity falls: they are least frequently used among Guruuswa farmers and most often among unqualified Mutadza farmers. Work parties in Guruuswa are small and seldom more than five or six farms send a member to a party. Most farmers are busy on their own land and reluctant to help their neighbours. Hence work parties in Guruuswa have few members and cannot complete much work.

The average Mutadza farm owner calls in some eight work parties a year and attends an equal number on the farms of his neighbours. Usually two members of a family attend the work party of a neighbour so that work parties consist on the average of some 15 to 20 people. This number is large enough to accomplish a significant agricultural task. The people in Mutadza purchase area rely to an even larger extent on work parties than do ordinary peasant cultivators in tribal trust lands. In tribal trust lands members of work parties contribute only 19·4 per cent of all working hours, but in Mutadza they contribute 34·5 per cent to the labour force of master farmers, and 42·2 per cent to the labour force of unqualified farm owners.

Since peasant farmers in purchase areas grow the same type of crops as peasant cultivators in tribal trust lands, their seasonal labour requirements are similar.[1] As in tribal trust lands, the peak periods for labour occur in November and December when the land has to be ploughed, sowed or planted and weeded, and in April–May when the crops are harvested. The November–

---

[1] See Appendix, Table 51, for the labour input for the various crops grown in the two purchase areas.

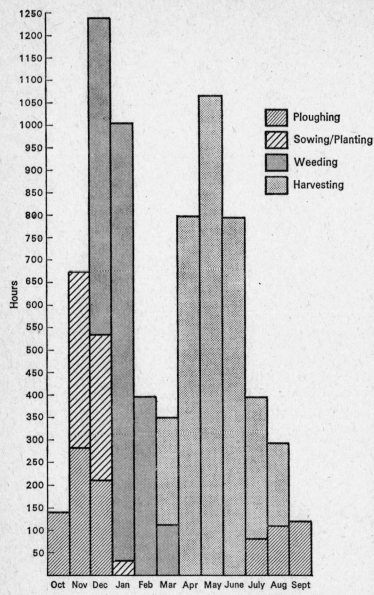

Fig. 4. Labour input on crops in Guruuswa purchase area

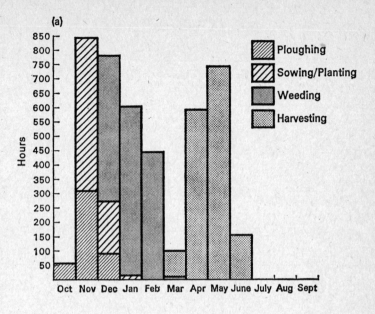

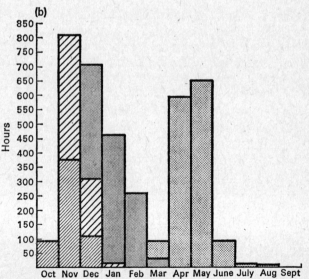

Fig. 5. Labour input on crops per household in Mutadza purchase area: (a) master farmers; (b) unqualified farm owners

December peak period is unnecessarily heavy for Mutadza
farmers because none of them winter plough their fields after the
harvest.

The more efficient cultivation of Guruuswa farmers results in a
great demand for extra labour at harvesting time. Whereas in
Mutadza purchase area harvesting is completed by the beginning
of June, in Guruuswa it lasts well into July. Guruuswa farm
families spend on the average 7,270 hours on crop production,
master farmer families in Mutadza 4,314 hours, and families of the
remaining farm owners in Mutadza 3,766 hours.[1] The low
labour input in Mutadza is partly due to two factors: firstly,
local farm owners are old and can no longer work hard and
secondly, women have to walk long distances to fetch water for the
household and this withdraws their labour from the fields.

Since the overall labour input of Mutadza farmers is low, their
labour input per acre is also inadequate. In fact, it is only about
half as high as is the labour input per acre in tribal trust lands.
This less intensive cultivation of land necessarily results in much
lower yields per acre. Even Guruuswa farmers spend less time on
each acre under crops than do tribal trust land peasants, though
their total labour input is almost three times as high as that of
ordinary peasant cultivators.[2]

A great strain on every peasant farmer's labour force is the need
for herd boys. Since cattle are generally grazed by each farm owner
on his own farm, each farmer must provide his own herder.
Cattle, sheep and goats have to be herded from October to July
to prevent them from damaging crops. Thereafter enterprising
peasant farmers stall feed some of their cattle. Consequently the
average farm family in Guruuswa spends 3,158 hours a year on
cattle maintenance. The average Mutadza family spends only
1,391 hours on herding.[3] This relatively low investment of time
is partly due to lack of interest in stall feeding, partly to partial
communal grazing on the land in which asbestos has been discovered. Here herd boys can look after the cattle of several farmers
so that each farm owner can reduce his hours of herding.

[1] See Appendix, Table 51.
[2] Johnson found in his study that the total input of work per family in a
purchase area is some two to three times as great as the labour input by a
family in a tribal trust land. He also stresses that due to the large acreage
cultivated, the labour input per acre is considerably less than in tribal trust lands.
Johnson, 1964a, p. 20.
[3] For further details see Appendix, Table 52.

Whereas in tribal trust lands women provide a third of the herding time, in Guruuswa they provide less than a fifth, and in Mutadza less than 5 per cent. Most cattle herders are men and especially boys so that the old Karanga custom, which left herding to men, re-emerges in purchase areas. Yet since farm owners lay great emphasis on their children's education, few of their own sons look after the cattle. Instead they hire boys from adjoining tribal trust lands. In Guruuswa 32 per cent of all herding hours are provided by hired herd boys, and in Mutadza as many as 40 per cent.

(4) CONCLUSION

This analysis of the economic resources of Guruuswa and Mutadza farm owners shows that there are only slight differences between the sizes of farms, cattle herds and labour forces available to the families in the two communities. Though Guruuswa farmers have slightly more land, slightly larger herds and a slightly larger labour force, these differences are not great enough to account for the significant differences in the agricultural output of these communities. More important are the lack of farming skills of most Mutadza peasant farmers and their apparent lack of interest in farming. For although the labour force of farmers in both purchase areas is approximately equal, Guruuswa farming families nevertheless spend twice as much time on their land and cattle as do Mutadza farming families. This work orientation in Guruuswa, as against the apparent greater leisure orientation in Mutadza, is rooted in the different attitudes of members of these communities towards agriculture.

Danckwerts who examined the causes of low productivity in peasant communities, found that peasant agriculture can only become more productive if people recognize 'the need to set aside income to provide increasing quantities of capital; the necessity for more regular and accurate application of work; the need for longer periods of learning to equip workers for increasingly complex duties; the need to continue to learn more about each specialization on the job and the need to adjust the mode of life of the whole society to each new form of production.'[1]

The social characteristics and agricultural yields of peasant farmers in Guruuswa and Mutadza confirm Danckwerts' findings.

[1] Danckwerts, 1970, p. 20.

Guruuswa farmers, and to a lesser degree master farmers in Mutadza, have set aside larger quantities of capital than ordinary peasant farmers in Mutadza; some of them sank boreholes, built dams and bought expensive machinery. They work harder, possess farming certificates, and continue to learn more about farming by attending demonstration lessons organized by the agricultural staff. As a consequence, the very community structure of Guruuswa purchase area differs from the community structure of Mutadza and reflects its peasant farmers' adjustments to the requirements of a modern cash economy.

These differences indicate that once a peasant community has extricated itself from a vicious circle of poverty, more factors are required to turn self-sufficiency into wealth than are necessary to turn a struggling peasant cultivator into a more progressive master farmer.

CHAPTER 10

AGRICULTURAL PRODUCTIVITY OF
PURCHASE AREAS

(1) INTRODUCTION

Whereas peasant cultivators in tribal trust lands gain a large proportion of their income from other than agricultural sources, peasant farmers in purchase areas depend for their income exclusively on their farms. Hence crops and cattle, and to a lesser extent milk, eggs, fruit and vegetables, are their only source of money. For people who rely so exclusively on agriculture, drought is even more serious than for people who derive part of their income from salaries and wages. To assess the effect of drought on peasant farmers, their incomes in a year of average rainfall and in a drought year, that is, in 1965–66 and 1966–67, are compared.

(2) CROP PRODUCTION

Tables 24 and 25 give a summary of the productivity of fields in purchase areas during a season of average rainfall and during a drought season.

These Tables show that maize and millet together account for about 80 per cent of all the crops grown in purchase areas. The other crops, including groundnuts, are of only minor importance.

Drought has a crippling effect on the economic activities of progressive farmers. The more crops a peasant farmer produces in a year of average rainfall, the greater is his loss in a drought year. Guruuswa farm owners, for example, who in a year of average rainfall harvest some 92 bags of crops, reap in a drought year only 28 bags, or 30·4 per cent of what they had expected to reap. Likewise master farmers in Mutadza who normally expect to harvest some 45 bags of crops, reap in a drought year only 18 bags, or 40·0 per cent of their normal harvest. The other Mutadza farmers, who in a year of average rainfall harvest some 34 bags, reap in a drought season only 18 bags, or 52·9 per cent of their normal harvest. Drought, therefore, narrows the income from

TABLE 24

Productivity of Peasant Farmers in a Year of Average Rainfall (1965–1966) (N=132)

| | Bags harvested | | | | | | Bags per acre | | | Bags sold | | | | | | Bags consumed per household or unaccounted for | | |
| | Guruuswa | | Mutadza M. Farmers | | O.P. Farmers | | Guruuswa | Mutadza MFs | OPFs | Guruuswa | | Mutadza M. Farmers | | O.P. Farmers | | Guruuswa | Mutadza MFs | OPFs |
	No	%	No	%	No	%				No	%[1]	No	%[1]	No	%[1]			
Maize	3,000	45·5	377	46·7	515	35·8	5·7	3·2	2·2	1,059	35·3	51	13·5	11	2·1	27·0	20·2	12·0
Millet	2,593	39·3	284	35·2	620	43·2	4·0	3·2	2·5	447	17·2	1	0·4	52	8·4	29·8	15·7	13·5
Sorghum	209	3·1	83	10·3	194	13·5	1·5	2·7	2·3	168	80·3	21	25·3	73	37·7	0·6	3·4	2·9
Groundnuts	552	8·4	59	7·3	100	7·0	1·9	0·9	0·8	285	51·7	15	25·4	24	24·0	3·7	2·4	1·8
Groundbeans	164	2·5	2	0·2	7	0·5	3·2	1·0	1·8	76	46·3	—	—	3	42·9	1·2	0·1	0·1
Other Crops	82	1·2	3	0·3	—		6·0	1·0	—	36	43·9	—	—	—		0·6	0·2	—
Total	6,600	100·0	808	100·0	1,436	100·0	4·0	2·6	2·1	2,071	31·4	88	10·9	163	11·3	62·9	42·0	30·3

MF = Master Farmer
OPF = Other Peasant Farmer

[1] Percentage of the total crop harvested

TABLE 25

Productivity of Peasant Farmers in a Drought Year (1966–1967) (N=132)

| | Bags harvested | | | | | | Bags per acre | | | Bags sold | | | | | | Bags consumed per household or unaccounted for | | |
| | Guruuswa | | Mutadza M. Farmers | | Mutadza O.P. Farmers | | Guruuswa | Mutadza MFs | OPFs | Guruuswa | | Mutadza M. Farmers | | Mutadza O.P. Farmers | | Guruuswa | Mutadza MFs | OPFs |
	No	%	No	%	No	%				No	%[1]	No	%[1]	No	%[1]			
Maize	640	32·1	172	54·5	305	40·0	1·2	1·5	1·3	24	3·8	25	14·5	25	8·2	8·6	8·2	4·3
Millet	939	47·1	82	26·0	390	51·2	1·4	0·9	1·6	68	7·3	—	—	—	—	12·1	4·6	9·3
Sorghum	111	5·6	28	8·8	40	5·3	0·8	0·9	0·5	19	17·1	—	—	—	—	1·3	1·6	1·0
Groundnuts	231	11·6	28	8·8	22	2·9	0·8	0·4	0·2	27	11·7	14	50·0	9	40·9	2·8	0·8	0·3
Groundbeans	68	3·4	—	—	—	—	1·3	—	—	—	—	—	—	—	—	1·2	—	—
Other crops	4	0·2	6	1·9	5	0·6	0·3	2·0	5·0	—	—	—	—	—	—	0·1	0·3	0·1
Total	1,993	100·0	316	100·0	762	100·0	1·2	1·0	1·1	138	6·9	39	12·3	34	4·5	20·1	15·5	15·0

MF = Master Farmer
OPF = Other Peasant Farmer

[1] Percentage of the total crop harvested

agriculture between progressive and backward farmers, and those who invest money in improved seed and fertilizer reap almost as little as those who invested no money in these items.

The crop yield per acre in a season of average rainfall is very low in both purchase areas when compared with the crop yield per acre in tribal trust lands. A comparison with Tables 11 and 12 in chapter 5 shows that master farmers in tribal trust lands reap consistently more of all crops per acre than do peasant farmers, including the farm owners in Guruuswa. The yield of Mutadza farm owners is so low that even ordinary peasant cultivators in tribal trust lands who lack a master farmer's certificate, reap more than Mutadza farm owners. This low yield in purchase areas is due to a variety of factors. Previous chapters showed that master farmers in tribal trust lands tend to cluster in certain sections of a larger tribal area, for example in Hove subchiefdom in the Shiri-Ngara tribal trust land and in the Shoko Museamwa community in Shoko tribal trust land. Since rainfall in Karangaland is very localized, peasant farmers who come from tribal trust lands lying in the same overall rainfall area as their purchase area, may nevertheless produce fewer crops per acre on their farms than they did before because of variations in the local rainfall pattern. Some peasant farmers even state that on the different parts of their farms rainfall varies and that they plant larger acreages in the hope of catching some rain on some of their fields. Other peasant farmers try to protect themselves against uncertain rainfall by planting some crops early, some late, so that at least some crops are saved if either the early rains fail, or if the later rains do not fall. Moreover, although many farm owners do not have much larger families than they had in tribal trust lands, they cultivate now much larger fields so that they suffer from an acute labour shortage. Consequently they now cultivate their fields less thoroughly than they used to do, and so the yields per acre fall. Irregular rainfall and labour shortage, therefore, are the main reasons for low output in purchase areas. But whereas local peasant farmers attribute low crop yields above all to unreliable rainfall, I consider insufficient labour input, and even more incompetent farm management, more important reasons. The Guruuswa farmers, who work harder on their land than the Mutadza farmers, and who are deeply interested in agricultural production, harvest many more crops per acre.

Though purchase area farmers produce more crops than tribal

trust land peasant cultivators, the proportion of the crops they
sell is relatively low. Whereas in a year of average rainfall master
farmers in tribal trust lands sell 40·9 per cent of their crops,
Guruuswa farmers sell only 31·4 per cent and Mutadza farmers
only about 11 per cent. The proportion of crops sold by Mutadza
farm owners is almost 2 per cent lower than the proportion of
crops sold by ordinary peasant cultivators in tribal trust lands.
In a drought year the average proportion of crops sold in purchase
areas is just about 7 per cent of the total harvest. Only a few
families can then draw on money from crop sales to pay for school
fees and clothing.

A drought year not only reduces farm income, but it even causes
food shortage in some families. For whereas in a year of average
rainfall all peasant farmers retain more crops than are enough
to feed their families, in a drought year food is only just adequate
in Guruuswa and definitely short in Mutadza purchase area.
Hence many families buy additional crops when the rains fail.

(3) CROP SALES

The fact that purchase area farmers grow the same types of
crops as are grown by tribal trust land peasant cultivators suggests
that farm owners look to tribal areas as markets for their surplus
crops. This is in fact the case: 50 per cent of all millet, 35 per
cent of all groundnuts, 30 per cent of all maize and 7 per cent of
all sorghum which come onto the market are directly sold to
tribal neighbours. These sales amount to 38 per cent of all crops
sold, for farm owners receive the highest prices for their crops
from buyers in tribal trust lands. These sales are strictly speaking
illegal, since purchase areas are administered together with
European farming areas and administratively separated from
tribal trust lands. But this does not disturb the people.

People sell 24 per cent of all surplus crops and over half
of all groundnuts through local stores. Mutadza farmers sell a
much larger proportion of their surpluses through stores than
Guruuswa farmers, even though they have to cart them outside
their purchase area to reach a store. They readily put up with this
inconvenience because they want to avoid selling their crops
through the cooperative society. In 1966, for example, they sold
twice as much maize through stores as through their cooperative
society. The aversion of Mutadza farm owners to the cooperative

society is due to their reluctance to repay loans. Since many took out loans but few repaid them, they were barred from taking out further loans. To avoid the repayment of debts they have to use other channels to sell their crops.

Cooperative societies handle about 25 per cent of all the surplus crops of the farm owners, especially sorghum, millet, and to a lesser degree maize and groundnuts. Guruuswa farmers make full use of their cooperative society and obtain through it loans for fertilizer and farming equipment. In 1962 Guruuswa farmers sold a total of 1,643 bags of crops through their cooperative society, and these crops were valued at £2,526. Maize accounted for 49·2 per cent of these sales, millet for 27·6 per cent, groundnuts for 5·4 per cent and the remainder came from a variety of crops. By 1967 Guruuswa had two depots where the surplus crops of members were sold, graded, weighed and stored until they could be taken to the Grain Marketing Board. Peasant farmers sell five times as large a proportion of their surplus crops through cooperative societies as do peasant cultivators in tribal trust lands. This shows that as soon as African peasants produce larger surpluses they are prepared to accept this modern marketing system, but as long as they have little to sell, they prefer the *ad hoc* transactions with tribal neighbours and store owners.[1]

Some 13 per cent of all crops are sold through a variety of channels. Some farm owners sell directly to the Grain Marketing Board, others sell crops in nearby mine compounds. But because most peasant farmers live far from mission stations and few have close ties with local missionaries, hardly any of them sell their maize to mission stations, a market which successful master farmers in tribal trust lands prefer.

The various buyers who obtain crops from peasant farmers pay different prices. Hence the value of locally produced crops has been calculated in the same way as has the value of crops grown in tribal trust lands, and the average price paid for each particular crop is used in the following analysis.

In 1965–66 the year of average rainfall, Guruuswa farmers grew on the average £182 worth of crops. Of these they sold crops worth £65 and retained the remainder for home consumption

[1] It may also be argued that peasant farmers are innovators who have voluntarily moved out of the tribal system, and as innovators are prepared to use a new marketing system. Likewise cooperative marketing is catching on in tribal areas among master farmers, another group of innovators, many of whom are marginal to the tribal system.

and other purposes. In the drought year of 1966–67 they reaped only £57 worth of crops. Some still sold a surplus. If these sales are averaged out among all farm households, sales amount to £6 worth of crops per farm. Yet most farmers had to buy crops. Purchase of crops amounted to some £24 per family. The average Guruuswa family, therefore, consumed crops worth £75 in the drought year, considerably less than they consumed in 1965–66.

The average master farmer family in Mutadza grew £94 worth of crops in 1965–66 and sold some £10 worth of crops. Thus they kept £84 for home consumption or other uses. In the drought year they grew only £22 worth of crops. Some still sold a small surplus which, if averaged out, comes to £5 per family. That year the average master farmer family in Mutadza bought crops for an average price of £31. Even so the total value of food at their disposal amounted to only £48.

Other peasant cultivators in Mutadza reaped on the average £93 worth of crops in 1965–66 and sold about £8 worth of crops per homestead. Thus they kept £85 worth of crops for home consumption. In 1966–67 the average family reaped £37 worth of crops, sold less than £1 worth of crops and bought crops worth some £20. Thus the average family had some £56 worth of crops to feed its members.

These average figures give a good impression of the different farming skills possessed by peasant farmers in the two communities. They conceal, however, the larger differences in income between individual farm owners. In Guruuswa, for example, one farm owner reaped in the season of average rainfall crops worth a mere £67, while another reaped crops worth £428. The large majority of Guruuswa farmers reaped crops worth £200 to £250. In 1965–66 the two worst peasant farmers in Mutadza reaped crops worth £10 and £19, the best between £200 and £250. The incomes of the remaining farm owners were evenly distributed between these two extremes. Thus, while the incomes of many peasant farmers in Guruuswa cluster around the average figure, the incomes of peasant farmers in Mutadza differ greatly.

Income from crops, expressed in relation to the acreage on which it is produced, is as low as £8 per acre in Guruuswa and £5.10.0 in Mutadza purchase area. In contrast, master farmers in tribal trust lands reap as much as £12 worth of crops per acre and even ordinary peasant cultivators reap as much as £6.15.0 worth of crops per acre.

In addition to their income from crops, a number of farm owners earn money from the sale of milk, eggs, fruit and vegetables. This income amounts to about £9 per Guruuswa farm family in a year of average rainfall, and rises to £19 in a drought year, because in a drought season every family saves as much milk for sale as possible in order to make money to meet family needs. Among master farmers in Mutadza such income also doubles in a drought year, but it is never significant: in 1965–66 the average family gained only £3 from this source, and in the drought year £6. Ordinary peasant farmers in Mutadza made in both years just about £2 from these sales. Since few Mutadza families have their own gardens, few can sell fruit and vegetables.[1]

To produce their crops, Guruuswa farmers spend about 15 shillings a year on improved seed, £3 on fertilizer and, in a season of average rainfall, some £10 on labour. Of this £10, £2 is spent on brewing beer and £8 paid out to wage labourers. In a drought season the expenditure on labour falls to £6 since harvesting costs are reduced. This gives a total outlay of £13.15.0 in a season of average rainfall, and of £8.15.0 in a drought season.

Mutadza peasant farmers spend about 10 shillings a year on seed, about £1 on fertilizer, and about £6 on labour, irrespective of the size of their harvest. Hence every homestead spends about £7.10.0 a year on crop production.

Compared with the outlay on these items by master farmers in tribal trust lands, the peasant farmers' expenditure is exceedingly low.[2] Moreover, since master farmers in tribal trust lands invest this money on a much smaller acreage than do peasant farmers, the peasant farmers' thin application of fertilizer and their occasional use of improved seed increase the negative effects of uncertain rainfall and labour shortage. It is true that in a drought year the

---

[1] For a summary of these figures see Table 26, p. 201.

[2] Master farmers in tribal trust lands spend £6 on seed and fertilizer; farm owners in Guruuswa £3.15.0; Mutadza farm owners £1.10.0. Johnson found that in the purchase area he studied the average farmer spent £9.14.0 on fertilizer. This is more than three times as much as the average Guruuswa farmer spends on it and nine times as much as the average Mutadza farmer pays for fertilizer (Johnson 1964a, p. 6). As a result of their high investment in fertilizer, peasant farmers in the purchase area harvest 9·6 bags of maize per acre (*Ibid.*, p. 4), whereas the average Guruuswa farmer harvests only 5·7 bags of maize per acre, the average master farmer in Mutadza 3·2 bags, the other ordinary Mutadza peasant farmer 2·2 bags.

investment in seed and fertilizer is to a large extent lost, but not every year is a drought year, and the increase in yield which fertilizer and improved seed bring if rain is adequate, more than makes up for their expenditure. Since due to their larger cultivated acreage the overall income of farm owners is high, most could afford this outlay. The use of fertilizer combined with heavy manuring—and again, peasant farmers have large enough herds to apply a heavy dressing every third or fourth year—would greatly increase their output per acre.

(4) ANIMAL HUSBANDRY

Income from cattle makes a great contribution to the income of peasant farmers. Hence many farm owners take great care in looking after their livestock. Most peasant farmers graze their cattle on their own farms. Many have paddocked their land so that one section of the pasture is always resting. Grazing land is therefore in good condition and hardly any erosion takes place on farms. The only places where erosion occurs is on the crown lands which contain the dip tanks, and on the bus roads, for where long and broad cattle tracks merge with these roads, the surfaces are easily washed away in the rainy season. Since both purchase areas are situated in marginal rainfall regions which are, however, ideally suited for animal husbandry, a greater emphasis on livestock could overcome the drought problems.

Cattle owners in Guruuswa are proud of their cattle, and most not only dip them regularly to clear them of ticks, but many also hand-tick them to improve their health. Quite a number of Guruuswa farmers have shown great interest in cattle fattening. Stall feeding became widespread in Guruuswa after the first chairman of the African Farmers' Union committee accepted the advice of the local extension assistant and built a modern cattle byre with several divisions. At this cattle byre many demonstrations on stall feeding have since taken place. Some farm owners now buy special cattle food through their cooperative society, and some cut grass along the rivers after the harvest to prepare hay as dry season fodder. Others carry maize stalks to their cattle byres for the winter. These activities are time-consuming and account for the much greater time spent on cattle maintenance in Guruuswa than in Mutadza purchase area. According to the report of the Secretary for Agriculture in 1970,

26·4 per cent of all African stall-fed cattle in the 1968–69 season were kept by purchase area farmers in the Victoria province, in which Guruuswa is situated, and 61·1 per cent of all top grade cattle sold by purchase area farmers came from that province.[1]

In spite of their large cattle herds, farm owners in neither Guruuswa nor Mutadza purchase area have their own auction sales. Instead they must drive their cattle to the auction sales in nearby tribal trust lands. As early as 1962, therefore, the farm owners in Guruuswa petitioned the district commissioner to arrange for regular auction sales in their purchase area, but they were told that not only were the installations for auction sales expensive, but auctioneers followed fixed rounds of sales and would find it difficult to include Guruuswa in their tight schedules. By 1967 no auction sales yard had been established in either purchase area.

Because cattle lose weight if they have to walk for many miles to a sale, many peasant farmers sell their beasts through other channels. Quite a number sell their cattle to the sons of neighbouring farmers who work in town, but who try to build up their own herds before they retire to a village. These sons generally graze their cattle on their fathers' farms. Other farm owners sell their cattle to a local butcher, others to friendly European ranchers. Some peasant farmers ask their European neighbours to take their cattle to an auction sale where European farmers sell. At these sales more buyers attend than at tribal trust land sales yards and competition drives up the prices.

Some farm owners sell their cattle directly to the Cold Storage Commission if they can take them there by lorry. Their cooperative society at times assists them with transport. Those who walk their cattle to the Cold Storage Commission have to put them into quarantine for a fortnight to ensure that they are free from disease. They then have to pay for their maintenance. Since prices are generally higher for slaughtered cattle than for cattle sold on the hoof, peasant farmers profit by selling their beasts directly to the Cold Storage Commission.

Though peasant farmers are more skilled in animal husbandry than tribal trust land peasant cultivators, they still do not obtain the maximum return from their herds because they sell their beasts when they are already five or six years old. If they would sell younger stock, prices would be still higher.

[1] Report of the Secretary for Agriculture, 1970, p. 63.

Cotton growing by a leading master farmer in the Shoko Museamwa community

Homestead of a polygamist in Guruuswa purchase area

Irrigation scheme at the Limpopo river

In a year of average rainfall, Guruuswa farmers sell about two head of cattle a year for which they receive some £57. In a drought year they sell two or three beasts, but receive only £46 on the average since the quality of the beasts is poorer. Master farmers in Mutadza also sell about two beasts a year if rains are normal, but they receive only about £34 for them since hardly any Mutadza peasant farmers stall feed their cattle. In a drought year Mutadza farmers sell twice as many beasts, but receive only £49. Ordinary peasant farmers in Mutadza sell about one beast a year for £20. In a drought year they sell two or three beasts for £47. The greater investment of labour in livestock maintenance by Guruuswa farm owners is therefore repaid when the cattle are sold.[1]

All farm owners receive much more money from their cattle than do peasant cultivators, for whereas master farmers in tribal trust lands receive only £15 from their cattle in a year of average rainfall, Guruuswa farmers receive £57, master farmers in Mutadza £34 and ordinary peasant farmers in Mutadza £20.

The less productive a peasant household is, the more heavily it relies on income from cattle, for most Karanga sell cattle only when they are in desperate need of money. Dependence on cattle is especially great in a drought season when families sell cattle to buy food. The only group of peasants which does not receive more money from cattle in a drought year than in a year of average rainfall are the Guruuswa farmers because they are such efficient crop producers.

Only progressive farmers sell cattle regularly because they have adopted a commercial attitude towards cattle and abandoned the traditional attitude which is determined by ritual needs and social values.

Just as the averages of crop production conceal great differences in income between individual farmers, so do the averages of cattle sales. In every year there are some farm owners in both Guruuswa and Mutadza who sell no cattle at all, and others who sell six or even seven beasts in one season. Such large sales, however, are the exception and only take place when a farm owner wants to drill a borehole, build a dam, or make some other heavy capital investment. Ordinary peasant farmers never sell large numbers of cattle because they never plan such great capital outlays. Most

[1] Johnson found in his study of a purchase area that the average income from cattle sales per farm amounted to only £8.13.0 (Johnson, 1964a, p. 10). This is far less than in either Guruuswa or Mutadza purchase areas.

frequently they sell livestock in order to obtain money for their children's school fees.[1]

Peasant farmers insist that the value of their cattle is larger than the income from cattle sales. If oxen had to be hired to plough the land, to pull the carts at harvesting time, to fetch water in the dry season from the nearest river and to bring manure to the field, much money would have to be paid for draught power by each household. But just as family labour has not been included in farm expenditure, so the labour of oxen is not included in farm income, since it would be too difficult to assess its exact contribution to each farmstead.

If only the income from cattle sales is considered, and if this income is expressed as a return per acre of grazing land, this return is as low as five shillings six pence in Guruuswa and four shillings six pence in Mutadza.[2] The difference in income from acres grazed or ploughed is therefore very great. Consequently some people have suggested that farm owners who have not enough labour to cultivate more land, should let some of it to tenants so that a fuller use be made of it.[3] Such a suggestion leaves out of account that much of the grazing land is unsuitable for cultivation because it consists of rocky outcrops, has only a very shallow top soil, or gets easily water-logged. Nevertheless, more land could be cultivated, and stall feeding could greatly increase the return from cattle. For both improvements, however, a larger labour force is required than most farm owners at present command.

(5) TOTAL INCOME OF PEASANT FARMERS

Table 26 summarizes the income of peasant farmers. If expenditure on seed, fertilizer and labour is subtracted, Guruuswa farmers have in a season of average rainfall an income of £234.5.0[4] and in a drought season an income of £113.5.0. Master farmers in Mutadza obtain in a year of average rainfall an income of £123.10.0.

---

[1] The average Mutadza farm owner spends some £23.10.0 a year on his children's school fees, the average Guruuswa farmer only some £13.

[2] Johnson found that in the purchase area he studied the average income from cattle per acre was worth about two shillings seven pence. Johnson, 1964a, p. 10.

[3] Makings, S. M. 1964 Problems in African Agricultural Development, p. 23 (Unpublished).

[4] The total agricultural income of Guruuswa peasant farmers is similar to that of peasant farmers in the purchase area studied by Johnson. Peasant farmers in that area had an income of £240.9.0. Johnson, 1964a, p. 12.

TABLE 26

Average Income of Peasant Farmers (N=132)

	Gurunswa				Mutadza							
					Master Farmers				O. Peasant Farmers			
	1965–1966		1966–1967		1965–1966		1966–1967		1965–1966		1966–1967	
Source of Income	£	Perc.	£	Perc.	£	Perc.	£	Perc.	£	Perc.	£	Perc.
Crops	182	73·4	57	46·7	94	71·7	22	28·5	93	80·9	37	43·1
Cattle	57	23·0	46	37·7	34	26·0	49	63·7	20	17·4	47	54·9·
Milk, eggs, fruit, vegetables	9	3·6	19	15·6	3	2·3	6	7·8	2	1·7	2	2·3
Total	248	100·0	122	100·0	131	100·0	77	100·0	115	100·0	86	100·0

and in a drought season £69.10.0, and other peasant farmers in
Mutadza £107.10.0 in a season of average rainfall and £78.10.0
in a drought season. A drought season, therefore, affects the farm
income of many peasant farmers by almost 50 per cent. Whereas in
a season of average rainfall crops provide about three-quarters of
all income, in a drought season cattle become the greatest money
earner, especially in agriculturally unproductive communities
like Mutadza.

Unlike tribal trust land cultivators, no purchase area farmers
can rely on income from salaries or wages to help them through a
drought season. At most they can rely on help from relatives.
Thus in 1966–67 two Mutadza farmers, whose farm income had
been well below £50, received £57 and £69 respectively from
relatives working in town. More often, however, peasant farmers
are approached for help in a drought season by relatives from
tribal trust lands. In Guruuswa, the average farm family gave
crops worth £14 to their kinsmen in tribal areas, but none of the
Mutadza farmers did so. Though these crops were handed over as
free gifts, many people who received help expressed their gratitude
by assisting their relatives in the next season with free labour on
their farms.

If the incomes of farm owners in Guruuswa and Mutadza are
compared with the incomes of master farmers and ordinary
peasant cultivators in tribal trust lands, they are in both the year
of average rainfall and in the drought year about twice as large as
those of their tribal neighbours. Even in the drought season
purchase area farmers gained as large an income from agriculture
as did peasant cultivators in a season of average rainfall from the
combination of wage labour and agriculture. Farm owners, therefore, are economically secure when compared with their tribal
neighbours and most peasant cultivators would like to be as well
off as are families in purchase areas.

(6) CONCLUSION

The data presented in this chapter show that peasant farmers
are richer than tribal trust land peasant cultivators. Because of
their relative wealth they are envied by their tribal neighbours and
many peasant cultivators would like to be as secure and affluent as
farm owners are. Yet although peasant farmers are richer than
peasant cultivators and economically secure, they do not use their

land as efficiently as do peasant cultivators. This less efficient use of the land is to a large degree caused by labour shortage.

Labour shortage could often be overcome by mechanization. Tractor ploughing could overcome the bottleneck at the plough- ing season, and combine harvesters could reduce labour require- ments at harvesting time. All-round mechanization, however, requires a great deal of capital. At present no individual peasant farmer is capable of raising so much money, nor have any of them sufficient land to make full use of such machinery. Yet if several farm owners clubbed together, more machinery might be bought.

By 1967 the peasant farmers in neither Guruuswa nor Mutadza purchase areas had evolved a strong enough cooperative spirit to purchase and use machinery on a community basis. In fact, the tractor purchased by Guruuswa farmers in the early 1960s had to be sold because no farm owner held himself responsible for its maintenance and all demanded priority of service. Until these communities evolve a strong enough spirit of responsibility for communal property, it should be possible to persuade special interest groups, such as the 'Who is the Champion?' club in Guruuswa, to band together to purchase more expensive machinery. Since these men are friends, trust each other, and are keen on increasing their farm output, they might be able to maintain larger machines and agree on their use. Moreover, as groups of successful farmers they will be able to obtain sufficiently large loans through their cooperative society to purchase these machines, for they possess enough property to guarantee repayment.

Just as in tribal trust lands progress has been pioneered through master farmers, so in purchase areas further development could be envisaged through groups of capable and interested farm owners. Their effect would be even greater than that of master farmers in tribal trust lands. For while the latter are to a large degree marginal to their communities and often keen on moving out into a purchase area, the former are the most important men in their communities. In well-to-do purchase areas, like Guruuswa, they fill leadership positions on committees and their example influences many of their neighbours. The extension staff already uses them to pro- mote modern farming methods. The mechanization of their farms, therefore, should not present insuperable problems.

In less progressive purchase areas, like Mutadza, such develop- ments are not yet likely to succeed since progressive farm owners are few in number and public opinion discourages the adoption of modern farming techniques. Only when most of the older farm owners are succeeded by their sons are developments likely to take place. Progress in Mutadza purchase area will require far-reaching changes in the attitudes of farm owners towards agriculture.

Other requirements for greater farm productivity will follow mechanization. For example, much more arable land could then be cultivated. Some acres could also be grown with fodder crops and so stall feeding cattle could become still more widespread. Since tractor ploughing is deeper and more efficient, yields are likely to increase.

More important still, and this is possible even without mechanization, peasant farmers could significantly increase their crop yield through a greater use of improved seed and fertilizer. The development potential in purchase areas is great, but it needs a new departure from present practices before it can be realized.

PROFILES OF PEASANT FARMERS

(1) INTRODUCTION

The analysis of the preceding chapters indicated that the great interest in agriculture of Guruuswa farmers has given rise to several voluntary agricultural associations in that purchase area and that these, in turn, gave Guruuswa its peculiar structural characteristics which make it different from Mutadza purchase area whose peasant farmers are less interested in agriculture. I suggested that the more stringent selection procedure in Guruuswa may have been partly responsible for attracting a more progressive type of peasant farmer to that community.

The following case histories of five farm owners from Guruuswa and three master farmers and four other peasant farmers from Mutadza draw pictures of typical people living in these communities. The case histories have been chosen to represent both successful, average and unsuccessful farmers in each area.[1]

(2) PROFILES OF GURUUSWA PEASANT FARMERS

(a) Gabriel, the Entrepreneur

Gabriel is one of the younger and better educated men in Guruuswa. He is also the most successful farm owner in that purchase area. Born in 1923 he completed his primary education and claims to have subsequently studied a correspondence course in philosophy and psychology. In his twenties he taught for three years in a village school, earning £5 a month. When he finished teaching he had a savings bank account of £50. In 1947 he joined the Ministry of Agriculture as junior assistant and received a monthly wage of £6. During these years he obtained his master farmer's certificate. From 1952 to 1954 he sold vegetables in Salisbury, making a profit of £50 which he again put in the bank. In 1955 his father employed him in his own bus company and paid him £10.10.0 a month. That year Gabriel saved £70.

---

[1] Appendix, Table 53 shows from which income groups the case histories have been drawn.

In 1956 his father sold all his buses and bought a large farm on unreserved land, that is, land open for purchase by both African and European farmers.[1] He gave Gabriel £60 to start his own farm, for in that year Guruuswa purchase area was opened and Gabriel's earlier application for a farm was successful.

Gabriel's education and financial experience before he came to the farm enabled him to plan his agricultural activities on a commercial basis. He immediately decided to grow vegetables for sale. He therefore bought a pump for £700 to irrigate three and a half acres of farm land. His cooperative society assisted him with a loan. He employed six to eight men for several months to prepare his land for irrigation farming. Their wages, plus the necessary equipment, cost him another £200. Next he bought a secondhand lorry to transport his vegetables to the nearby towns and mining centres. By the mid-1960s he had made an annual profit of £300 from his vegetables, especially on tomatoes, potatoes and sweet potatoes. In an exceptionally good year he makes some £500, and even in the drought season of 1966–67 he made £200 from his vegetables. In 1965–66 he had a total agricultural income of £1,127. By 1964 he had repaid all his debts and still had £200 in the bank.

Once his farm made a profit, Gabriel built a spacious house for himself and his two wives. This house cost him £500 which he raised from the sale of twenty head of cattle, four sheep and his vegetables. By 1967 his wives had given birth to 14 children, seven of whom still stayed with him on the farm. The older children had found work in town or had returned to the tribal trust land from which Gabriel had originally come. To increase his labour force, Gabriel permanently employed two boys, one to herd his cattle, the other to help around the house or wherever his services were needed.

Since Gabriel's farm lies at the very boundary with a tribal trust land, he is never short of labour. His tribal neighbours come to work for him whenever he requires their services and are paid daily wages worth two shillings in either cash or vegetables. At times Gabriel employs as many as ten hired labourers. People from the tribal trust land also come to his farm to buy vegetables.

Gabriel possesses all the necessary farming equipment. He is the best farmer in Guruuswa and highly respected by his neigh-

---

[1] This land category has since been abolished.

bours. For several years he was elected as chairman of the local cooperative society, and his neighbours repeatedly chose him as secretary of the African Farmers' Union committee.

Education, a close association for several years with members of the Ministry of Agriculture, as well as entrepreneurial experience equipped Gabriel to become a successful farm owner. In spite of his determination to make money, he did not alienate his neighbours. Because they held him in great esteem, his influence was widespread and many looked to him for guidance to increase their own farm profits. No other farm owner in Guruuswa has even half as high an income from his farm as Gabriel.

(b) George, the Polygamist

Another successful farm owner is George. In 1965–66 he made a total profit of £411 from his farm. His farm income is more typical of good peasant farmers in Guruuswa than that of Gabriel.

Born in 1910, George attended school for only four years, and then worked from 1923 to 1928 as a domestic servant for £2 a month in a small mining town in the Victoria province. He saved every penny he could spare and bought five head of cattle, two goats, two ploughs and a cultivator, for he had no intention of spending his life as a labour migrant but looked forward to becoming a farmer.

On his return to his village, George married his first wife. His father contributed six head of cattle to his bridewealth. When in 1935 his sister married, he used her bridewealth to marry a second wife. All in all, George had married ten wives by 1967, two of whom died and four of whom he divorced. His wives gave birth to 23 children, six of whom died.

In 1945 George applied for a purchase area farm and began training as a master farmer. He obtained his certificate in 1949. Like Gabriel, he was one of the first settlers in Guruuswa. Besides his equipment and livestock, George brought with him £50 in cash, part of which he had obtained from selling surplus crops, part of which remained from bridewealth he had received at the marriage of his eldest daughter.

Since he had a large family, George needed little help to open up his farm. He was himself a skilled builder, and only once did he employ a man for £2 to help him mould bricks. All the other work he did together with his wives and children. His children, who went to school, helped him during their holidays. Together with his sons, George cleared eight acres of land during the first year, and over the years cleared 38 acres of arable land.

By 1967 George's large family had dispersed. Only four wives and eight children remained with him. Five of his sons were in European employment and each of them looked only after his own mother. None of them sent money to him. Because his children neglected him, he made a will bequeathing his farm to his younger brother. In appointing his younger brother and not his eldest son as heir, George went contrary to local custom. He argued that if he left his land to one of his sons, this man would use all the wealth for his own mother and his uterine brothers and sisters, neglecting the other wives and their children.

But although George made a will, he is not thinking of retiring for a long time. In 1967 he made arrangements to marry another wife and applied for a second farm in Guruuswa to join to his first.

For some years George was chairman of the African Farmers' Union committee. He is well liked by his neighbours. He is a traditionalist and in spite of his unusual testament clings staunchly to traditional values.

(c) Gerald, the Former Farm Tenant

Unlike most of his neighbours, Gerald was not born in a tribal trust land but on a European farm. As the son of a tenant farmer on a European estate he had little chance of education and went to school for only four years. In 1927, at the age of fourteen, he worked for three months in a nearby European settlement for seven shillings six pence a month. On his return to his father, the European owner of the estate employed him as a mill hand for ten shillings a month. Gerald gave some of his wages to his father for safe keeping until he should have earned enough to buy a cow. Later he worked for four years in a mining town as a domestic servant and earned fifteen shillings a month. With his earnings he bought a bicycle and gave £9 to his father for safe keeping. He stayed another three years as a domestic servant, this time with three different families, and then he returned home. There he learned that all his savings had been stolen.

Determined to build up his own cattle herd, Gerald set out to find work in Gwelo. For three years he worked as a domestic servant and was paid £3 a month. With his savings he bought four head of cattle. In 1941 he joined the army and was paid £3 a month. Again he saved his earnings and bought cattle.

In 1944 Gerald returned to the European's estate and married his first wife. He helped his father, who by then had rented 14 acres from the European owner. When his father died, Gerald entered a lease agreement in his own name. He proved a successful peasant farmer. During the first season he harvested 50 bags of maize, 30 bags of sweet potatoes, 22 bags of potatoes and 20 bags of groundnuts. With some of the proceeds he bought a plough and a planter.

Some years later the European owner died and left his property to his wife. The woman retired to a nearby town but often visited her land. On these occasions Gerald cooked for her. She took a liking to him and when she saw that he farmed the land successfully, she suggested that he train as a master farmer. She made an application on his behalf to an agricultural training centre near Fort Victoria, Makoholi, where Africans were taught modern farming methods. She also paid Gerald's fees. Gerald obtained his certificate in 1956 and applied for a purchase area farm.

Just before he obtained his certificate, the woman also died and the new owner of the estate gave notice to all the tenants to leave. Gerald was allowed to stay until 1959 when he was offered a purchase area farm in Guruuswa.

On his return to the estate in 1956, Gerald immediately implemented the new farming skills he had learned. During the first season he harvested 126 bags of maize, 45 bags of groundnuts, 50 bags of sweet potatoes and six tons of pumpkins. While waiting to move to Guruuswa he married a second wife. By 1967 his two wives had borne him 13 children. When he finally came to his own farm, he already possessed a plough, a harrow, a cultivator, a cart, a shelling machine and 60 head of cattle. In addition he had £724 in a bank savings account.

Gerald invested much money in opening up his farm. He employed workmen to mould bricks and paid them £50. Next he hired a builder to put up two huts, a granary and a five-roomed house. He paid him £40. Some people thatched his huts and he paid them £6. He also employed labourers to clear the land; this cost him £15. Other men dug two wells for him and again others dug his contour ridges. For these services he paid £36.

In 1962 Gerald drilled a borehole. To find the necessary £592 he drew on his savings and also sold 17 head of cattle for £293.

In 1964 he bought a secondhand car for £171. He had saved the necessary money from the sale of surplus crops during three preceding seasons.

Gerald's income in 1965–66 was £387. His crop yields are generally good because he uses a great deal of fertilizer. He also continued growing tomatoes, sweet potatoes and potatoes. In a year of average rainfall, these bring him some £72. In 1967 Gerald thought of building a dam. He had another £300 in the bank and decided to apply for a loan of £400. His aim was to grow vegetables under irrigation on the same scale as Gabriel does. His sister's daughter who is unmarried, his younger wife's sister and a child live with him, but these were not sufficient for his labour requirements; he also employs a herd boy. In addition he obtains regular help from neighbours in the adjoining tribal trust land. Gerald is a member of the African Farmers' Union committee and liked by his neighbours.

(d) Godfrey, the Moderately Successful Peasant Farmer

With an income of £236 Godfrey is considered only moderately successful in Guruuswa. Born in 1910, he went to school for the first time when he was eleven years old. He wanted to learn reading and writing and stayed in school for two years. Then he returned to his village to help his parents in the fields and after two years once again went back to school for a further year. At the age of fifteen he found employment with a European in a small urban settlement and earned £1 a month. He stayed with his employer for a year, saved every penny, and with his savings bought three head of cattle. He then returned home. In 1931 his sister married and with her bridewealth he himself married.

Godfrey's family increased rapidly because twice his wife gave birth to twins. By 1967 she had given birth to 13 children, four of whom died. To provide for his growing family, Godfrey sought work in Gwelo. A building company employed him for £2 a month. He saved his earnings and bought his wife a sewing machine and himself a bicycle. He put £20 aside in a savings account. In 1940 he bought a plough. In 1943 the local district commissioner employed him as a messenger and paid him £3 a month. Godfrey again saved his money and bought a second plough, a cultivator, a harrow and eleven head of cattle. In 1952 he returned to his village and trained as a master farmer. He obtained his certificate in 1956. The following year he came to

Guruuswa, bringing with him his livestock, farming equipment
and £40 in cash.

To open up his farm, he hired three men to mould bricks,
paying them £4. He paid £10 to a builder who constructed three
huts for him. He later built a fourth hut with the help of his wife
and children. Then his brother from the tribal trust land helped
him to clear the land for the first crop and was paid in maize and
millet. To clear more land, Godfrey hired two labourers whom he
paid £2 each. When all the preparatory work was done his wife
brewed beer for a work party, and people came from the adjoining
tribal trust land to dig the necessary contour ridges. Finally his
son-in-law helped him to plough the land.

To raise the money necessary for the opening of the farm,
Godfrey received a gift of £20 from his son who was working in
Salisbury. He himself earned £4 a month for half a year by work-
ing as a dip attendant in the purchase area.

While on the farm Godfrey bought two carts, eight sheep and
five head of cattle. In 1967 he thought of buying a pump to overcome the water shortage on his farm, but he felt uncertain as to
whether the cooperative society would advance him the loan.
Since he possessed little equipment, and since his annual harvests
were only moderately good, he could offer little security to repay
a large loan.

Godfrey is chronically short of labour. He has never served
on any committee in Guruuswa. In a tribal trust land, and even
in Mutadza purchase area, he would be considered a rich man, but
in Guruuswa he is an unimportant peasant farmer. His heavy
reliance on kinsmen in the opening up of his farm shows that he is
still dependent on traditional support.

(e) Guido, the Late Settler

Guido, who came to Guruuswa as late as 1963, is also one of the
less successful farmers. Born in 1930, he went to school for only
three years. As a young man he worked as a domestic servant in a
mine settlement for fifteen shillings a month. He spent all his
money on clothing and food. In 1947 he found work in Gwelo and
for two years received a monthly wage of £3. He saved £10 and
gave it to his elder brother who was collecting his own bridewealth. In 1949 Guido found work with the Rhodesia Railways in
Umtali and received the relatively high monthly wage of £8. He
saved much of this and bought four head of cattle, a plough, a

cultivator and two goats. In 1950 he returned home and married. His brother then assisted him in paying his bridewealth. That year Guido decided to become a purchase area farmer and applied for a farm.

From 1953 to 1955 he acted as a small entrepreneur. He bought shirts at wholesale prices and resold them at a profit, thus earning some £94. In 1956 he went with his wife to a tribal trust land to live with a rich master farmer. He worked for him and in return for his labour received instruction in modern farming methods. In 1958 when he enquired why his application for a farm in 1950 was still unsuccessful, he was told that he would not be allowed to buy a farm unless he possessed a master farmer's certificate. He therefore began training at a rural centre where an extension assistant instructed master farmer trainees. In 1961 he obtained his certificate and in 1963 was offered a farm in Guruuswa which had just been vacated by a master farmer who had been imprisoned because of political activities.

At that time Guido possessed £55 in cash and the basic farming equipment. But he had only one wife and small children. He therefore needed help to open up his land. He employed two men to cut trees and paid them £5. His father-in-law helped him to build two simple huts and gave him a present of £2. Four women from his church came over from the tribal trust land to help his wife smear the huts with clay. To prepare his land, Guido hired three men to dig contour ridges. This cost him £4.

During his first years on the farm, Guido's brothers and sisters from the nearby tribal trust land came to help him in the field. But in return for their labour they took back with them many bags of grain. Still, since he was short of labour and reluctant to repudiate kinship obligations, he accepted their expensive help.

Guido would like to have married additional wives, but was reluctant to give up his church membership. In 1965–66 he had an income of only £149, and after he had repaid his relatives he was left with very little indeed. Hence both he and his wife and children are poorly clad. Only by living very frugally has he been able to buy a cart and six head of cattle, and recently a sewing machine for his wife. Guido is an unimportant man in Guruuswa. He has never served on any committee.

(3) EVALUATION OF CASE HISTORIES

The major social characteristics of the five Guruuswa farm owners are set out in Table 27.

TABLE 27

Characteristics of Five Guruuswa Farm Owners

Name	Agricultural Income £	Year of Birth	Education in Years	Labour Migrat. in Years	Investment in opening up of farm £	Office in Agricultural Association
Gabriel	1,127	1923	9	12	1,700	chairman of coop. soc., secretary of A.F.U.
George	411	1910	4	6	2	chairman of A.F.U.
Gerald	387	1913	4	15	929	committee member of A.F.U.
Godfrey	236	1910	3	7	20	—
Guido	149	1930	3	6	9	—

Like the master farmers in tribal trust lands, so the more successful farm owners in Guruuswa seem to have more education than the less successful peasant farmers. Yet this is accidental and may be explained by the small number of case histories here presented. The larger sample does not bear out a close relationship between farming ability and education in purchase areas. The length of labour migration too bears little relation to farming success. What counts is rather the wages men earned and the proportion of money they set aside while in wage employment to buy farming equipment. Apart from George, the polygamist, the successful farm owners invested much money in their farms, bought expensive capital equipment and did everything in their power to turn their farms into economic enterprises. If they had insufficient labour, they hired more.

The less successful farm owners, by contrast, came with limited amounts of capital to the purchase area. They invested little money in their farms and when additional labour was required relied on kinsmen. This reliance, however, proved more expensive than hired labour. Guido found this out to his cost. Once farm owners replace the assistance offered by kinsmen with contractual labour, they are well on the way to running their farms at a profit, for such a change indicates a far-reaching break with past values.

Table 27 also shows that the more successful peasant farmers are, the more likely they are to hold important leadership positions in their community. The best peasant farmers are also those who settled in Guruuswa when the purchase area was first opened. Length of residence, high income and leadership positions, all contribute to their influence in the community.

Farming expertise is also closely related to agricultural training. Gabriel, the best farmer, had been employed by the Ministry of Agriculture and while thus employed underwent master farmer training. Gerald took a special course for master farmers at an agricultural institute. George had had since early youth the ambition to become a prosperous farmer and only engaged in wage labour to buy farming implements and cattle. Godfrey trained as a master farmer in his tribal trust land. He needed four years to obtain his certificate and, as has been pointed out in the analysis of master farmers in tribal areas, the longer a man takes to become a master farmer, the less successful a peasant he tends to be. Guido's agricultural training was haphazard, and even after learning farming from a master farmer, he still needed three years of training to obtain a certificate.

(4) PROFILES OF MUTADZA PEASANT FARMERS

To gain a picture of farm owners in Mutadza, three master farmers and four ordinary peasant farmers have been chosen. The master farmers include the best, a typically average and the worst of the master farmers. The ordinary peasant farmers are drawn from men in the largest income brackets.[1]

(a) Alban, the Richest Farm Owner in Mutadza

Alban has devoted his whole life to agriculture and never sought European employment. His father also owns a farm in Mutadza purchase area and Alban learned from him a love of farming. Born in 1919, Alban went to school for only two years. In 1942 he applied for a purchase area farm and shortly afterwards began training as a master farmer. He obtained his master farmer's certificate in less than two years. When he came to

[1] For further details of their selection see Appendix, Table 53.

Mutadza, he brought with him three wives and five children. Since then he has married two more wives and now has 22 children, all of whom are still alive. Those of school age all attend school.

On opening up his farm in 1950, Alban employed four men for one year to make bricks, clear the land and dig contours. He paid each man £3 a month. He also hired a builder to construct his huts and granaries; this cost him £16. He then fenced his farm-stead, spending £4 on wire and a gate. In 1960 he bought a grinding machine for £500 and built a shed for it which cost him £20. Alban is the only African in Mutadza purchase area who ventured into business. His grinding mill now earns him some £30 in the months following the harvest, and less during the remaining months of the year. In 1966 he built his own dam, paying £226 for cement and wages. Alban already paid the full price of his farm and was the first farm owner in Mutadza who obtained his title deeds.

Like some of his neighbours, Alban experimented with cash crops. In 1954 he grew tobacco for the first time. He reaped 15 bales from half an acre which he sold for £90. In 1957 he received £11 for six bales, in 1960 £8 for one and a half bales, £9 for three bales in 1961, in 1964 £25 for ten bales, in 1965 £3 for two bales, and in 1966 £2 for four bales. After an initial success, therefore, returns from tobacco became very low and hardly justified the heavy labour input. In 1964 Alban also tried to grow cotton. He received £15 for four bags. If his wives and his many children had not assisted him, he could never have coped with the extra work.

In 1966 Alban began stall feeding his cattle and was reasonably successful. He received £80 for three beasts. Alban is also one of the few Mutadza farm owners who still has his vegetable garden and several fruit trees. In 1965–66 he had an income of £374.

Alban works hand in hand with the agricultural staff and always consults them about the best way of treating his land and cattle. Demonstration lessons are occasionally held at his farm. His wives and many children are always well dressed and Alban is respected by his neighbours. For several years they elected him as a member of the local African Farmers' Union committee; but this committee is less important in Mutadza than the council.

(b) Alex, the Council Chairman

With a farm income of £174, Alex is a good average peasant

8

farmer in Mutadza. Born in 1912, he went to school for six years, but is now almost illiterate. He married in 1934 and by 1967 his wife had borne him ten children, nine of whom are still alive.

In 1940 Alex sought work in Gwelo and for four years was employed as a domestic servant for £2 a month. Thereafter he went to a mining town where he worked in the same occupation for three years at a wage of £1.10.0 a month. In 1947 he returned to his tribal trust land, applied for a purchase area farm, and immediately began training as a master farmer. He obtained his certificate in 1950. During these three years he bought most of his farm implements, such as a plough, cultivator, rake, cart and wheelbarrow.

The opening of his farm cost him £223. He hired two men to cut trees and construct contour ridges and paid them £9. He then had a house built which is the envy of his neighbours. He hired six men to make bricks and paid them £25. A builder put up the house for £88. Alex then paid £85 for door frames, windows and corrugated iron sheets for the roof. On his instructions the builder erected four huts which cost him £16.

Alex started growing tobacco in 1952. That year he received £28 for the crop. In 1953 he received £16 for his tobacco, and £5 in 1956 because wild animals had destroyed most of his field. In 1967 he grew two acres of tobacco and expected a good return.

With only one wife and all his older children in school, Alex is chronically short of labour. In most years, therefore, he employs two labourers all the year round and pays them wages of £1.10.0 a month. During the two months following the harvest, that is, from July to August, his wife makes clay pots for sale which brings in some £6 a year.

Alex is fairly popular among his neighbours and was for several years chairman of Mutadza council until the council was closed in 1967. He paid the full price of his farm and obtained the title deeds.

Alex is pleased with his farm. He considers its soil slightly better than the land he ploughed in the tribal trust land. Though the unreliable rainfall jeopardizes some harvests, Alex emphasizes that since he has much more land than he had before, he will always have enough food for his family. He believes himself to be economically secure for the rest of his life.

(c) Alfons, the Failure

Born in 1914 Alfons attended school for three years and at the age of 19 began looking for work. First he was employed for three years as a waiter in a hotel in Gwelo for a monthly wage of £2. Then he worked for one year as a waiter in Bulawayo. In 1938 he returned home and began to train as a master farmer. As early as 1935 he had applied for a farm, and when Mutadza purchase area was opened in 1950, he was offered one.

When Alfons came to the farm, he possessed no farming equipment at all. His wife and three small children were inadequate to cope with the work needed to open up the farm. He therefore hired three men for four months to dig his contour ridges, paying them £3 a month each. He then hired a builder to erect five huts. Each hut cost him £9. Because there was no water near his farm, Alfons also hired men to dig a well. This cost him £5.

Since Alfons had little money and no implements, he took out a loan of £16 from his cooperative society to buy a plough, a cultivator and a rake. Yet he never repaid this loan, and, moreover, he never paid a single instalment towards the cost of his farm. Yet he married a second wife for whom he paid a bridewealth of £90 and four head of cattle. By 1967 his wives had borne him eleven children.

In 1967 Alfons was served with an eviction order. That year he had a farm income of £23. He had seldom been at his farm, but instead spent his time visiting friends in town. His wives were not eager to do the farm work alone, and so fields and cattle—he possessed only four—were left largely unattended.

Though a failure as a peasant farmer, Alfons was liked by his neighbours who discerned in him some leadership qualities. They elected him to their council because he was a fearless man and often challenged the district commissioner when he made proposals which did not meet with the approval of the community.

(d) Raphael, the Former Farm Labourer

Raphael is one of the many peasant farmers in Mutadza who do not possess a master farmer's certificate. Born in 1908 he went to school for only one year and is now illiterate. Early in his youth he found work in a European family as a domestic servant and was paid 15 shillings a month. He stayed in that family for three years, and then became a farm labourer on a European farm. There he was paid 10 shillings a month. Raphael stayed with the European farmer for 22 years. In 1945 he took up a job on a government owned farm and was paid £10 a month. He stayed for four years and during this time applied for a purchase area farm. But he never trained as a master farmer.

When in 1950 Mutadza purchase area was opened, Raphael was among the first who were offered a farm. He arrived with a wife and six children, all of whom were old enough to help him open up the land. One of his sons was a builder and helped him to put up six huts and two granaries. In subsequent years Raphael married two more wives. By 1967, they had borne him eleven children. He invited his old father to live with him and so had a large family to look after.

By the standards of Mutadza farm owners Raphael has been reasonably successful. He has paid the full price of his farm, but has not bothered to obtain his title deeds. He owns three ploughs, a cultivator, a planter, a rake, a cart and a wheelbarrow, and also 31 head of cattle and 51 sheep. In 1964 he sank a borehole of 12 feet for which he paid with his own savings. He also fenced his farm. To obtain four rolls of wire he took out a loan from the cooperative society, but never repaid it. Consequently he no longer uses the cooperative society to sell his surplus crops. Since 1964 Raphael has fattened some cattle, and annually sells an ox for the average price of £23. In 1965–66 he had a farm income of £151.

Raphael ploughs some 23 acres each year. Two of these, however, are water-logged since he cleared his land in a vlei. Still, Raphael is reasonably satisfied with his land. He has never held a leadership position in his community.

(e) Reginald, the Old Man

Reginald is an old Karanga who last left the rural area in 1915. Born in 1894 he went to school for five years and then found employment in a mining township. He was paid ten shillings a month. Later he worked for two years in Bulawayo for a monthly wage of £1.10.0. In 1914 he worked for one year on a European farm earning £1 a month. After that he returned to his village. He married his first wife in 1929, and two more wives in 1943 and 1945. By 1967 his wives had borne him 19 children, all of whom are alive. His oldest sons and daughters had married and the younger ones still attended school.

Reginald had been living on the land which became Mutadza purchase area and moved to an adjoining tribal trust land while Mutadza was being surveyed. When applications for farms were invited, Reginald came forward and was offered one. At that time he possessed only one plough, a planter and a little cash. He employed six men for five months to clear the ground and dig the contour ridges, paying each a monthly wage of £1.15.0. Later he re-employed them for one and a half months to mould bricks. He then hired a builder who constructed him a house for £8.10.0 and six huts for £1.10.0 each. He paid an additional sum of £5.10.0 for flooring material and £24 for doors and windows. He also bought wire for £4 to fence in his homestead and paid £3.15.0 in wages to have the fence put up. Since most of his children were working in town, he had few helpers on the land.

Reginald paid the full price of his farm, but has not bothered to obtain his title deeds. Since his arrival on the farm he has bought a second plough, a cultivator, wheelbarrow and a cart. He ploughs some 31 acres a year, but in 1965–66 his total farm income was only £107. This is reasonably good for unqualified peasant farmers in Mutadza, but low when compared with that of Guruuswa farm owners.

Reginald possesses only nine head of cattle. To increase the number of oxen during the ploughing season, he offered to herd eight beasts for the Cold Storage Commission and expects to be paid for their maintenance.

Reginald never experimented with modern cash crops; he never stall fed his cattle. He has no great ambitions and is satisfied with his present economic position. He feels secure. His neighbours elected him as a committee member of the African Farmers' Union.

(f) *Richard, the Heir*

Richard is the youngest of all Mutadza farm owners. His father came to Mutadza as an old man. Richard was born in 1934, completed his primary education and found employment in Bulawayo as a clerk where he earned £14 a month. Richard liked his white-collar job and saved some money for a sewing machine, a plough and a harrow.

In 1950, when his parents moved to Mutadza, Richard was still a youth and helped his father to open up the land. He remembers that his father employed six men to clear the land and build contour ridges and two men to mould bricks. These services cost his family £28. Later his father bought a wire fence for £4 to enclose his homestead. His father built personally all the huts for his family.

When his father died in 1961, Richard was called back from Bulawayo and asked to take over the farm for he was an only child. He had also to take over responsibility for three children of his mother's sister, whom his father had taken care of, and to pay their school fees.

Richard knew nothing about farming. He worked the farm together with his mother, and when his mother died in 1965 he stood alone. Richard then married, and together with his wife tried to build up the farm. The farm was in a derelict state. Richard therefore made friends with the extension assistant and tried to learn from him as much as he could. For example, he started cotton growing and in the first year received £10 for three bags. Still, in 1965–66 his farm income was as low as £86, far less than the money he earned as a clerk. That season he had ploughed 16 acres, for labour shortage prevented him from culti-vating more.

Though still young and inexperienced, Richard is determined to develop the farm. He has already built up his cattle herd to 14 beasts. He possesses two ploughs, a rake, a cultivator, a cart and two wheelbarrows.

(g) Robert, the Disillusioned Peasant Farmer

Robert is one of the very few peasant farmers who is tired of life in a purchase area. Born in 1896 as the son of a labourer on a European farm, he sought work in Bulawayo to earn money for school fees. At the age of 26 he attended school for the first time and persevered for six years. Missionaries then employed him for ten years as an assistant teacher at a mission school. In 1938 he gave up teaching and became a tenant farmer on a European owned estate. There he stayed until 1950, when he came to his farm in Mutadza.

In his mid-thirties Robert married, and over the years his wife has given birth to seven children. His youngest son was born on the farm. Robert paid school fees for all his children, as well as for two illegitimate children of his eldest daughter. Since he sent all his children to school, he had little labour at hand when he came to Mutadza to open up the land. He therefore hired four men to make bricks, build his huts and dig his contour ridges. This cost him £20. Apart from paying these wages, he invested no money in his land. By 1967 he had paid the full price of his farm, but he had not obtained his title deeds.

Although his neighbours like him and elected him vice-president of the African Farmers' Union committee, Robert is unhappy on his farm. He is a very unsuccessful farmer. Initially he reduced labour costs by clearing fields in the vleis, but now his soil often gets water-logged. In 1965–66 he had a farming income of only £23. His wife makes a small contribution to the annual budget by making mats, which brings in some £2 a year. During the drought season of 1966–67 his sons sent him money from town to buy food. Robert would like to sell his farm and retire to a tribal trust land. Since he has never lived in a village, he thinks that village life is the best life an African can lead.

(5) EVALUATION OF CASE HISTORIES

Table 28 sets out some of the characteristics of farm owners in Mutadza purchase area.

TABLE 28

Characteristics of Seven Mutadza Farm Owners

Name	Agricultural Income £	Year of Birth	Education in Years	Labour Migrat. in Years	Investment in opening up of farm £	Office in Agricultural Association
Alban	374	1919	2	—	766	Member of A.F.U. committee
Alex	174	1912	6	7	223	Council chairman
Alfons	23	1914	3	4	86	Councillor
Raphael	151	1908	1	29	—	—
Reginald	107	1894	5	4	83	Member of A.F.U. committee
Richard	86	1934	8	4	32	—
Robert	23	1896	6	13	20	Vice-chairman of A.F.U. committee

Table 28 shows little correlation between education and farming ability and so confirms the earlier statement that the close correlation between education and farming success in Guruuswa was accidental. There exists, however, a striking relationship between farm output and agricultural skills. Apart from Alfons, the failure, the other master farmers have much better incomes than those of unqualified farm owners.

As in Guruuswa, so also in Mutadza, only the very good peasant farmers invested much money in opening up their farms. But unlike Guruuswa farm owners, there is no correlation in Mutadza purchase area between leadership and farming ability. I have already stressed this in an earlier chapter and explained it by the lack of interest Mutadza farm owners show in modern farming methods. Thus the chairman of the council, which was the most important administrative body in Mutadza until 1967, had only an average farm income, and Alfons, a councillor, was evicted from the purchase area for poor farming practices. Also on the less important African Farmers' Union committee, positions were offered to farm owners irrespective of their farming ability. Its vice-chairman even wanted to leave the purchase area and move into a tribal trust land.

Mutadza farm owners, like peasant farmers in Guruuswa, come from a rural background, many had been peasant cultivators for most of their lives, one had been a farm labourer and one a tenant on a European estate. Yet few came with special skills or much farming equipment to the purchase area. Most bought their implements after they had settled on their farms. Few invested much money in their land. Rather they spent larger sums of money on education. One Mutadza peasant farmer stated explicitly: 'We invest our wealth in the education of our children.' Mutadza peasant farmers resemble tribal trust land peasant cultivators in doing everything in their power to provide their children with a good education. This indicates that they envisage their children's future in urban areas, not on the land.

The analysis of peasant cultivators in tribal trust lands indicated that only those are ready to experiment with modern cash crops who are either very successful and can afford running a risk, or the very poor who have nothing to lose. In the two purchase areas, no family in Guruuswa experimented with either cotton or tobacco, though the best farm owners tried to run their own irrigation schemes. In Mutadza, however, quite a number of peasant farmers tried to grow cotton or tobacco. Yet since these crops require great care and much labour, neither of which Mutadza farm owners were willing or able to provide, their yields were very low. Thus, whereas the more experienced Guruuswa farmers ignored the recommendations of extension assistants to experiment with cotton and tobacco and rather listened to their advice on how to improve traditional crops, the less experienced Mutadza peasants rejected extension advice concerning traditional crops, but accepted the proposal to try the new cash crops. Yet they failed. The major reason for their failure seems to be the same as that of the woman cultivator in Hove subchiefdom who grew tobacco and failed: inadequate labour in tending the new crop.

Low labour input seems a major reason for the low yields of Mutadza farm owners. Many stressed that they were short of labour, yet few men were ready to pay for hired labourers apart from the time when they opened up their farms. Alex is an exception, and his yields are relatively high. So are the yields of Alban whose family is large enough to provide an adequate labour force. The high value placed on education, which withdraws child labour from the farms, accounts for the inability of most men, however large their families, to cultivate their land effectively. This eagerness to fit their children for other than farm labour indicates that few of the Mutadza farmers regard agriculture as a vocation.

I suggested that in Mutadza purchase area no far-reaching improvements in agricultural productivity are likely to take place as long as the old men, who bought the farms, are still in control. The case history of Richard, which is typical of those of other young men who inherited their fathers' farms, shows that even after a take-over progress will be slow because of the young men's inexperience, lack of capital and shortage of labour. Richard's close cooperation with the extension assistant, however, holds out the hope that over the years his farm income will increase.

One interesting difference between master farmers and other peasant farmers in Mutadza is that all master farmers except Alfons paid the full price of their farms and obtained their title deeds, but none of the other farm owners obtained his title deeds, though most of them paid the full price of their farms. This is true not only for the farm owners included in the case histories, but of all farm owners in Mutadza. These farm owners stated that they saw no reason for paying stamp duties to obtain a certificate of ownership; they thought that they had spent quite enough in re-paying their debt to government.

A few Mutadza farm owners regret having come to the purchase area. They declare that they had under-estimated the amount of labour required on a farm and the degree of supervision exercised by the extension staff. The least successful added that when he first came to the farm he had been rich in cash. The opening up of the farm, however, and the ever increasing school fees for his children had made him poor. Now he has no money left to make a new start.

Most farm owners, however, are satisfied with the life they lead. The majority had come from tribal trust lands and they know of the land shortage and hardships in those areas. Most farm owners think that their present land is not only larger but also of better quality than the land they formerly cultivated. They state that they came to the purchase area to get more land and to own larger herds of cattle. The more progressive express the same idea in the words: 'We came to make money.'

PART III
IRRIGATION SCHEMES

CHAPTER 12

GOVERNMENT POLICY AND
ADMINISTRATIVE CONTROL

(1) INTRODUCTION

In the Introduction to this book I stressed that changes in the economic life of peasants are likely to take place when new methods of production become available and when peasants either desire to adopt them or when their adoption is forced on them by higher authorities. Since most peasant societies are slow to adopt new ways of crop production, many governments in underdeveloped countries have seen themselves forced to impose development plans on their people.

When changes have to take place within a short time and private capital and skill is lacking, governments must direct and guide these changes. If they are to succeed, credit and marketing facilities must be provided. Irrigation farming, which requires a high degree of skill and much capital, must be closely supervised lest the invested capital be lost. Such supervision of necessity restricts the freedom of settlers and may lead to dissatisfaction unless the supervised have great confidence in their supervisors. The Rhodesian government's approach to this problem is analysed in this and the following chapters.

(2) GOVERNMENT RESPONSE TO LAND SHORTAGE IN AFRICAN AREAS

As pointed out in the first chapter of this book, the first African irrigation scheme in Rhodesia was started in 1931 in the Sabi valley when drought had caused widespread starvation among Africans. For many years government left small irrigation schemes in the hands of the African people who had built them. Only in the late 1960s did government pay serious attention to irrigation farming in African areas, for by then land shortage in tribal trust lands had become acute and the fully entrenched government policy of separate development did not allow for a transfer of land from Europeans to Africans. Moreover, Africans living on

European farm land, who were not employed by the European farm owners, were to leave and return to the tribal areas.[1] The natural population increase of purchase areas, as described in the second part of this book, had also to be absorbed by tribal trust lands, and the Africans who failed to find work in the towns were ordered to return to their villages. Thus tribal trust lands became the shock absorbers of all surplus population from all parts of Rhodesia.

To support this ever growing tribal population without departing from the policy of separate development, government had to introduce drastic changes in peasant agriculture and decided that irrigation schemes might be a first answer. Those areas in tribal trust lands, therefore, which could be irrigated from nearby rivers or dams, were earmarked for irrigation, and many schemes sprang up all over Rhodesia.

Since some 2,200 persons per square mile can be supported on irrigation schemes, and since on most schemes two crops can be grown per year, many more people can be settled there than on dry land, and all of them will be employed the whole year round, thus preventing them from seeking urban employment. A number of agriculturalists have warned that irrigation schemes cost so much money that only if they are farmed efficiently—more efficiently, they implied, than African peasants were capable of doing—would the capital investment be justified. Moreover, they stressed that without great precautions irrigation would increase the salt content of the land to such a degree that the soil might be ruined for future generations. This plea was repeatedly made by Savory, a former conservationist and later member of parliament. Yet government declared itself willing to pay this price if only its segregationist policy could be preserved.[2]

In establishing irrigation schemes in tribal trust lands, government strained its good relationships with African chiefs, for once an irrigation scheme has been established in a chiefdom, its land is removed from the direct control of the chief and placed under personnel responsible to the Ministry of Internal Affairs. Moreover, the people living on a scheme have to follow a completely different work life to other people in a tribal trust land because of the

[1] One whole tribe, the Tangwena, were forcibly removed from their home area which had been declared European land. See Clutton-Brock, 1969.

[2] In 1971 Savory stated plainly that irrigation schemes were 'political palliatives' and that the money would be better spent on other agricultural projects. *The Rhodesia Herald*, 24.9.71.

necessary regimentation by the scheme personnel to convert peasant cultivators into irrigation plotholders.

District commissioners stated that irrigation schemes did not aim at making plotholders rich, but at feeding them, enabling them to grow a surplus with which to feed their neighbours in tribal trust lands, and to tie men and women to the land throughout the year and so prevent them from seeking work in European areas.

(3) MVURA AND ZUVA IRRIGATION SCHEMES

The two irrigation schemes studied in this book, Mvura and Zuva, represent two different types of government controlled irrigation schemes. Zuva, the older scheme, is irrigated by flood irrigation, Mvura, the more recent scheme, by overhead irrigation. Overhead irrigation, common on European owned farms in Rhodesia, is new in African areas.[1] It has many advantages over flood irrigation since it makes a finer distribution of the water possible, and since water clocks control the water supply no special drainage system is necessary. Moreover, sprinklers do not use up land as water canals do. From a technical angle, therefore, the Mvura irrigation scheme is more efficient than the Zuva scheme.

Both Mvura and Zuva irrigation schemes lie at rivers which form the boundaries of the tribal trust lands in which the schemes are situated. Mvura lies 65 miles away from Gatooma, its administrative centre. Gatooma is a small town on the Rhodesian high veld on the main highway which connects all the major cities of Rhodesia, namely Bulawayo, Gwelo, Salisbury and Umtali. Mvura irrigation scheme is connected to Gatooma by a good dirt road. The immediate neighbours of the Mvura plotholders are the peasant cultivators of the tribal trust land and peasant farmers in two purchase areas across the river. Zuva irrigation scheme is 90 miles from Beit Bridge, its administrative centre, and over 200 miles from Bulawayo, the nearest larger town of Rhodesia. The marketing of surplus crops, therefore, presents a much greater problem to plotholders in Zuva than to plotholders in Mvura.

---

[1] Only since 1970 has overhead irrigation become more widespread in African areas. By then 40 per cent of the acreage irrigated in the western part of Rhodesia was watered by overhead irrigation. *The Rhodesia Herald*, 11.11.70.

Both schemes lie in very hot areas of the country. Mvura has an annual mean temperature of 75 degrees Fahrenheit and a mean maximum temperature in October of 95 degrees. Though its average rainfall is 24 inches, evaporation is high and dry land cultivation hazardous, though possible. Zuva has an annual mean temperature of 96 degrees, a mean maximum temperature in October of 107 degrees, and an average rainfall of only 10 inches.[1] Only every seventh year is rain adequate for dry land cultivation.

The Zuva scheme has a fertile sandy loam soil. Luxuriant tropical trees surround the irrigated land, though its immediate neighbourhood, which lacks water, is desert-like country. The Mvura scheme is built over an earlier bed of the river, which now provides the water for irrigation. Consequently river sand lies immediately below a thin layer of top soil which in most parts of the scheme is only a few inches thick. The top soil increases, however, to a depth of 12 inches at the northern end of the scheme. Since the top soil is itself sandy, water penetrates quickly and little moisture is retained for plant growth.

The area of the present Zuva irrigation scheme was opened up in 1956 when a dirt road was constructed from Beit Bridge, the only larger settlement in the area. In 1964 the district commissioner began holding meetings with the people, telling them about the plans for an irrigation scheme. In 1965 the first 178 acres of a potential 1,060 acre scheme were prepared for irrigation farming. For about a year government employed local men to clear the land. Since employment opportunities in this border land of Rhodesia are limited, many men took advantage of this offer. Under the supervision of the district commissioner, extension officer and extension assistant, water canals were dug, the land was levelled and ploughed by tractor and the fields were pegged. Then the first applicants were invited to settle on two-acre plots and were given instructions on how to complete the levelling of their fields. Soon 48 more plotholders were allowed to settle. By 1970 Zuva had 88 plotholders. The later settlers were not helped by tractors to level their land but had to do it themselves without mechanical assistance. Since some were more skilled than others, some fields are less adequately watered than the rest.

The first maize crop, which was planted in November 1966,

---

[1] The area is so hot that the local people greet each other with the words: 'How hot the sun is!', instead of the more customary 'Makadiko', 'How do you do?'

gave a rich harvest. Though the settlers used no fertilizer, they reaped an average of 40 bags per acre. They sold their surpluses at £2.10.0 a bag to the people of their tribal trust land. Since in the first year they had to pay a water rate of only £2.10.0, they made a great profit and many more people volunteered to join.

In May 1967 the people planted their first wheat crop. Since the wheat could not be sold locally, the plotholders hired a lorry and sold their harvest in bulk in Bulawayo for a standard price of £3.7.0 a bag. Transport costs amounted to £1 per bag. The next maize crop was again sold locally. During their second year on the scheme, the plotholders had to pay £14 water rate, and by 1968 it had increased to £28 annually. This is the standard rate for two acres of irrigated land in African areas.

During their second year on the scheme, people received fertilizer and improved seed from the district commissioner at subsidized prices. During their third year they were asked to form a cooperative society. This, however, they were reluctant to do. Plotholders on other irrigation schemes in the same district had told people at Zuva that a cooperative society would exploit them, that it would regulate their sales and force them to buy excessive amounts of seed and fertilizer. Hence, when after much persuasion the cooperative society was established, most plotholders boycotted it. Meetings called by visiting cooperative officers were seldom attended by more than the chairman and one or two committee members. Though the people were told that soil tests, carried out in laboratories, had established the ideal amount of fertilizer per acre, they believed that the officers of the co-operative movement forced them to buy more fertilizer than was necessary or even good for their crops, in order to get money from them. Many expressed their resentment by letting the pockets of fertilizer, which they were forced to buy, lie unused all over the scheme.

Unfamiliarity with the credit system also caused resentment against deductions from crop sales at harvesting time.[1] When in 1968 the cooperative society deducted previously advanced loans from the price paid for wheat, the plotholders complained that their money had been taken from them. They also resented that in 1968–69 they had to pay £3 for 60 lbs of maize seed, whereas in the preceding year, when the seed had been subsidized, they had

[1] Weingrod, in his study of Oriental Jews on an Israeli moshav, describes similar difficulties of cooperative farming and marketing. Weingrod, 1966, p. 86.

paid the same sum for 100 lbs. Moreover, the cooperative society charged £1.15.0 transport costs for each bag, or 15 shillings more than they had paid when they had hired their own lorry to bring their wheat to Bulawayo. They therefore complained that they were no longer working for themselves but for the cooperative society.

To avoid the deductions made by the cooperative society, many plotholders sold their crops privately. By 1970 some owed the cooperative society as much as £60. Since the cooperative movement had no power to force the repayment of debts, the cooperative officer handed his problem over to the district commissioner and the debts were transferred to the African Loan Fund administered by the Ministry of Internal Affairs. The African Loan Fund can instigate court action against debtors and in this way much of the money was repaid. In 1970 no more loans were made available to the people and the district commissioner informed the plotholders that before the new season started they had to produce £14 to buy seed and fertilizer or leave the scheme. Few families possessed that much money and many went to their relatives in surrounding tribal trust lands to raise the necessary sum. By the time this research was completed, the Zuva irrigation scheme was almost deserted by its plotholders, most of whom had left their plots temporarily in the care of hired labourers while they themselves went begging money.

In 1969 a scheme manager was introduced to supervise the agricultural activities of the plotholders on the scheme.

The Mvura irrigation scheme is slightly newer. The clearing of the land started in 1966 when first 80, then 129 acres were prepared and divided into 36 plots of about three and a half acres each. Mvura plots are therefore almost twice as large as plots on the Zuva scheme. In November 1967 36 families moved in, but by 1970 only 29 families occupied the land; some of these cultivated two allotments. All families were offered a small irrigated vegetable garden of 20 by 22 yards to the east of their fields.

Some of the early settlers from the surrounding tribal trust land continued to cultivate land in their chiefdoms to graze cattle on the tribal pasture. When the first harvest proved successful, the district commissioner asked the people either to give up their land rights and cattle in the tribal trust land, or to leave the irrigation scheme. Many feared the uncertainty of a completely new agricultural environment and left the scheme. Some of their places were taken by newcomers.

Since quite a number of plotholders in Mvura had been labourers or sons of farm owners in the adjoining purchase areas, they were familiar with the working of cooperative societies and the local cooperative society was established without difficulty. Difficulties, however, arose when the scheme manager told the people to join a cooperative union, the Producers' Cooperative Society, which included several societies more distant from the market than Mvura. Transport costs then increased from 15 to 20 per cent of the crop value and both the people and the district commissioner opposed the incorporation. In 1968 the people left the union and the cooperative society again became popular among the plotholders.

Mvura, therefore, is a much smaller scheme than Zuva, its settlers have almost twice as much land as the plotholders in Zuva, and the irrigation system itself is technically more efficient. On the other hand, the soil on the Zuva scheme is much more fertile. These differences must be kept in mind when comparing the success or failure of the two schemes.

(4) THE ADMINISTRATION OF IRRIGATION SCHEMES

The administrative framework of all government controlled irrigation schemes is identical. The Ministry of Internal Affairs controls all irrigated land in tribal areas through its civil servants and through other employees. The district commissioner is responsible for the admission and expulsion of plotholders.

Applicants to irrigation schemes must be approved by the district commissioner. Before taking up their plots, they must sign a lease agreement, the terms of which reproduce the Tribal Trust Land (Control of Irrigation Schemes) Regulations of 1967. As soon as men have signed this lease agreement they are bound by its various clauses, including the stipulation that they must personally reside on the scheme. Initial payments include five shillings to cultivate the irrigated land, one shilling to occupy a residential stand, and £1.5.0 per acre during the first year for water. This water rate, which in the second year increases to £7 and in all subsequent years to £14 per acre, is paid into the African Development Fund.[1] Expulsion of plotholders lies with the provincial commissioner who generally acts on the advice of the district commissioner. The provincial commissioner may at any

[1] Land Tenure (Control of Irrigable Areas) Regulations, 1970, para 12.

time order plotholders to leave an irrigation scheme immediately for any 'reason which the provincial commissioner considers good and sufficient.'[1] This arbitrary power gives rise to great insecurity among plotholders.

The lease agreements do not require special agricultural knowledge from the lessees, nor capital assets or equipment. Hence district commissioners have great freedom to choose men whom they consider suitable. Different district commissioners look for different abilities in the applicants. The district commissioner at Beit Bridge, for example, at first thought that settlers should pay £200 towards the development of the Zuva scheme. When no people applied he lowered the sum to £100. Even then only five men came on these terms. Thereupon all contributions to the cost of the scheme were dropped and applications were accepted from all local people who volunteered to live on the scheme.

The district commissioner of the Mvura scheme demanded that all plotholders be master farmers. When few master farmers applied, he requested that those applying for irrigated land be willing to undergo master farmer training while on the scheme. This the people agreed to do and by 1970 twelve of the 29 plotholders were master farmers and seventeen master farmer trainees. Mvura irrigation scheme, therefore, has many more agriculturally knowledgeable plotholders than the Zuva scheme.

People can leave an irrigation scheme of their own accord, and they can be evicted. A great turnover of plotholders in a scheme indicates local discontent and insecurity. By the end of 1969 no family had left the Zuva irrigation scheme, but of the first 36 settlers in Mvura 26 had left. Few Zuva families wanted to leave their scheme since dry land cultivation is almost impossible in their area[2]. In the surroundings of the Mvura scheme, however, dry land cultivation, though hazardous, is possible.

Ten of the first settlers in Mvura had come from the adjoining purchase areas, the rest from the tribal trust land. Most people from the tribal trust land left. They preferred the greater freedom of village life to the supervision on the scheme. They were also appalled by the high production costs and the necessity for repaying their loans at harvesting time. Moreover, since no cattle

[1] Land Tenure (Suspension of Irrigation) Regulations, 1970, para 3 (1) (e).
[2] On revisiting the scheme in 1974 I found that all but six plotholders had left, so that the scheme was practically deserted.

were allowed on the scheme, they felt insecure, for like most Karanga peasants they regarded cattle as their basic security.

Those who were left were forced to pay their debts. Those who had no means of doing so were ordered to work on the roads of the tribal trust land for a monthly wage of £4.10.0. By 1970 five men were still working on the roads, having outstanding debts of £20, £40, £95, £105 and £110. Their unsuccessful irrigation farming, therefore, involved them in heavy financial losses which took them years to repay. Their failure discouraged many peasant cultivators from joining the scheme and Mvura irrigation scheme has had vacant plots ever since.

None of the settlers from the purchase areas, however, left Mvura because they possessed no land of their own. Yet even these men had no intention of staying permanently on the irrigation scheme. They rather hoped to make enough money to buy their own purchase area farms.

People not only left the scheme of their own accord; some were evicted for breaking the rules and regulations of the scheme administration. One plotholder, for example, placed an irrigation pipe in such a position that it watered only his own field. A sprinkler covers an area within a radius of 60 feet. This is slightly more than the width of one field. The position of pipes has been exactly calculated so that all fields receive an even water supply. A repositioning of a pipe, therefore, deprives part of a field of water. The neighbour of this plotholder complained, the case was taken into court and the plotholder evicted. Another plotholder broadcast his wheat instead of planting it in rows, as the scheme manager had instructed him. The scheme manager saw in this a challenge to his authority and had an eviction order issued to the plotholder. Every eviction increases the feeling of insecurity among the people who stay on the scheme.

When irrigation schemes are first opened, all plotholders are offered plots of equal size. The same facilities are granted, and the same restrictions are placed on all. Yet these identical conditions never standardize performance. Those who work harder and are more successful soon distinguish themselves from the rest and may occasionally be allowed to cultivate two allotments. This happened, for example, in Mvura where in 1969 several plots were vacant. Four enterprising and successful plotholders volunteered to cultivate a second allotment on the understanding that should new settlers arrive they would hand back their second plot.

District commissioners, who control the admission and expulsion of plotholders from irrigation schemes, are also responsible for the administration of the schemes. Plotholders can appeal to them in any difficulties, whether these arise from disputes with the scheme personnel or from their environment. Crops, for example, are often destroyed by wild animals, and in Zuva even the lives of the people are endangered by lions. Since Africans are not normally allowed to bear firearms, district commissioners take the responsibility of protecting the life and property of the people in their districts.

To guarantee the efficient running of a scheme, the district commissioner appoints a manager[1] who normally resides at the scheme. This man, always a European, is an employee of the Ministry of Internal Affairs, but not a civil servant. Scheme managers differ in their farming skills and knowledge of irrigation farming. Some have been farm managers on European owned farms and have little sympathy for African peasants. These often fail to win the confidence of the plotholders.

Difficulties between scheme managers and plotholders have been especially marked on the Mvura irrigation scheme. By 1970 the people had had three managers in succession. The first manager had some previous experience on a European farm, but had never handled irrigation equipment. His stay was marked by the 'bean episode'. He knew little about irrigation equipment and experimented with the water pressure as best he could, but failed to adjust it correctly so that the plants near the sprinklers were pressed to the ground through a too heavy application of water, while those further away withered through lack of water.

A lack of communication between scheme manager and plotholders further increased the people's losses. When the manager thought that all beans had been harvested, he ordered the tractor driver to plough the land and the still unharvested beans were ploughed in. Many of the plotholders incurred heavy financial losses and left the scheme. Those who stayed, but were unable to repay their loans to the cooperative society, were given an extension of time to repay their debts.

The failure of that harvest was also due to an over-ambitious crop programme. The scheme manager thought that two crops could be grown on all land. He planned that half of the acreage be planted with maize and wheat in succession, and the other half

---

[1] Land Tenure (Control of Irrigable Areas) Regulations, 1970, para 6.

with cotton and beans. To achieve this goal, especially fast work was required on the bean-cotton sequence, and the need to prepare the land for the next crop caused the destruction of the still unharvested beans. Since then no more beans have been grown in Mvura, and half of the acreage now carries only one crop a year, cotton.

The first scheme manager in Mvura was not only technically incompetent and failed to cooperate with the plotholders, but he also clashed with the district commissioner and the extension assistant. Moreover, he sensed political agitation whenever plotholders objected to any of his plans. In 1968 he was replaced by another manager.

The second manager showed little interest in the scheme itself and was often absent. The people resented especially that he placed orders for seed and fertilizer without informing them. During his stay the actual responsibility for the scheme shifted from the European manager to the African extension assistant. In 1970 he was replaced by a third scheme manager who was relatively new when the research took place.

The Zuva plotholders have been more fortunate in their first scheme manager and no difficulties marred their relationship with him.

Every irrigation scheme has its own extension assistant. Many of these assistants have attended special courses in irrigation farming. Though their formal authority is less than that of the scheme managers, their influence is often greater. Yet since extension assistants see themselves as advisers not as authority figures who issue orders, they prefer that scheme managers see to the implementation of their advice. Ideally scheme managers and extension assistants should cooperate closely. Many extension assistants show a real interest in the scheme, they understand the African plotholders and district commissioners, to whom, since 1969, they are responsible, often trust them and even ask them to examine applicants to the scheme.

The scheme manager and extension assistant together regulate practically the whole working life of the plotholders. They instruct them daily in the work that has to be done, tell them what equipment to use and how to carry out their tasks. Every year after the harvest they send soil samples to the laboratories in Salisbury to ensure the correct treatment of the soil and then order seed, fertilizer and insecticides according to the findings of the laboratory workers. This procedure is necessary if yields are to be high, yet it excludes plotholders from decision making. If the plotholders were informed of the laboratory findings and their implications explained to them before the orders were placed, a greater degree of trust might be established.

Whereas the Mvura irrigation scheme had two unsuccessful scheme managers in succession, it had a most competent extension assistant whom the people trusted. By contrast, Zuva plotholders were relatively satisfied with their scheme manager, though they did not always follow his instructions, but their extension assistant was grossly incompetent. In 1970 this man was expelled from the civil service.

The relationship between scheme personnel and plotholders is of great importance for the success of a scheme. Scheffler, who studied a tobacco scheme in Tanzania, found that schemes which require a high initial capital investment can only succeed if plotholders trust the scheme management and are willing to submit to its instructions.[1] On the two irrigation schemes, Zuva and Mvura, success or failure seems to a large extent to depend on the extension assistants.

On schemes where people are willing to follow agricultural advice, as in Mvura, harvests are generally satisfactory. On schemes where people resent agricultural guidance, as in Zuva, harvests tend to be very low. As stated above, non-cooperation in Zuva goes so far that plotholders refuse to apply to their fields the fertilizer which has been bought for them and for which they have paid.

In addition to scheme managers and extension assistants, some employees of the African Development Fund and of the Ministry of Water Development work on irrigation schemes. Those paid by the African Development Fund tend to be unskilled labourers working at the behest of the scheme manager. They see to the maintenance of the canal system, help in the loading and unloading of lorries, and assist wherever their work is needed. Zuva irrigation scheme has ten such employees, one of whom is himself a plotholder who wants to earn some extra money. Mvura has only one general labourer. Employees of the Ministry of Water Development in Zuva see that the main canal is regularly opened to allow

---

[1] In fact, Scheffler goes further and states that a scheme will only succeed if the people feel politically one with the scheme management. Scheffler, 1968, p. 302.

plotholders to water their fields. In Mvura three African pump assistants of the Ministry of Water Development and one coloured man in charge of the water supply see to the pumps and various machines of the irrigation scheme. This coloured man stands in an intercalary position on the scheme. With a monthly wage of £75 he is richer than any of the Africans, but poorer than the scheme manager. The second scheme manager, in fact, refused to associate with him and communicated with him only in writing, instructing him at what times water was wanted on the plots. The Africans on the scheme, however, like him. They invite him to their homes and treat him as a member of their community. The three pump assistants receive a monthly wage of between £11 and £13. One of them is a Malawian married to a local woman. Like his two colleagues, he lives with his family on the scheme. All three men have little education but many years practical experience in their work.

This administrative system of irrigation schemes shows that authority runs from the district commissioner who lives outside the scheme, to the scheme manager who controls the day to day administration, to the extension assistant who possesses the technical knowledge of irrigation farming. The plotholders are subject to the instructions of all these officials. Employees of the Ministry of Water Development and of the African Development Fund provide manual services and are expected to help both the scheme personnel and the plotholders.

(5) THE PEOPLE'S RESPONSE TO CLOSE SUPERVISION

The close supervision of the plotholders by the scheme personnel and the complete control of the latter over the running of the scheme, prevent the people from participating in the local administration and create in them a feeling of insecurity. The growth of voluntary associations is discouraged and those which start tend to be short-lived.

One difference between the Mvura and Zuva schemes is that the Mvura plotholders made a real effort to form voluntary associations whereas the Zuva plotholders did not. Like the peasant farmers of Guruuswa purchase area, the first arrivals on the Mvura irrigation scheme tried to form their own administrative body. As early as 1967 they formed the Mvura Management Board which consisted of a group of plotholders but had no chairman. The management board met once a week with the scheme manager to inform him of the problems and complaints of the plotholders. The manager was then invited to explain his policies and, when necessary, forward the people's wishes to the district commissioner. Since the board was formed by the people, all initiative came from them. Unexpected actions of the scheme manager could be discussed only after they had taken place. This explains the unanticipated destruction of the bean crop. The management board also helped to organize work. For example, it divided the plotholders into three divisions, each of which was directed by a member of the board regularly to change the irrigation pipes in the fields.

Since the management board was critical of the scheme manager, it was abolished in 1968 and replaced by a coordinating committee. This committee protested against the higher transport costs and the higher charges for seed and fertilizer when the manager joined the local cooperative society to the Producers' Cooperative Society. The manager suspected the committee of political agitation, had it disbanded and its chairman arrested.

The chairman of the coordinating committee was the only powerful leader who ever represented the plotholders of Mvura to the scheme personnel. Before he came to the scheme, he had been an extension assistant and was therefore very knowledgeable about farming. The plotholders trusted him and had earlier on elected him to the Mvura Management Board. Since he also understood the intricacies of marketing, he led the protest against the Producers' Cooperative Society, whose vice-chairman he was. After his arrest the homes of other committee members were searched and thereafter no man dared to come forward to speak up for the people. Police investigation later proved that the chairman had never engaged in political activities and that he had merely voiced the general dissatisfaction of the plotholders. In spite of these findings, however, he was not allowed to return to the scheme.

As a result of these events both the plotholders and the scheme personnel looked unfavourably at voluntary associations. Apart from a young farmers' club and a natural resources club for teenagers, no other voluntary associations were formed. When, therefore, in 1970 a senior agricultural officer recommended that the plotholders form some body through which to present their opinions to the scheme manager and district commissioner, the plotholders were most reluctant and the district commissioner also discouraged the formation of a new society. The local extension assistant said: 'There is no need for leaders on the scheme, nor for any association of plotholders, because everything is done for the people. All they have to do is to carry out our instructions.'

After the plotholders had repeatedly failed to participate effectively in the administration of their irrigation scheme, they became apathetic and regarded themselves merely as workers who had temporarily come to the scheme to make money, but they did not regard it as a new home.

In 1970 a new type of leader came forward who organized small self-help schemes when emergencies arose. When, for example, the maize sheller which the people had purchased with money from their cooperative society broke down, he asked the plotholders to collect money for its repair, and when a plotholder fell sick he asked his neighbour to weed that man's field. But he never became the spokesman of the plotholders *vis-à-vis* the scheme personnel. This man had been a detective before he came to the scheme, had been living in Mvura since its inception, and in 1970 cultivated two irrigated plots. He was the most successful man on the scheme.

Zuva plotholders are even less interested in voluntary associations than Mvura plotholders. Apart from the enforced cooperative society, which never found popular support, the people in Zuva formed only once an *ad hoc* committee when disputes arose over water distribution. In their daily lives plotholders look rather to some relatives of their chiefs who live on the scheme and who have taken over some leadership functions. In this way the people in Zuva are more closely linked to the tribal system than are plotholders on the other irrigation scheme. In fact, they highly esteem traditional values and view modern institutions with scepticism.

The analysis of this chapter has shown that although the overall administrative framework of the Zuva and Mvura irrigation schemes is the same, the people's adjustment varies. Whereas Mvura plotholders attempted to set up a modern bureaucratic structure, those in Zuva treat the scheme as an extension of their tribal system, and whereas the leaders in Mvura are former civil servants, in Zuva they are relatives of chiefs. In contrast to Zuva plotholders, those in Mvura cooperate closely with the agricultural staff. Their link with the tribal system is weak and their general orientation seems to be towards the modern cash economy. Zuva plotholders on the other hand, are still bound by traditional values and seem little concerned with increasing their agricultural yields.

Since basic value orientations of people are conditioned by their background, and since without an understanding of this their economic behaviour cannot be fully understood, the following chapter examines the social background of plotholders on the Mvura and Zuva irrigation schemes.

CHAPTER 13

PLOTHOLDERS ON
IRRIGATION SCHEMES

(1) INTRODUCTION

Since plotholders on irrigation schemes have little say in the administration of their communities, and since they are liable to eviction if they fail to comply with the instructions of the scheme personnel, many feel insecure and often regard their stay as temporary. Their inability or refusal to settle down permanently is reflected in their lack of investment in housing, which contrasts strongly with the high investment in brick buildings made by peasant farmers in purchase areas.

Though the general administration of irrigation schemes is fixed by the Ministry of Internal Affairs, individual schemes often differ markedly in their character because their plotholders come from different tribal and social backgrounds.

(2) THE LAYOUT OF IRRIGATION SCHEMES

All irrigation schemes are fenced off from their tribal trust lands. On the Mvura irrigation scheme the huts of plotholders are situated within the enclosed area and surround the irrigated land on the north, south and south-east. Each hut, built of poles and mud and much inferior to the huts of villagers in the adjoining tribal trust land, stands on a plot of 50 x 50 yards.[1] Few huts contain any furniture. Some plotholders say that if they could obtain title deeds to their stands and irrigated fields, they would build better homes, but under their present lease agreement they consider investment too risky.

The irrigated land itself forms a large rectangular block which is divided into 36 parallel strips, marked by beacons, which represent the standard holdings on the scheme. One path runs round this block, one dissects it from the north to the south, and

---

[1] Plotholders who came from purchase areas put up their huts immediately, those who came from tribal trust lands built them only in subsequent years.

two paths run from the east to the west. To the west of the
fields, where the land slopes down to the river, stand two powerful
engines which pump the water from the river to a large cylindrical
concrete tank. Next to the tank stands the pump house with three
engines, two of which are working at a time, pumping the water to
the plotholders' fields. The pump assistants live in government
built brick houses next to the pump house. Their homes are
superior to those of the plotholders, an indication that however
temporary the plotholders consider their stay, government
considers the scheme permanent.

To the east of the irrigated land, opposite the pumping in-
stallation, stand two large water tanks from which a vegetable
garden and an orchard are watered. Next to the gardens stands the
office building for the scheme personnel and not far away a store
house and shed where the crops are assembled before being
taken to the market.

All these buildings and irrigation installations are inside the
fence. The only person working on the scheme but living outside
this enclosure is the extension assistant whose house is five minutes
distant from the scheme boundary. The people of Mvura, therefore, form a concrete entity in their tribal trust land.

The Zuva irrigation scheme is laid out similarly to the Mvura
scheme, only the huts of the plotholders lie outside the fenced
enclosure. The irrigated land lies at the confluence of two rivers,
and on the third side a little stream forms a natural boundary.
This stream, however, and one river seldom carry water.

The Zuva scheme is divided by the main canal, which runs
from the south to the north, and by seven minor canals which
run from the east to the west, into broad strips, which are again
subdivided into narrower strips in such a way that each field
converges on a canal. Every plotholder has two fields of one
acre each which meet at one of the river canals.

To the south of the irrigated land, next to the Limpopo river,
stand three pumps which pump the water from the river into the
main canal. To the east of the scheme, following a bend in the
river, stand the engine house, a store room, a rest house for civil
servants and houses for the employees of the Ministry of Water
Development and of the African Development Fund. A second
rest house, generally used by the district commissioner, stands to
the north of the irrigated land in the shade of magnificent tropical
trees. Some banana trees grow all around the irrigated land.

This whole area is fenced in, and plotholders have to cross the river or stream when they come to work in their fields.

The road from Beit Bridge runs straight into the scheme. Where it ends there are a store room and the office of the local cooperative society, the house of the extension assistant and, further east, a grinding mill, a grocery store, the local school and a dip tank. Most of the plotholders live to the north and south of the road; a few live to the east of the scheme. The huts of the people at Zuva are even poorer than those of the people at Mvura and a visitor to an irrigation scheme gets the impression that plotholders belong to the poorest section of Rhodesian peasants.

(3) THE TRIBAL BACKGROUND OF PLOTHOLDERS

Since government created irrigation schemes to relieve population pressure in tribal areas, and since schemes are built in tribal trust lands, the first plots are generally offered to local people and only when these refuse them are Africans from other areas invited. The more readily, therefore, a scheme is accepted by the local people, the more homogeneous is its population, and the less readily it is accepted, the more heterogeneous is its people.

In Mvura, which is situated at the northern boundary of Karangaland, 44 or 53·7 per cent of the 82 adults are Karanga, 26 or 31·7 per cent are other Shona speakers. Six or 7·3 per cent come from Ndebeleland which borders on the west of Karangaland, and a further six adults, that is another 7·3 per cent, come from Zambia and Malawi. The Karanga and other Shona are therefore dominant in the area and the social customs of the people in Mvura are similar to those of the tribal trust lands and purchase areas studied in the first two parts of this book. As a consequence of their common background, social ties quickly evolved and plotholders freely lend and borrow from each other.

The Zuva irrigation scheme differs from all the other communities studied in this book. For the first time in my research I was not allowed to choose the areas I wanted to study, but was told by the Ministry of Internal Affairs which schemes I could enter. On stating that I wanted to study one successful and one unsuccessful irrigation scheme, I was given permission to carry out research in Mvura and Zuva. Mvura was ideally suited for a comparative study of peasant agriculture in Karangaland, but Zuva lies outside this cultural area. Of 190 adults on the scheme, only 7 or 3·7 per cent are Karanga. However, 101 or 53·2 per cent are Pfumbi or Venda, a tribal group closely related to the Karanga. The Shangaan, a tribe related to the Ndebele, represent 70 or 36·9 per cent, and 6 or 3·1 per cent are Ndebele. A further 6 or 3·1 per cent come from South Africa. The non-Karanga element in Zuva is, therefore, very large. This complicates a comparison of farming success or failure by introducing a new element, that of cultural and tribal differences. Moreover, Pfumbi and Venda plotholders do not easily mix with the Shangaan and this gives rise to many tensions in the community. To avoid unnecessary contact, most Pfumbi and Venda live as a group south of the road coming from Beit Bridge, and most Shangaan live north of this road and to the east of the scheme.

Tensions between the Pfumbi and Venda on the one hand, and the Shangaan on the other, are caused both by cultural differences and by their tribal history. Like the Karanga, the Pfumbi and Venda are used to a mixed economy of agriculture and animal husbandry; the Shangaan, however, have been pastoralists, food gatherers, fishermen and hunters until the 1950s when their area was opened up by a new road. Hence, when the scheme was opened, they were much more reluctant to settle on it than were the Pfumbi and Venda, and when they finally did so they were much less willing to cooperate with the scheme personnel than were the other plotholders. When the cooperative society was formed, the Shangaan boycotted it from the beginning, and when the society was finally closed, the officer of the cooperative movement attributed its failure to a clash between the Shangaan and Pfumbi. Outwardly too, the people are distinguished from one another. Whereas the Pfumbi and Venda have accepted European clothing, Shangaan women still walk about in blankets, their traditional tribal dress. Moreover, the Shangaan speak a completely different language from the Pfumbi and Venda, and to interact successfully, people have to be bilingual.

The people's keen awareness of their tribal history makes them reluctant to assimilate each other's cultures. Until the early 19th century the Venda lived south of the Limpopo river and the Pfumbi to the north. Through pressure from later invaders, the Shangaan, the Venda split into two groups, one moved further south, the other north and intermarried with the Pfumbi so that in the area around the present Zuva scheme it is difficult to distinguish between the Pfumbi and Venda.

The Pfumbi share the dialect and customs of the Karanga, especially their belief in a high God whose cult centre is in the Matopo hills near Bulawayo. The Pfumbi used to send an annual delegation to the cult centre to implore their God for rain, and their delegates also pleaded for the Venda. The Venda could not send their own delegations, since they practise circumcision, and the cult rules lay down that no mutilated person may enter the presence of the high God. Since the irrigation scheme started, no more delegations were sent to the Matopos for rain and the religious dependence of the Venda on the Pfumbi ceased.[1]

The Shangaan came into the area in the 19th century, broke the power of the Venda and Pfumbi at the Limpopo, and displaced many of them to the north. The Zuva irrigation scheme, therefore, lies in traditional Pfumbi territory, but the nearest chief is a Shangaan. In spite of a strong Shangaan population, government declared that the scheme falls within the sphere of influence of the Pfumbi chief who lives several miles to the north and has never succeeded in exercising control over the plotholders. Relations between the Shangaan and Pfumbi were further strained when the Pfumbi readily took to irrigation farming, and so settled on land occupied for many years by the Shangaan. The Shangaan agreed only reluctantly to settle on the scheme in order not to be expelled from their homes. Hence all who formerly lived on the land that was now irrigated stayed, even single women, so that a fifth of all plotholders at Zuva are widows and divorcees.

In contrast to the Zuva plotholders, then, those at Mvura are not divided by tribal custom and affiliation. Moreover, Mvura lies in an area which only in recent years has been freed from tsetse fly. Hence most peasant cultivators in that region are new-comers. Since the area has little water, government had to sink boreholes in order to make settlement possible. The first chief who settled in that region, chief Shumba, arrived with his people just before 1950. A second chief, Chapungu, arrived with his followers in 1952. The followers of each chief built their villages around the government-sunk boreholes so that no territorially defined chiefdoms were formed. Instead of laying claim to a particular territory, each chief has to rely on the personal allegiance

---

[1] The officials at the cult centre of the High God in the Matopo hills are hostile to the cooperation of the people with government officials, and are especially opposed to the building of dams and irrigation schemes. See, for example, Weinrich, 1971, pp. 85–7.

9

of his followers, wherever they live.[1] The chiefs' relationship
with plotholders, therefore, also depends on personal allegiance.
Such a relationship between chiefs and people is unusual in
Rhodesia.

Government declared both chiefs of equal status, but the people,
including chief Chapungu himself, regard chief Shumba as the
senior chief because he arrived first. Chief Shumba strongly
opposes irrigation farming and calls the scheme 'family destroying'
because it forces men to leave their extended families in the tribal
trust land and to move to the scheme with only their wives and
children. He regards plotholders as 'government servants' who
work for nothing but seed and fertilizer. Four of his people
initially settled on the scheme against his advice, but all left after a
crop failure and still work on the roads to pay off their debts.
Chief Shumba claims no authority over the Mvura scheme and
disowns all the people who settle there.

Chief Chapungu is himself a progressive peasant cultivator and
master farmer and has begun growing cotton on dry land. He
approves of irrigation farming and encourages his people to settle
on the scheme. The district commissioner, therefore, refers
quarrels between plotholders to him, and when once a man was
evicted who still owed government a debt of £40, he asked chief
Chapungu to collect the money. This embarrassed chief Chapungu
who is keenly aware of his junior status and knows that chief
Shumba regards him as an intruder. This refusal of chief Shumba
and the hesitancy of chief Chapungu to claim authority over the
Mvura irrigation scheme leave plotholders effectively free from
all supervision by chiefs, and when asked what authority the chiefs
had over them, they answered 'none'.

(4) THE SOCIAL CHARACTERISTICS OF PLOTHOLDERS

The plotholders in the two irrigation schemes of Mvura and
Zuva differ markedly in their social characteristics. As Table 29
shows, the people at Mvura are much younger than the people at
Zuva. Whereas in Mvura most people are in their twenties and
thirties, Zuva has about the same proportion of people in the
higher age groups as have tribal trust lands. Since irrigation

[1] The only other society in South and Central Africa known to me in which no
territorial boundaries determine the people's affiliation to chiefs are the Lozi
at the upper Zambezi in Zambia. See Gluckman, 1951, pp. 1–93.

schemes are labour intensive and since the younger plotholders at
Mvura are more energetic than the older people at Zuva, Mvura

TABLE 29

De facto Adult Population of Two Irrigation Schemes (N=272)[1]

| | Mvura | | | | Zuva | | | |
| | Men | | Women | | Men | | Women | |
Age	Freq.	%	Freq.	%	Freq.	%	Freq.	%
15–19	3	7·5	8	19·0	2	2·3	7	6·7
20–24	6	15·0	13	31·0	10	11·6	21	20·2
25–29	5	12·5	7	16·7	9	10·5	18	17·3
30–34	5	12·5	5	11·9	15	17·4	16	15·4
35–39	8	20·0	3	7·1	9	10·5	7	6·7
40–44	6	15·0	2	4·8	9	10·5	9	8·6
45–49	1	2·5	3	7·1	3	3·5	6	5·8
50–54	3	7·5	—	—	9	10·5	5	4·8
55–59	3	7·5	1	2·4	7	8·1	3	2·9
60–64	—	—	—	—	3	3·5	3	2·9
65–69	—	—	—	—	—	—	1	1·0
70–74	—	—	—	—	3	3·5	3	2·9
75–79	—	—	—	—	1	1·2	—	—
80–84	—	—	—	—	4	4·6	4	3·8
85–89	—	—	—	—	2	2·3	1	1·0
Total	40	100·0	42	100·0	86	100·0	104	100·0

plotholders are likely to make a better use of their irrigated land
than those in Zuva.[2]

The labour force of Zuva plotholders is not only older but also
smaller than that of Mvura. Whereas the average plotholder in
Mvura has 4·2 dependants living with him on the scheme, the
average in Zuva is only 3·5. This small labour force of Zuva
plotholders is due both to their frequent absences from the scheme
and to their endeavour to maintain two households simultaneously,
one on the dry land and one on the scheme. For quite a number of
Zuva plotholders break their lease agreement and leave the scheme

[1] The adults on the Mvura irrigation scheme have 113 children living with
them, and the adults in Zuva 204. On both schemes therefore, but especially in
Mvura, the child population is larger than the adult population.

[2] There is a widespread association between youth and the adaptation of
modern farming techniques. See, for example, Weingrod's study of an Israeli
moshav. Weingrod, 1966, p. 73.

for longer periods of wage employment. In 1970 four men were absent as labour migrants. One of these was working in a South African mine, another was employed as a messenger by the local district commissioner. Whatever may be the legal position of the other absentees, this man at least must have obtained permission to leave the scheme. In addition to these men, 27 wives and their children are permanently absent from the scheme. Most of these are Pfumbi and Venda whose homes lie further to the north. Polygamous plotholders—30 out of 88, or 34·1 per cent of all Zuva plotholders are polygamists—like to leave some of their wives in their home villages to herd their cattle and to keep a place to which they can retire should the irrigation settlement prove a failure. Those plotholders, whose families are separated, regard the scheme in a similar light as European employment, namely as a place where a man earns money. In Mvura only 3 out of 29 plotholders, or 10·4 per cent, are polygamists and all of these have their wives staying with them on the scheme.

To compensate for the absence of wives and children, Zuva plotholders have invited various relatives and strangers to stay with them. Of all adults in Zuva 17·4 per cent are brothers and sisters, grandparents and grandchildren, or parents of plotholders. Hired labourers represent 4·2 per cent. In Mvura only 9·7 per cent of all plotholders are brothers and sisters or other kinsmen. No hired labourers reside permanently on that scheme.

Since the Shangaan, Venda and Pfumbi live in a remote district of Rhodesia, they have had less contact with Christian missionaries than the people in Mvura. Consequently their education is very low. Whereas all but four out of 82 adults in Mvura, or 95·1 per cent, are Catholics or Protestants, in Zuva only 57 out of 190 adults, or 30·0 per cent, are Christians belonging to mission churches. Twenty-six or 13·7 per cent belong to African independent churches and 109 or 57·4 per cent are religious traditionalists. Thus in Zuva only 7 men out of 86, or 8·1 per cent, attended school for six years or more, but in Mvura 24 men out of 40, or 60·0 per cent. Zuva plotholders belong to the least educated section of Rhodesian peasants, and those in Mvura to the best educated, for even in tribal trust lands only about 38 per cent of all men have attended school for six years or more.

In Mvura all but two families send their children to school; some children attend boarding schools for secondary education and four young men study at home through correspondence courses. The average Mvura plotholder pays £10 a year for his children's education.

The parents in Zuva, on the other hand, who themselves have little education, are not keen on sending their children to school. In 1959 missionaries of the Church of Sweden opened a school in their area which employed one teacher for three classes. At first attendance was moderate, but when the irrigation scheme was started, enrolment dropped to seven pupils because the parents then needed their children both on the scheme to help on the land and in their home villages to herd their cattle. In 1969 a new teacher came to Zuva. He tried to persuade the parents to send their children to school and by 1970 the enrolment had increased to 40. Yet the Shangaan resented his pressure and through their leader complained about the new teacher to the district commissioner. Before the year ended, the teacher was transferred.

The educational background of the plotholders not only influences their attitude towards their children's education, it also determines their earlier labour migration. Of the 29 plotholders in Mvura, 28 had been labour migrants before they came to the scheme, and although all are still relatively young, they have on the average had eight years of European employment. Only 25·3 per cent of their labour trips lasted less than one year, 32 per cent lasted one to three years and 42·7 per cent lasted four years or longer. This very high percentage of long-term employment— only 37 per cent of the labour trips of peasant cultivators in tribal trust lands lasted this length of time—is a reflection of the men's education and skill in holding down good jobs for many years. Most of their labour trips took the men to the cities and towns of Rhodesia.

The male plotholders in Zuva have equally long, or even longer, migration histories, yet they mostly sought work in South Africa. Of all trips of Zuva plotholders 21·3 per cent lasted less than one year, 40·4 per cent lasted one to three years, and 38·3 per cent four years or more. The labour experience of men going to South Africa differed from that of those Africans who found employment in Rhodesian towns. Not only are Africans in South Africa more rigidly segregated from Europeans than they are in Rhodesia, but Africans there frequently divide themselves into two groups, those of the 'school people' and of the traditionalists.[1] The 'school

---

[1] For excellent studies of this division among migrant workers in South Africa see P. Mayer, 1961 and Wilson and Mafeje, 1963.

people' resemble urban Africans in Rhodesia, traditionalists cling to their tribal customs and encapsulate themselves so that their contact with European culture has little effect on them. The present plotholders at Zuva, especially the Shangaan, associated with the traditionalists during their stay in South Africa so that their urban employment affected them but little.

These different experiences of labour migrants partly account for the greater interest of Mvura plotholders in modern association and their eagerness to participate in local administration, and the desire of Zuva plotholders to preserve their tribal values.

(5) RELATIONS OF PLOTHOLDERS WITH THE WIDER COMMUNITY

Plotholders on the two irrigation schemes interact with their tribal neighbours in the political, social and economic spheres. Yet the people in the two schemes place different values on these three spheres. Zuva plotholders are primarily concerned with political relations because where two distinct tribal groups compete for leadership, enmeshment with the tribal system is intense. As stated above, administratively the Zuva scheme is under the Pfumbi chief. His son is a plotholder on the scheme and for some years tried court cases for his father. Yet the local Shangaan do not accept his leadership and one Shangaan, also a plotholder, whose father had ruled the area for the Shangaan chief before the scheme was established, claims the leadership; his claim is accepted by the local Shangaan, but not by the administration. Tribal politics, therefore, divide the plotholders and link each group back to its own chief.

Mvura plotholders hardly recognize any ties to local chiefs. Their indifference to chiefs is partly due to their own emancipation from the tribal system, accounted for by their higher education and urban employment, and partly to the fact that their scheme is situated in a resettlement area whose chiefs disclaim authority over plotholders.

Yet if Mvura plotholders recognize few political ties with the tribal trust land, they carefully cultivate social and economic ties with their neighbours. Unlike Zuva, Mvura does not have its own store and school. A small township with a couple of stores lies just outside the scheme, and two more townships lie within walking distance. All the stores serve villagers and plotholders alike.

Since Mvura plotholders are used to a high standard of living—their breakfast generally includes bread, jam and tea with milk and sugar, and paraffin lamps are used for longer hours in their homes than in the homes of peasant cultivators—plotholders frequently visit the stores and there meet their tribal neighbours.

Plotholders also send their children to the same school as do peasant cultivators. This school is about three miles from the scheme. Religious services, which may take place either at a nearby mission or in the open, further unite the people. If religious meetings are held near the irrigation scheme, plotholders often accompany fellow worshippers back to their homes. No such links exist in Zuva which has its own school and grocery store.

Mvura plotholders sell much maize and vegetables to people in the tribal trust land, but they also barter their maize with farm owners in the nearby purchase areas for groundnuts, sorghum and millet, which may not be grown on the irrigated land, or for milk, meat and eggs which they also cannot produce for themselves since no livestock may be kept on the scheme.

Like peasant farmers who rely on their tribal neighbours for agricultural labour, so plotholders look to villagers in the tribal trust land for help during the sowing, weeding and harvesting periods. Many of their relatives then come to help them, and this assistance strengthens the kinship ties between the people on the scheme and in the tribal area. Unrelated villagers also offer their labour and are repaid in either crops, vegetables or cash.

Villagers often visit their relatives on the scheme, but plotholders visit their home villages only rarely because they claim to be too busy on their fields all the year round. Moreover, plotholders should obtain permission from the scheme manager if they want to leave the scheme for any length of time, and though this regulation is often ignored, people cannot absent themselves frequently without running the risk of eviction. Kinship ties, therefore, are preserved, and their preservation assures plotholders of a home should they be evicted or leave the scheme of their own accord.

Kinship ties between plotholders in Zuva and their relatives are still closer than in Mvura, because either the plotholders' relatives live close to the scheme, or plotholders left some of their wives and children behind to form an effective link between them and their kinship group. The economic dependence of villagers around Zuva on the plotholders further strengthens their ties with them, for if dry land harvests succeed in only one out of seven years, the surplus maize grown by the Zuva people is eagerly bought up.

Plotholders are not only engaged in economic exchanges with their African neighbours, but also with the wider Rhodesian society. Since half their crops, such as cotton and wheat, cannot be sold locally, they must offer them to the national market. Moreover, since plotholders cannot grow these crops without investing heavily in fertilizer, seed and insecticides, they also have to deal with European firms and agents from whom these products can be bought. Hence African plotholders on irrigation schemes are closely involved in the complex network of Rhodesian commerce.

(6) CONCLUSION

In the tribal trust lands and purchase areas, studied in the earlier parts of this book, the soil, climate, ecology and the tribal background of the people was kept constant so that a quasi laboratory situation was created in which those factors could be studied which give rise to high or low agricultural productivity among peasants. These earlier sections of the book showed that a close similarity in the natural environment does not result in an equal agricultural output among peasants.

In this study of two irrigation schemes, the natural environment and the tribal background of the people could not be kept constant. Yet ecological factors may be held less important on an irrigation scheme than in dry land farming because of the greater scientific control of irrigated land, though the different systems of overhead and flood irrigation in Mvura and Zuva might well affect output. Had not the earlier analysis proved that identical factors do not necessarily lead to an identical agricultural output, but that high and low productivity are rather determined by a variety of personal characteristics of African peasants, a comparative study of these two irrigation schemes would contribute little to the analysis. Backed by the previous findings, however, it seems reasonable to assume that social factors may again be primarily responsible for agricultural success or failure. Thus the younger, better educated population of the Mvura scheme, whose plotholders spent many years in apparently well-paid European employment, is likely to be much more successful in their farming activities than the older, less well-educated population of the Zuva scheme.

The larger farming profits of master farmers in tribal trust lands and the greater incomes of purchase area farmers also suggest that a break with the tribal systems makes for greater agricultural success. Mvura plotholders, therefore, should for this reason too be much more successful than those in Zuva, for not only does the Mvura scheme lie in a resettlement area where chiefs are reluctant to exercise control over the plotholders, but many of the plotholders themselves try to save their money to buy their own farms and so to move completely away from the control of chiefs. The proximity of two purchase areas, which are the homes of a large proportion of the people on the scheme, constantly reminds the plotholders of this goal.

Zuva plotholders are not only handicapped by tribal bonds, but they also inherited the traditional conflicts between their tribes which even in as modern a settlement as an irrigation scheme prevent cooperation and thus have an adverse effect on crop production. Moreover, the pastoral background of a large section of the Zuva population, the Shangaan, who have very little experience in agriculture, may be further expected to lower the potential output of this irrigation scheme.

The proposition, therefore, is that Mvura plotholders will be much more successful in irrigation farming than those in Zuva, not because the facilities on their scheme and its environment are better but because of the personal characteristics of its plotholders.

CHAPTER 14

ECONOMIC RESOURCES
OF PLOTHOLDERS ON
IRRIGATION SCHEMES

(1) INTRODUCTION

If land shortage is to be overcome by such intensive cultivation as irrigation farming, much capital and many new skills, none of which most African peasants possess, are required. The previous chapters showed that the Rhodesian government made both skills and money available to Africans to start irrigation farming on an economic basis. Peasants were only invited after irrigation schemes were ready for occupation so that new settlers had no such expenses as peasant farmers had who had to open up their farms with their own capital. Weingrod, who studied settlement schemes of Oriental Jews in Israel, wrote that far-reaching changes in the economic and social lives of peasants can only be brought about if the new settlers are guaranteed an initial economic security.[1] Plotholders on Rhodesian irrigation schemes are given this initial security.

All plotholders on an irrigation scheme start off with identical opportunities. Table 30 sets out the gross agricultural income of plotholders in Mvura and Zuva during the 1968–69 season.

Both the productivity census, and the labour input survey for the two irrigation schemes, include every Mvura plotholder who has been in the scheme since 1968. Twelve of the present 29 plotholders arrived less than twelve months before the research took place so that they had not yet reaped a full year's harvest in Mvura and could not be included. In Zuva every third plotholder was included.

Table 31 shows that the spread of incomes is narrow on the Zuva scheme, but that in the more prosperous Mvura area differences in income are greater. These differences will be accounted for in a later chapter which presents case histories of Mvura plotholders.

[1] See Weingrod, 1966, especially page 201.

TABLE 30

Gross Income of Plotholders on Two Irrigation Schemes 1968–69
(N=46)

Gross Agricultural Income	Mvura		Zuva	
	Freq.	Per cent	Freq.	Per cent
Below £50	—	—	7	24·1
£50– £99	—	—	17	58·6
£100–£149	—	—	5	17·3
£150–£199	—	—	—	—
£200–£249	7	41·2	—	—
£250–£299	4	23·5	—	—
£300–£349	5	29·4	—	—
£350–£399	1	5·9	—	—
Total	17	100·0	29	100·0

More important than the differences in income between plot-holders on each of the two schemes are differences in income between the schemes, for not even the best plotholder in Zuva reaps as much as the worst plotholder in Mvura. This chapter analyses how far adequate equipment, cattle, acreage and labour account for the differential output on the two schemes.

(2) ECONOMIC RESOURCES

The importance of personally-owned equipment to cultivate the land varies between the two schemes. In Mvura the land is ploughed by tractor so that plotholders have no need of ploughs and oxen. In Zuva, however, each plotholder has to plough his own land. Of the 88 Zuva plotholders only 22 or 25·0 per cent own a plough. These ploughs are barely adequate to plough all the land on the scheme. Only twelve or 13·6 per cent of all plotholders own a cart to transport their crops. In addition to their farming equipment, 32 or 36·3 per cent of all Zuva plotholders own a bicycle and 7 or 8·0 per cent own a radio. These are the only property items which Zuva plotholders have taken over from European culture.

In Mvura, where plotholders need no agricultural equipment at all, seven out of 29 nevertheless own a plough, three a cultivator and one a harrow. However, they keep these implements in their home villages or on their fathers' farms in the purchase areas, where also three plotholders have built their own brick houses. On the scheme itself plotholders keep some tools and means of transport: 23 men own a bicycle, two a car, three a wheelbarrow, three a sewing machine, one a maize sheller and one a typewriter. Three plotholders also have a radio in their huts. Most own a cotton sprayer, the only necessary farm implement not provided for them. Mvura plotholders are, therefore, not only fully equipped for their work whereas Zuva plotholders are short of implements, but those in Mvura own also better means of transport and other possessions which indicate that they are more fully integrated into Rhodesia's cash economy than are Zuva plotholders.

No plotholder may keep cattle on an irrigation scheme. Since Mvura plotholders have their land ploughed by tractor, they have no need of cattle. Yet like all Karanga they are reluctant to sell their livestock. In 1970, the 29 Mvura plotholders owned 136 head of cattle, or four to five beasts per family, as well as a few sheep and goats. These they kept with their relatives in their home villages or on their fathers' farms.

Zuva plotholders, however, need oxen to plough their fields. Since they live either close to their kinsmen around the scheme, or have left some of their wives and children in their dry land villages, cattle rearing presents no great problems for them. Because of their pastoral background, most Shangaan possess large herds of cattle so that they have enough oxen to pull their ploughs. The Venda and Pfumbi are in a more difficult position at ploughing time because their herds are farther away from the scheme. Some of them plough their fields with donkeys or hire a team of oxen.[1]

Owing to recent government moves to limit livestock in the area to prevent the erosion of pastures, it was difficult to obtain exact information on cattle ownership. One man, for example, said to my field assistant that he possessed 80 head of cattle. At about the same time the extension assistant carried out a survey for the Ministry of Internal Affairs and this plotholder declared that he possessed only 35 head of cattle. When after some weeks he came to trust my field assistant he confided to him that he owned 150 head, but that he did not want government to know this. The following figures of livestock owned by Zuva plotholders must therefore be taken with many reservations. Sixteen out of 88 plotholders were willing to have the number of their cattle, sheep

[1] Thirty-one out of 88 plotholders own three to four donkeys each.

and goats recorded. According to their statements, they owned together a total of 330 head of cattle, 256 goats and 18 sheep. This means that the average plotholder had some 21 head of cattle and 17 goats or sheep.

In spite of the district commissioner's pressure on Mvura plotholders to choose between dry land and irrigation farming, many not only rely on tribal trust lands to graze their cattle, but still retain rights to cultivate dry land. For example, six out of 29 plotholders in Mvura lay claim to 6 to 10 acres each of dry land, and most of those in Zuva continue cultivating land outside the scheme. Since no information about income from dry land farming could be obtained, and since this income in the very hot areas which have a low rainfall and high evaporation rate is likely to be low, it is ignored in the following analysis.

More important than any of these economic resources are the land and water available to plotholders on the irrigation schemes. On each scheme land holdings are of a standard size. All Zuva plots cover 2 acres; 23 plots in Mvura cover 3·5 acres, and the remainder 3·75 acres. In addition every Mvura plotholder has his own vegetable garden and orchard so that they have almost twice as much irrigated land as Zuva plotholders.

No disputes over land ever occur because all irrigated land is allocated by the district commissioner. Access to water, however, gives rise to many disputes. In Mvura, for example, some plotholders accuse their neighbours of occasionally turning off their irrigation pipes. In Zuva disputes arise over the order in which fields should be watered. Those who plant early receive water whenever they need it, but once all fields are planted the irrigation circulates from field to field. This cycle is difficult to interrupt and any plotholder who misses his turn must ask permission to irrigate his field at night or on a Sunday. Some fields, moreover, where soil evaporates faster than in others, need additional irrigation. It is the duty of the employees of the Ministry of Water Development under the direction of the extension assistant to ensure that water is fairly distributed and that all the fields are adequately irrigated.

(3) LABOUR INPUT AND THE AGRICULTURAL CYCLE

Although the average family of plotholders on the Mvura and Zuva irrigation schemes has about three members who can contribute to work in the fields, as can be seen from Table 31, labour input differs greatly in these communities.

TABLE 31

Average Household Composition of Plotholders
on Two Irrigation Schemes (N=117)

Household Composition	Mvura	Zuva
Men	1·0	1·1
Women	1·1	1·3
Children aged 7–14	1·1	1·1
Children aged 0–6	2·0	1·1
Total	5·2	4·6

The different labour input is partly dictated by the different requirements of overhead and flood irrigation, by the larger acreage at the disposal of Mvura plotholders and by their additional cotton crop; but it is also due to the different attitude of the people towards agricultural labour.

In Zuva the agricultural cycle begins in October when the people plough their land for the maize crop. Shortage of ploughs causes some difficulties and delays, and though the Shangaan have enough oxen, many Pfumbi and Venda have not. Their donkeys are less efficient than oxen, and hired oxen increase production costs.

The average Zuva family spends some 42 hours in October and November ploughing its land. Of these, 17 hours or 40·4 per cent are provided by hired labourers, often the owners of the hired team of oxen.

Planting, which takes place during November and December, requires 51 hours per family. Several Zuva families call in small work parties of about six people to help them plant their maize so that this task can be completed in less than a day. Members of work parties contribute 19 hours or 37·2 per cent of the planting time.

From December onwards the maize has to be weeded and the crop has to be watered about six times. Weeding takes up 162 hours of which 13 or 8·2 per cent are contributed by hired labourers or work parties. As in tribal trust lands weeding is mainly left to women; watering the land, however, is the men's task. Each time the sluices of a canal are opened to water a field, its plotholder ought to be present for the four hours to see that the water runs evenly over his land. If the ground is uneven he has to level it by hoe. Some plotholders find this task very burdensome and neglect it, with the result that some of their crops receive no water at all.

The maize harvest begins towards the end of February and lasts until May. All harvesting is done by family members. It takes 219 hours. All in all, therefore, Zuva plotholders invest 498 hours in their maize crop.

The wheat crop requires more labour. As soon as the maize is harvested in May, the land is ploughed for wheat. Again about 42 hours are needed for this task. Of the ploughing time 12 hours or 28·6 per cent is contributed by hired labourers. Zuva plotholders spend on the average only 9 hours on sowing their wheat; none of them plants it in lines. Weeding the wheat, too, takes little time, and families finish this task in about 15 hours. Watering the wheat takes up to 24 hours. The wheat harvest begins in August, and it is this task which requires much hard and careful work. The average Zuva family spends 600 hours on reaping its wheat, of which 33 or 5·6 per cent is contributed by hired labourers. All wheat must be reaped by October to get the fields ready for the new maize crop. Because harvesting demands so much labour, many families try to plant only a portion of their two acres. This was forbidden in 1970 when the district commissioner ordered that all plotholders grow their full two acres of wheat. Some plotholders reacted to this order by not harvesting their full crop. Labour input on wheat amounts to 690 hours per family.

The average Zuva plotholder therefore, invests only 1,188 hours in crop production. Of these hours his family members contribute 77·0 per cent and hired labourers 20·2 per cent, which is a much higher percentage than in purchase areas. Members of work parties contribute as little as 2·8 per cent.

In spite of the high labour input by hired labourers, most of whom are men, women still contribute 59·7 per cent of all working hours. This shows that the plotholders themselves work very little in their fields. As traditional pastoralists the Shangaan abhor work in the fields and are happiest when they can supervise the labour of others. They would rather pay wages than cultivate their own fields. Hired labour in Zuva is therefore not an indication of progressive farming but of the plotholders' aversion to agriculture. The total labour input per family is so low that most plotholders work only a few hours a day[1].

---

[1] The very hot climate is partly responsible for this.

Since Zuva plotholders invest little labour in their wheat crop until the harvest starts, the months from May to August are those of greatest leisure. They are the months for visiting friends and relatives, for social gatherings and beer drinks. During these months, too, people re-thatch their huts and repair their equipment.

The agricultural cycle in Mvura is more complex because three different crops are grown. Work on the maize and wheat crops, which in 1968–69 were planted on 1·6 acres of each standard holding, takes place in the same months as in Zuva. Yet because all ploughing is done by tractor and all wheat is reaped by combine harvester, labour requirements on these tasks are less than in Zuva. In spite of this, Mvura plotholders work harder. The average Zuva plotholder spends only 51 hours on planting two acres of maize and 9 on sowing two acres of wheat, but the average plotholder in Mvura spends 73 hours on planting his maize and 130 hours on wheat. Of these, 22 hours or 10·8 per cent are contributed by hired labourers. Planting is therefore a busy time in Mvura and most families start work in their fields at 5 or 5.30 a.m. and continue until 6 or 6.30 p.m., with only short breaks for meals. Ambitious plotholders, who take on a second holding, may work until it is quite dark.

Weeding the maize takes 241 hours of which 22 or 9·1 per cent is provided by hired labourers. Wheat needs only 39 weeding hours, all of which is provided by family members. The maize harvest takes 142 hours, 14 or 9·9 per cent of which is contributed by hired labourers. The wheat is reaped by combine harvester in 10 working hours, 3 or 30·0 per cent of which are provided by the hired driver of the harvester. But the plotholders must be present to carry the wheat to the store room or shed.

The overhead irrigation system in Mvura demands more labour than the flood irrigation system in Zuva. Moreover, overhead irrigation must be carried out according to the clock and therefore ties plotholders to the scheme. At 7.30 a.m. the engine starts pumping the water to the fields. By this time a plotholder must have removed the pipes from his neighbour's field to his own, a work which takes him and his wife about an hour and a half. After two hours or more, depending on the dryness of the land, the irrigation bell is sounded and the plotholder has to change the sprinklers on the pipes to different positions to give his whole crop an even supply of water. This takes a plotholder half an

TABLE 32

Labour Input on Two Irrigation Schemes (N=46)

Agricultural Activity	Maize		Wheat		Cotton		All Crops			
							Mvura		Zuwa	
	Mvura	Zuwa	Mvura	Zuwa	Mvura	Zuwa	Hours	Per cent	Hours	Per cent
Ploughing	4	41	4	42	4	—	12	0·5	84	7·1
Sowing/Planting	73	51	130	9	87	—	290	12·2	60	5·0
Weeding	241	162	39	15	390	—	670	28·3	177	14·9
Harvesting	142	219	10	600	1,027	—	1,179	49·8	819	69·0
Pest Control	—	—	—	—	84	—	84	3·6	—	—
Irrigation	48	24	30	24	54	—	132	5·6	48	4·0
Total	508	498	213	690	1,646	—	2,367	100·0	1,188	100·0

hour. The maize crop has to be irrigated about 16 times and the wheat crop 10 times so that the average plotholder spends about 48 hours on irrigating his maize and 30 on his wheat crop. All in all, therefore, Mvura plotholders spend 508 hours on their maize and 213 on their wheat crops, 9·7 per cent of which is provided by hired labourers, including the driver of the tractor and combine harvester.

Cotton, which in 1968–69 was grown on 1·9 acres of each allotment, requires more labour than maize and wheat together. It is planted in November and remains in the land until August. Again, ploughing is done by tractor. Planting requires 87 hours, 8 or 9·2 per cent of which are performed by hired labourers. Weeding eeds 390 hours of which hired labourers contribute 32 or 8·2 per cent.

Since the cotton crop has to be watered about 18 times, irrigation takes up 54 hours. The cotton has to be sprayed about 14 times a year. Cotton spraying is very hard work and is always done by men. A cotton field in Mvura consists of 33 lines, each of which is about 80 yards long. The worker has to carry a four-gallon sprayer on his back filled with liquid insecticides. When the cotton is about one foot high, the spray pump has to be refilled four to five times; when the cotton is taller it has to be refilled eight to nine times. Each spraying lasts five to six continuous working hours so that pest control takes a cotton grower 84 hours a year.

The cotton harvest extends from May to August. Cotton picking is more time-consuming than any other agricultural task. The average family spends some 1,027 hours on it, of which 214 or 20·9 per cent is contributed by hired labourers. The cotton crop, therefore, requires 1,646 working hours, of which 258 or 15·7 per cent is provided by hired labourers.

Unlike Zuva plotholders who employ hired men all the year round, those in Mvura employ them only on a piecework basis. During cotton picking they pay a worker two shillings for filling one plastic bag with cotton. This takes the average worker a day, but fast workers may fill two to three bags.

Mvura plotholders never employ work parties, for like master farmers in tribal trust lands they believe that their work is often careless and so endangers their expensive investment in the irrigated land. If a family cannot cope with the work because of illness or some other misfortune, neighbours help out without expecting a reward.

Though part of their work is mechanized, Mvura families work 2,367 hours, or twice as long on their land as Zuva plotholders. Moreover, a much larger proportion of their work is done by family members. In contrast to Zuva plotholders, the men in Mvura work hard in their fields. Whereas the women in Mvura contribute 37·2 per cent of all working hours on the land, men contribute 41·8 per cent and children 21·0 per cent. Even half the weeding which is generally regarded as the women's work is done by men. This personal involvement of Mvura plotholders in the agricultural production directly affect their agricultural output.

The findings of this labour input survey are corroborated by general remarks entered by the extension assistants in Mvura and Zuva in their notebooks about each plotholder. The extension assistant of Mvura recorded in 1970 that of the 29 plotholders then on the scheme, 12 or 41·4 per cent were 'hard and successful' workers, 9 or 31·0 per cent performed 'reasonably good' work and 8 or 27·6 per cent were 'careless or inadequate' in irrigation farming. The extension assistant in Zuva on the other hand, noted down that only 9 out of 88, or 10·2 per cent, worked 'hard', that 24 or 27·3 per cent performed their work 'adequately', a further 24 or 27·3 per cent worked 'not hard' and 31 or 35·2 per cent were written down as 'lazy'. The extension assistant often entered such comments behind the name of a plotholder as 'crop wasted through laziness', 'crop not harvested', 'harvested nothing from his wheat crop', or 'used no fertilizer on his maize'. Low productivity in Zuva, then, can to a large extent be attributed to careless work in the field.

In addition to putting much labour into crop production, Mvura plotholders also spend about an hour a day throughout the year on their vegetable gardens and orchards. During 1968–69 they also spent 37 hours on stall-feeding their cattle, a practice which was discontinued in the following year. In addition, the average Mvura family spend some 90 hours on repairing their huts and other maintenance work. Zuva plotholders spend practically no time on gardening since only four families have planted vegetables. They never stall-feed their cattle but have their livestock herded by their wives and children.

(4) CONCLUSION

A most outstanding difference between Mvura and Zuva plotholders, emerging from this chapter, is their attitude towards crop production as it reveals itself through the labour which plotholders are ready to invest in their land. Other economic factors, such as the better equipment and larger acreage of Mvura plotholders, seem less important. In fact, had Zuva plotholders more land, they would most likely not use it. This can be deduced from their reluctance to plant their full two acres with wheat. An earlier chapter stated that Zuva plotholders often let the fertilizer which they were obliged to buy lie unused all over the scheme. This chapter quoted from the extension assistant's notebook that a number of plotholders did not even fully reap their wheat crop.

An explanation for this neglect of the wheat may be gathered from the same notebook. For apart from one entry that a plotholder had put no fertilizer on his maize, there are no entries about a neglect of the maize crop. Maize is the staple food of the people, but wheat is of little use to the Shangaan, Pfumbi and Venda, except as a source of money. But as yet they have developed few needs which can be satisfied with money. They still count their wealth exclusively in cattle and their herds can be increased by other means than making money from wheat. In fact, were they to invest their money proceeds from wheat in livestock, over-stocking would soon take on such proportions that government would step in and reduce their herds. Hence there is little incentive for them to work harder and increase their output. Their different attitude towards maize and wheat may, therefore, be interpreted as a reluctance to participate in the cash economy of Rhodesia for which their past life has not prepared them.

In Mvura the situation is different. Not only are plotholders through their previous life attuned to the cash economy, but many of them have the ambition to become rich and, if possible, to buy their own purchase area farm. Consequently they view their stay in Mvura as a means to make as much money as possible in a short time. They are therefore willing to work hard on their land, to make full use of all the facilities offered them, and welcome crops which find a ready market and fetch a high price. No Mvura plotholder would ever let part of his field remain unharvested, and when a former scheme manager by accident ploughed in a bean crop, unrest broke out.

The different cultural backgrounds of the people on the two irrigation schemes, their different contact with western civilization and their consequently different attitude towards the cash economy, seem to be the major factors which determine their labour input and thereby their agricultural success or failure.

CHAPTER 15

AGRICULTURAL PRODUCTIVITY OF IRRIGATION SCHEMES

(1) INTRODUCTION

Plotholders on irrigation schemes, like peasant farmers in purchase areas, are prevented by their lease agreement from seeking work outside their scheme, and the wages of the few who succeeded in getting away from Zuva are so low as to be insignificant in the total income of plotholders. Also they are not allowed to keep cattle on the irrigation schemes, yet most are able to leave their livestock in the care of their relatives. This enables them to draw on their herds for at least some occasional income.

Because of these restrictions on wage employment and cattle ownership, plotholders on irrigation schemes depend more exclusively on the land than any other section of Rhodesian peasants. Thus, whereas ordinary peasant cultivators in tribal trust lands derive only 57·1 per cent of their total income from the land, and master farmers and purchase area farmers 70 to 80 per cent, Mvura plotholders derive 92·1 per cent and those in Zuva 91·3 per cent of their total income from irrigation farming. This dependence on the land is made possible by their independence from rain, for drought years, which cause grave problems to dry land farmers, have little effect on irrigation farmers unless rivers dry out and water levels sink considerably after successive drought years. This has not yet happened in Mvura and Zuva. Hence no comparison between a drought year and one of average rainfall is necessary in this study of productivity on irrigation schemes.

(2) CROP PRODUCTION

In the Introduction to this book it was suggested that high yields per acre are related to high investment. Not only is irrigation farming much more expensive than dry land farming and should therefore be much more productive, but also, as the previous chapters showed, Mvura plotholders are more ready to invest in the land than are those in Zuva. In 1968–69 the average Zuva plotholder bought £12 worth of fertilizer and £4 worth of seed. This is much more than peasant farmers in purchase areas or peasant cultivators in tribal trust lands invest in seed or fertilizer, yet Mvura plotholders invest still more. The average plotholder on that scheme paid in 1968–69 £60.10.0 for fertilizer, £9.10.0 for seed and £16.10.0 for insecticides to spray the cotton crop. Hence all irrigation farmers should reap much higher yields per acre than dry land farmers, and plotholders on the Mvura scheme should reap many more crops per acre than those in Zuva.

The crop yields on the two irrigation schemes are set out in Table 33.

Table 33 shows that the yield of maize per acre in Mvura is 33·3 bags, in Zuva 12·1 bags; and that the yield of wheat per acre in Mvura is 16·1 bags and in Zuva 3·0 bags. The district commissioner at Beit Bridge estimated that his plotholders reaped 20 bags of maize and 10 bags of wheat per acre, but this is not borne out by this survey. Moreover, on an older African irrigation scheme in the lowveld, Nyanyadzi, plotholders reaped in 1967, according to a report of the agricultural staff, 12·6 bags of maize and 3·1 bags of wheat per acre.[1] I therefore suggest that my figures are more accurate than the district commissioner's estimates.

From Table 33 it can also be calculated that Zuva plotholders sow only 1·3 of their two acres with wheat. Since Zuva plotholders invest less seed, fertilizer and labour in their crops then Mvura plotholders, they reap only about a third of the maize and a fifth of the wheat which Mvura plotholders reap per acre. In fact, their maize yield is not much higher than that of the average master farmer in tribal trust lands. Even with low yields, however, most Zuva plotholders can easily feed their families for they retain about 16 bags of grain for home consumption.

Mvura families, whose agricultural yields are much higher, can enjoy a high living standard. They retain on the average 22 bags of grain so that they have enough to barter for groundnuts, millet and sorghum, which they cannot grow on the scheme, as well as for milk, meat and eggs.

Table 33 also shows that plotholders on irrigation schemes sell a very large proportion of their agricultural produce to the national market. Wheat, and especially cotton, are grown predominantly for sale. Only a few Africans have begun to eat wheat.

[1] Conex, Umtali, 1967, p. 7.

TABLE 33

Productivity of Plotholders on Two Irrigation Schemes (N=46)

Crops	Acres		Yield in Bags/Bales[1]		Yield in Bags/Bales per Acre		Bags/Bales Sold		% of Bags/Bales Sold		Bags consumed or stored per household	
	Mvura	Zuwa	Mvura	Zuwa	Mvura	Zuwa	Mvura	Zuwa	Mvura	Zuwa	Mvura	Zuwa
Maize	27·2	58·0	905	685	33·3	11·8	552	239	61·0	34·9	19·6	15·4
Wheat	27·2	36·9	437	111	16·1	3·0	390	81	89·3	73·0	2·8	1·0
Cotton	32·3	—	121	—	3·7	—	121	—	100·0	—	—	—

[1] Cotton is sold in 'bales'. A bale in Mvura weighs about 500 lbs.

These crops are therefore viewed as money earners. Mvura plotholders also sell 61·0 per cent of their maize and those in Zuva 34·9 per cent. These sales, however, are mainly made to local tribesmen.

Both maize and wheat fetch different prices in the two areas, partly because of the shortage of wheat around the Zuva scheme, which pushes up the price paid by local tribesmen, and partly because of the better quality of the wheat produced by Mvura plotholders whose wheat being reaped by combine harvester is generally graded higher than that produced in Zuva where it is harvested by hand. Thus in 1968 Zuva plotholders received an average price of £2.5.0 for each bag of maize, but those in Mvura received only £1.10.0; on the other hand Zuva plotholders were paid an average of only £2.10.0 for maize, whereas those in Mvura were paid £3.[1]

In 1968–69 the average Zuva plotholder reaped £53 worth of maize. He sold part of it for £18.10.0. Of his total wheat harvest worth £9.10.0, he sold the major part for £7. The total cash income in Zuva from irrigation farming amounted therefore to £25.10.0. After repaying £16 for seed and fertilizer they were left with £9.10.0 to pay their water rates and labourers. But for the average Zuva plotholder this expenditure amounted to £21 so that each family had to find £11.10.0 from other sources.

The average Mvura plotholder reaped maize worth £79 of which he sold a proportion worth £48. His wheat harvest had a value of £57 of which he sold £51 worth. He sold all his cotton valued at £105. His total cash income from irrigation farming amounted therefore to £204. From this he could easily pay his £86.10.0 on seed, fertilizer and insecticides, as well as £29 for water rates and labour, and still retain £80.10.0. in cash.[2]

Previous chapters showed that when master farmers, who in tribal trust lands reaped crops worth £12 per acre, moved to purchase areas, their yields per acre fell to £8 in Guruuswa and to £5.10.0 in Mutadza. It was stressed that even ordinary peasant cultivators in tribal trust lands reaped more per acre than Mutadza farm owners whose income per acre was £6.4.0. It seemed, there-

---

[1] These figures differ again from those obtained from the district commissioner at Beit Bridge who informed me that the average price of a bag of maize was £2.2.6 and that of wheat £3.2.6.

[2] Roder, in a study of nine irrigation schemes in the south-east of Rhodesia, calculated that the average cash profit per family from irrigation farming was about £81. Roder, 1965, p. 189.

fore, that with increasing acreage at the disposal of African peasants, the yield per acre dropped. This however, is not borne out by the study of the two irrigation schemes. Zuva plotholders, who have only two acres on which to grow their crops, reap grain worth £31 per acre, and those in Mvura who have three and a half acres of irrigated land, get a return of £69 per acre. Economic factors can therefore not be fully interpreted without taking into account social factors.

(3) OTHER AGRICULTURAL INCOMES

Apart from crops, plotholders on both irrigation schemes make money from growing vegetables and from their cattle. Since the Mvura scheme provides each family with a small vegetable garden and orchard, the average family gains £13.10.0 a year from the sales of fruit and vegetables. Many families have asked their scheme manager to allow them to plant part of their fields with vegetables because these would bring them a higher return than crops. They also know that they will always be able to sell their vegetables, for a mission station with hospital and secondary school is not far from their scheme. Local villagers are eager to buy vegetables and the scheme itself is only 65 miles distant from Gatooma and the main road which connects all the major cities of Rhodesia. The scheme administration, however, refused permission and insisted on the crop rotation of maize, wheat and cotton on all the fields of the irrigation scheme.

Only four Zuva plotholders have planted small vegetable gardens and none of them grows enough for sale. Some families, however, have planted a few banana, pawpaw, orange and lemon trees in their fields and sell some of their fruit. These sales however, amount to only some ten shillings per family. Unlike the Mvura scheme personnel, those in charge of Mvura never objected to the plotholders growing vegetables in their fields, and one extension assistant actually encouraged them to grow cucumbers and cabbages. Some people followed his advice, but found no markets for their vegetables. The local Shangaan are not accustomed to eating cucumbers and cabbages and refused to buy them. One man sent several bags by bus to Beit Bridge, paying 7s. 6d. transport cost per bag, but Beit Bridge had been oversupplied with vegetables from other irrigation schemes during that season and the local hotel had just ordered its supply from

Messina, a South African town across the border. Nobody, therefore, bought the vegetables grown in Zuva and they rotted away. Zuva plotholders realized that their great distance from markets makes vegetable growing unprofitable for them, just as those in Mvura realized that available markets would bring them a high return from vegetables. Discouraged by their failure to sell their vegetables, Zuva plotholders went to the other extreme. In 1968–69 vegetables were in such short supply on their scheme that 53 out of the 88 plotholders each spent £15 on buying fruit and vegetables, as well as eggs, milk and fish.

All plotholders in Mvura and Zuva could supply their own fish requirements from the local rivers, yet few do. They prefer to buy their fish from villagers.

Cattle contributed more money to the budgets of both Mvura and Zuva plotholders in 1968–69 than did fruit and vegetables. Of the 17 Mvura plotholders, 11 sold one head of cattle each for an average price of £35. If this income is averaged out among all 17 plotholders, cattle contributed about £23 to each family budget. This high contribution from cattle in that season was due to the scheme manager's experiment with stall-feeding. The people, however, were dissatisfied with the result, thinking that the prices for their cattle ought to have been higher still and so did not fatten any cattle in the following year. In 1970 a new scheme manager again tried to persuade plotholders to stall-feed some beasts, but by the time this research was completed, no plotholder had agreed.

In 1968–69 the 29 Zuva plotholders included in the productivity survey sold 13 head of cattle for which they received an average price of £14. These sales, if averaged out among all the plotholders of the sample, contributed £6 per family budget. This very low contribution from livestock, considering the large cattle herds of the Shangaan, Pfumbi and Venda, is due to their traditional attitude towards cattle. Even less than the Karanga do these tribesmen regard cattle as a commercial asset. The district commissioner's suggestion in 1970 that they stall-feed some of their cattle was rejected out of hand.

(4) THE TOTAL INCOME OF PLOTHOLDERS

Table 34 sets out the total income and expenditure of 17 plotholders in Mvura and 29 in Zuva.

TABLE 34

Income and Expenditure of the Average Plotholder
on Two Irrigation Schemes, 1968–1969 (N=46)

	Mvura £	Zuva £
Income		
Crops	241 0 0	62 10 0
Cattle	23 0 0	6 0 0
Fruit and Vegetables	13 10 0	10 0
Total	277 10 0	69 0 0
Expenditure		
Seed	9 10 0	4 0 0
Fertilizer	60 10 0	12 0 0
Insecticides	16 10 0	—
Water Rates	24 10 0	14 0 0
Labour	4 10 0	7 0 0
Total	115 10 0	37 0 0
Net Income	162 0 0	32 0 0

Table 34 shows that production costs are very high on both irrigation schemes. In Mvura they amount to 41·6 per cent of the total output and in Zuva to 53·6 per cent. On both schemes the highest outlay is on fertilizer. Since both irrigation schemes are situated in very hot areas, organic matter oxidizes quickly in the soil and large amounts of artificial fertilizer are necessary to supply the plant nutrients. In Zuva the actual input of fertilizer is lower than the figure for the money spent on it indicates because many pockets are left lying unused all over the scheme. If Zuva plotholders were to apply more fertilizer to their fields yields would increase, and they would be able to pay for their production costs as well as make a profit. In 1968–69 they had to rely on gifts or loans from relatives and friends to raise about £5 per family to pay debts to the cooperative society and water rates.[1] The budget

[1] Money from crop sales amounted to £25.10.0, income from the sale of cattle, fruit and vegetables to £6.10.0; their total expenditure to £37. Hence £5 remains unaccounted for. Gifts and loans from relatives are frequent and many plotholders in Zuva obtain some money from their kinsmen.

of the average Mvura plotholder shows that as production increases, expenditure, though higher in absolute figures than on the Zuva scheme, presents a lower proportion of the total income.

The reluctance of the Zuva plotholders to invest money in their land is due to their particular tribal values. They have not yet accepted the modern cash economy and still regard a cooperative society and its credit system as an alien and objectionable institution which they do not need because they have little use for money; most of the things they desire can be obtained without it. This explains both their relative neglect of the wheat crop as well as their overall low investment in the land. Mvura plotholders, who no longer feel bound to tribal values and who, moreover, had already fully accepted the modern cash economy before they went to the scheme, are ready to invest money in the land because they see that their investment pays them dividends. They have also fully accepted cooperative marketing and the credit system and look at irrigation farming as a commercial enterprise.

Mvura plotholders invest more in fertilizer and seed than those in Zuva, but the latter pay out more money in wages. The labour expenditure of Mvura plotholders is mainly confined to paying the drivers of the tractor and combine harvester and cotton pickers, whereas Zuva plotholders pay hired labourers for practically all agricultural tasks, even if these could easily be carried out with family labour. The pastoral background of the Shangaan, therefore, not only equips them badly for agricultural work, it also causes them to invest their limited financial resources less profitably than they could do.

All scheduled production schemes are expensive to run and their high costs frighten off African peasants. Baum, who investigated a sugar production scheme in Tanzania, found that 81 per cent of the scheme's income was absorbed by its running costs.[1] By comparison with this scheme, Rhodesian irrigation schemes have a wider profit margin for plotholders. The differences in income between the people in Zuva and Mvura indicate that the more fully peasants accept irrigation farming as a commercial enterprise, the lower will the proportion of production costs become. The profitability of an irrigation scheme, therefore, depends on the plotholders' readiness to accept the principles of the modern cash economy.

[1] Baum, 1968, p. 47.

(5) CONCLUSION

If the *per capita* incomes in the various peasant communities studied in this book are compared, plotholders in Mvura emerge as the richest, those in Zuva as the poorest of all peasants, for the *per capita* income of Mvura plotholders is £31, that of Guruuswa peasant farmers £23, that of master farmers in tribal trust lands £15, that of master farmers in Mutadza purchase area £12.10.0 and that of other peasant farmers in Mutadza £11; *per capita* income of ordinary peasant cultivators in tribal trust lands is also £11, and that of Zuva plotholders £7.

This great difference in productivity of plotholders on irrigation schemes seems to be due to their backgrounds and to the intention with which they settled on the schemes. Mvura plotholders who do not want to stay on the irrigation scheme, see it merely as a place where they can become rich in a short time, after which they might buy their own purchase area farms and so become free and independent peasant farmers. Hence their high yields per acre spur them on to leave the settlement in which they are not allowed to administer their own community and to make their own economic decisions. They know how to make money and they resent being guided in all their activities. Their cooperation with the scheme personnel is based on their realization that what is ordered is mostly to their economic advantage. Zuva plotholders on the other hand, who are less concerned with making money than with growing food, are happy to stay on the scheme as long as they grow enough maize for their families. Since they have no intention of increasing crop yields in order to make money, any force exerted on them to produce more will have no lasting effect. Zuva plotholders will only produce more if their aspirations change and if they greatly desire things which can be bought only with money.

CHAPTER 16

PROFILES OF PLOTHOLDERS
ON IRRIGATION SCHEMES

(1) INTRODUCTION

The case histories recorded in this chapter present a stratified sample of all plotholders on the two irrigation schemes in the labour input survey. All plotholders were numbered, and against each number the family's net income was entered. Then a sample of one to three persons was drawn from each income group on both schemes without taking into account tribal affiliation or any other social characteristics.[1] It so happened that of the six Mvura plotholders three of the better ones came from purchase areas, and that of the eight from Zuva the three best are all Pfumbi. The Shangaan all fall into the lower income groups. Two of the eight Zuva plotholders selected are women. One is a Shangaan, one is of mixed Venda-Ndebele ancestry. This chapter sets out to confirm the previous findings that social characteristics are very important in determining the agricultural success or failure of African peasants.

(2) PROFILES OF MVURA PLOTHOLDERS

(a) *Jacques, the Most Successful Mvura Plotholder*

Jacques was born in 1931 in a Karanga tribal trust land. His father was a semi-literate Christian and keen on his son's education. Since the local school provided only five years of elementary education, his father sent Jacques for three years to a boarding school run by missionaries. Jacques completed his full primary education in 1949, and in 1950 was employed by the missionaries as an assistant teacher. As such he earned £3.10.0 a month.

Jacques was a restless young man. After a year he threw up his job for a clerical post in Bulawayo where he earned £4 a month. Soon he left this job too and was employed as a clerk at the Gatooma Cotton Ginnery for £2.10.0 a month. In 1952 he

---

[1] For details on the selection of these case histories see Appendix, Table 54.

joined the British South Africa Police and underwent fifteen months' training. This training steadied Jacques and he remained in the police force until 1965.

First he was posted to a small provincial town, from there to a tribal trust land, and in 1958 he became a detective in Fort Victoria. In 1961 he was promoted to the rank of detective sergeant and transferred to Bulawayo. From there he retired. Jacques' first salary as a police constable amounted to only £2.10.0 a month, but at his retirement in 1965 it had risen to £29.

Jacques' long service with the police entitled him to gratuities. With these he bought a grinding mill for £406 and set it up on crown land in a purchase area adjoining the present irrigation scheme of Mvura. His father owns a farm in that purchase area and after his retirement Jacques lived with his father on the income of his grinding mill. In 1970 he also opened a grocery store.

Jacques' businesses prospered. First with the profits from his mill and store, and later also with his income from irrigation farming, Jacques bought a maize sheller for £43, a sewing machine for £44, a radio for £68, a secondhand car for £65, two bicycles, a typewriter and a plough. He also built himself a brick house and bought a complete set of sitting-room and bedroom furniture. He left this property, except for the two bicycles and the maize sheller, on his father's farm, as well as ten head of cattle and fifteen sheep. Jacques also opened a bank account. He hopes one day to inherit his father's farm.

When the Mvura scheme was started, Jacques registered as one of the first plotholders and soon became one of the most successful men on the scheme. In 1968–69 he had a gross income from irrigation farming of £356. He was one of the few who took on a second irrigation plot in 1970 after some settlers had left. His wife is equally keen on farming and possesses a master farmer's certificate. Jacques himself is still training as a master farmer.

Jacques is trusted by his neighbours and when the chairman of the now extinct coordination committee was arrested, Jacques became the unofficial leader of the scheme.

Yet Jacques is not satisfied with irrigation farming. Like most of his neighbours he resents receiving constant work orders from scheme managers whom he suspects of knowing little about irrigation farming. He also objects to the prohibition of keeping livestock on the scheme. In fact, he hopes to get off the scheme as soon as he can and to settle permanently in the purchase area.

This is why he built himself only a simple pole and mud hut on the scheme and why he transferred all his property to his father's farm. He regards his stay in Mvura as a transitional stage in his life, a step towards a secure future in a purchase area.

(b) James, the 'Irrigation Master Farmer'

Born in 1936, James went to school for several years but he failed his school examinations twice and finally left after passing the fifth class. He helped his parents till the land, and in 1956 looked for work in town but found none. He therefore hired himself out as a farm labourer and worked for fifteen months on a European-owned farm. He then worked for two years in a mine. After this spell of wage labour he returned home for half a year and in 1959 once again looked for work. He tried unsuccessfully to find work in three towns before he got a job as a packing operator in a factory. After less than three years he retired permanently to rural life.

In 1962 James accompanied his brother-in-law to a purchase area adjoining the present Mvura scheme. He helped open up the land and in 1963 began training as a master farmer. He obtained his certificate in 1965. In contravention of the law, his brother-in-law allowed him to cultivate for his own profit a small section of the farm, and with his agricultural surplus James paid bridewealth for his wife, a sister of Jacques whom he later joined on the irrigation scheme. By 1970 his wife had borne him two children.

James moved to the irrigation scheme in 1967 and soon became popular with his neighbours. They elected him as a member of the now defunct management board.

James is very interested in irrigation farming. As soon as he had settled down in Mvura he underwent further agricultural training, and in 1970 obtained the certificate of 'irrigation master farmer'. His gross agricultural income in 1968–69 amounted to £331. He bought a cotton spray and a bicycle, but otherwise he possesses no property. He owns no cattle and no furniture and lives as simply as his neighbours. James is happy on the scheme. For the first time in his life he feels economically secure and therefore has decided to stay permanently in Mvura.

(c) John, The Former Teacher

John was born in 1926 in southern Karangaland. He completed

10

his full primary education of eight years and found employment
as a teacher in a village school run by Methodist missionaries.
After ten years teaching, he returned to his tribal trust land in
1959 and took up farming. Since he hoped one day to buy a
purchase area farm, he trained as a master farmer. For this end he
had saved his salary for years and bought 26 head of cattle, nine
sheep, twelve goats and six donkeys, as well as two ploughs, a
cultivator, a harrow, a planter, a cart and some furniture.

John first married in 1953, and after retiring from teaching he
married in 1960 a second wife, a Coloured woman. By 1970 his
wives had borne him ten children, all but the youngest of whom
attend school.

When in 1966 some people moved from his overcrowded
tribal trust land to the re-settlement area around the present
irrigation scheme, John moved with them. Soon afterwards he
came to the irrigation scheme itself, but this was due to a misunderstanding. He wanted to go to a purchase area and was
asked to fill in an application form. John thought that the application form was for a purchase area farm, but it was for an irrigation
plot in Mvura. Through this misunderstanding John became
one of the first settlers on the new scheme.

Although John is a good irrigation farmer—in 1968–69 his
gross income was £302—he manages to save little. Since he has
been on the scheme he has bought nothing but a bicycle for
himself and a sewing machine for his wives. To make more money,
he took on a second irrigation plot in 1970, for he has enough
labour. Besides his two wives, his eldest daughter who has
completed her full primary education, lives with him and also a
distant relative of one of his wives, a man from Moçambique
who has no home of his own.

John never ceases to regret his mistake in signing a lease
agreement for an irrigation plot. He greatly resents the high
production costs of irrigation farming and is deeply dissatisfied
with life on the scheme. If he could get a purchase area farm he
would leave Mvura immediately. He still hopes one day to get his
own farm and for the time being has left his livestock with
relatives in the nearby tribal trust land.

(d) Joseph, the Disappointed Plotholder

Born in 1933 in a village in Karangaland, Joseph went to school
for five years and as a youth of seventeen found work in Gwelo

as an assistant to a builder. He received a monthy wage of £3.10.0 and after a year went back to his parents. From 1952 to 1954 he found work in Salisbury with the Dairy Marketing Board and earned £4.10.0 a month. After a holiday with his parents he set out for a last labour trip and found work in Bulawayo, earning £6.10.0 a month. In 1961 his parents acquired a purchase area farm near the present Mvura scheme and Joseph accompanied them. He stayed with them for seven years, helped them to open up the land and trained as a master farmer. He also built himself a house on his father's farm.

While still a labour migrant Joseph married, and by 1970 his wife had borne him seven children, the three eldest of whom are in school.

In 1968 Joseph took up an irrigation plot in Mvura. He hoped that through irrigation farming he would get rich quickly and so be able to buy his own purchase area farm. After two years on the scheme, however, Joseph became disillusioned. He found that the production costs were so high that once he had repaid his loan to the cooperative society he was left with little money to show for his hard work. In 1968–69 he had a gross income of £270. His most valued possessions—five head of cattle—he left on his father's farm. On the scheme he keeps merely some basic furniture and a cotton spray.

Joseph has no plans for the future. He has despaired of getting his own farm and said fatalistically: 'I shall stay here until I am sent away. What else can I do?'

(e) Jude, the Disgruntled Young Man

Jude is one of the youngest plotholders in Mvura. Born in 1945, he went to school for nine years, that is, he attempted secondary education but failed his 'junior certificate'. In 1964 he found work as a domestic servant in Gatooma for a wage of £2.5.0 a month. In 1967 he came to Mvura as an assistant builder, helping to construct the tanks on the irrigation scheme. There he earned £4.10.0 a month and watched the plotholders settling down. He decided to try his own hand at irrigation farming and in 1968 signed a lease agreement as a plotholder. He immediately began training as a master farmer.

Jude had hoped to make much money by growing two crops a year, but soon he was bitterly disappointed at the high production costs and especially resented the way in which the scheme manager handled the loans. He objects to accepting an overall statement of his debt and wants to know exactly how this sum is compounded. In 1968–69 Jude had a gross income of £246. This he thinks is too little for a young man with a wife and child. Since he has a right to cultivate ten acres of land in his tribal area, he does not depend on irrigation farming. He said: 'It does not pay for me, a young man, to waste my life on this scheme while the other young men enjoy themselves in town. I have land and two head of cattle and five sheep in my home village. I shall return there in 1971 with my family, and when necessary look for work in town.'

(f) Julius and Justin

Julius was one of the least successful plotholders in Mvura. Born in 1937 on the eastern border of Karangaland he went to school for five years, and then helped his parents plough the land. In 1962 he attached himself to chief Chapungu in the re-settlement area around the present irrigation scheme and trained as a master farmer. At the chief's suggestion he joined the scheme in 1967. His neighbours soon elected him vice-chairman of the cooperative society.

Julius' harvests were among the lowest on the scheme. In 1968–69 he had a gross income of only £205. Once the high production costs were deducted, little remained to support his family. Julius therefore left the scheme after the 1969 harvest and returned to chief Chapungu, having nothing to show for his two years of hard work on the scheme.

Julius' plot was immediately taken over by a young bachelor. This man, Justin, was born in 1947 and attended school for seven years. After that he stayed with his parents, cultivating the land. When his parents joined chief Chapungu in the re-settlement area in the early 1960s, Justin went with them.

Justin saw that dry land farming in his new home was very hazardous and asked chief Chapungu to recommend him to the district commissioner as a plotholder. As soon, therefore, as Julius left, Justin was offered the plot. His first aim now is to make enough money to collect his bridewealth so that he can marry. If he succeeds in making a profit, he intends to stay.

(3) EVALUATION OF CASE HISTORIES

Table 35 sets out the most salient characteristics of the six plotholders whose case histories have just been presented.

TABLE 35

Characteristics of Six Plotholders on Mvura Irrigation Scheme

Name	Net Income £	Year of Birth	Education in Years	Years in Employment	Agricultural Qualification	Past or present leadership position	Attitude to Irrigation Scheme
Jacques	356	1931	8	15	MFT[1]	unofficial leader	to leave for P.A.[3]
James	331	1936	5	6	wife MF[2] twice MF	member of MB[4]	to stay
John	302	1926	8	10	MF	—	to leave for P.A.
Joseph	270	1933	5	5	MF	—	would like to leave
Jude	246	1945	9	5	MFT	—	to leave in 1971
Julius	205	1937	5	—	MFT	vice-chairman of coop. soc.	left

[1] MFT = master farmer trainee
[2] MF = master farmer
[3] P.A. = purchase area
[4] MB = management board

Table 35 shows that Mvura plotholders have many social characteristics in common. All are relatively young and reasonably well educated and all, except Julius who left, have been labour migrants. In 1970 an editorial in *The Rhodesia Herald* pleaded that since irrigation schemes had not caught on among Africans because government had offered plots to 'heads of established families', irrigation plots should in the future be offered to African youths, preferably to those with some secondary education.[1] The six case histories indicate that well educated, enterprising young men, especially those who proved their ability to work hard and conscientiously by holding down responsible jobs for many years—such as Jacques who served for thirteen years in the police force and John who was a teacher for ten years—indeed make good irrigation farmers.

Yet good irrigation farmers are not necessarily permanent plotholders on irrigation schemes. Of the six men in the sample only one, James, is happy with his lease conditions and has decided to stay. All the others either hope to leave, are determined to leave in the near future, or have done so already. This is true even of the most successful among them, Jacques. Moreover, the Mvura irrigation scheme is not unique in this respect. The chairman of the Tribal Trust Land Development Corporation warned against the hope that Africans would rapidly take to irrigation farming and said that 'a drop-out of more than 50 per cent' of all plotholders is to be expected. The remainder, he said, would stay simple because they had surrendered their 'soul to the quartermaster's store.'[2] The case histories of Mvura plotholders indicate that those who stay do so in order to make money, yet not in order to buy goods at 'the quartermaster's store' but to obtain their own farm in a purchase area.

The desire of Mvura plotholders to move into a purchase area is due to their love of freedom and independence and their resentment against the scheme administration, especially against the scheme manager's handling of money. Not only Jude and Jacques but many other plotholders as well, want to know the cost of seed, fertilizer, insecticides and other expenditure, and they also want to know as much about the wider market as possible and then make their own decisions where to sell their crops and where to purchase their fertilizer. Unless they are given these opportunities, they will continue to leave the irrigation scheme.

[1] *The Rhodesia Herald*, 18.6.70.   [2] *The Rhodesia Herald*, 24.9.70.

Their suspicion of the scheme administration could be overcome by an open bookkeeping system, such as is in use on Israeli moshavim[1] where every peasant can check his accounts, and by a committee of plotholders which could discuss the marketing of produce with the scheme manager. These two innovations would go a long way to creating a relationship of trust between the administration and the people. Mvura plotholders are potentially interested in their scheme. Their various attempts to form committees and their readiness to serve on them prove their eagerness to take on administrative responsibilities. Moreover, all Mvura plotholders have a fair degree of agricultural knowledge. If they were allowed to participate in the administration of their scheme, and if they were given a higher degree of security by enabling successful plotholders after some years to change their lease agreements into title deeds, many might decide to stay permanently in Mvura.

(4) PROFILES OF ZUVA PLOTHOLDERS

(a) Martin, the Pfumbi with a Bank Account

Martin was born in 1919 and went to school for the first time when he was fourteen years old. He left after two years and is still illiterate.

In 1940 Martin found work as a domestic servant in Beit Bridge and, though he earned only twelve shillings a month, kept his job for six years. He then went to Messina in South Africa and worked for two years in a mine for a monthly wage of £3.5.0 On his return to his village he married his first wife who by 1970 had borne him five children. In 1951 Martin went once more to Messina and became foreman at the mine, earning £7.10.0 a month. After this he never again left the rural area, but he continued wage employment. For from 1955 to 1966 roads were built in his tribal trust and Martin was engaged as gang leader. During these years he married three more wives who by 1970 had borne him nine children.

Martin has been associated with the Zuva irrigation scheme since its beginning. When government looked for men to clear the land he volunteered, and when the district commissioner called for the first plotholders, Martin came forward. Yet Martin did not take his whole family to the scheme. Like many Pfumbi,

[1] Weingrod, 1966, pp. 80–1 and elsewhere.

he split his family. He left two of his wives in the tribal trust land to cultivate his twelve acres of dry land and to look after his cattle, sheep and goats, and took two of his wives and their children to Zuva. He also took with him his donkeys for ploughing.

Martin is one of the most successful Zuva plotholders and one of the few who welcomed the cooperative society of which he became a committee member. He always repaid his loan. In 1968–69 he had a gross income from agriculture of £131. This was more than he needed and enabled him to open his own bank account.

Martin is the only Zuva plotholder who invested his surplus in a bank rather than in cattle. This decision shows that he has freed himself to a greater degree from tribal values than have his neighbours. His previous employment as a foremen in a mine and leader of a road gang indicate his ability to adjust himself successfully to new circumstances and to take on new responsibilities. This ability also contributed to his success on the irrigation scheme.

(b) Matthew, the Successful Pfumbi

Matthew was born in 1910 of a Venda mother and a Pfumbi father. He never went to school. As a youth he went to Messina and became a street sweeper, earning first ten shillings a month, later £2.10.0. In 1938, still in Messina, he found work in a factory and was paid £3.15.0 a month. After ten years he went to another town in the Transvaal and found work as a store assistant, earning £14 a month. After a further ten years, in 1958, he returned to his home village.

During these 23 years of continuous employment, Matthew founded his family. At the age of 27 he married his first wife who by 1970 had borne him six children. On his return from South Africa he married three wives, paying their bridewealth with the wages he had earned. For one wife he paid his father-in-law £30 and six head of cattle, for another £30 and for the third £10.5.0 plus eight head of cattle. The remainder of his savings he invested in livestock.

Over the years Matthew discovered that two of his junior wives were barren, and so he divorced them. The other wife bore him three children. Matthew sent four of his children to school for five years, that is, for as many years as they could study at the local village school.

When the Zuva scheme was opened in 1966, Matthew decided to try his hand at irrigation farming, for during successive drought years he had had to sell cattle to buy food for his family. He therefore took his youngest wife with him to the scheme and left the older wife with her children on the dry land to look after his livestock. He took only his donkeys to the scheme to help him plough the land.

Matthew proved a successful plotholder by Zuva standards. In 1968–69 he had a gross income from agriculture of £123. He grows enough maize to feed both his family on the scheme and his wife with her children on the dry land, and enough wheat to pay with his proceeds his expenditure on fertilizer, seed and the water rates. Though production costs are much higher than he had expected, especially the cost of fertilizer, Matthew has decided to stay because he is loath to sell more cattle to buy food.

Matthew's long stay in South Africa accustomed him to living apart from his family, and it also prepared him for work under completely new conditions. These two experiences have helped him to adjust to the situation on the irrigation scheme. He looks at irrigation farming as an economic insurance policy for his cattle herd.

(c) Maurice, the Chief's Son

Maurice is the son of the late Pfumbi chief in whose territory the Zuva irrigation scheme falls. Born in 1928 as the second of fifteen children, Maurice was sent to a boarding school in South Africa and after ten years' study became a teacher. Only two of his brothers went to school and only one of them completed his primary education. Maurice is therefore the most educated member of his family. He is also the best educated plotholder in Zuva.

From 1951 to 1955 Maurice taught in an African school in Natal and in 1956 worked as a court interpreter in Rhodesia. In 1957 his father asked him to return home and teach at a local school in order to be near him in his old age. In 1966 his father died and Maurice expected to become chief because his only elder brother was away from home. The Rhodesian government, however, appointed another man as chief. This hurt Maurice deeply and because his eyesight began to fail he retired from teaching in 1967 and took up a plot on the Zuva irrigation scheme, leaving all his livestock—fifteen head of cattle and ten goats—in the tribal trust land.

Maurice came to Zuva not to make money—for as a teacher he had earned £24 a month, much more than he could hope to make on the scheme—but in order to become a political leader. He thought that as son of the late Pfumbi chief he had a right to rule the plotholders, but he ran up against Max, the leader of the Shangaan. Max would not recognize Maurice's claim and when, therefore, in 1970 the new Pfumbi chief offered Maurice the position of secretary at his court, he was pleased and considered leaving Zuva.

Maurice's stay on the irrigation scheme had been a relative failure. His gross income in 1968–69 was only £85 which left him with a mere £48 after the deduction of production costs. Since he had not come to make money, possessed no property in Zuva, and had a secure future as court secretary awaiting him in the tribal trust land, he saw no reason for staying on the irrigation scheme.

(d) Max, The Leader of the Shangaan

Max, the leader of the Shangaan in Zuva, was born in 1900. He never went to school. His father had been appointed by the Shangaan chief to look after the Shangaan living under the Pfumbi chief, and when his father died Max was entrusted with this responsibility.

In his youth Max married two wives who bore him three children. Both wives died in the 1950s. In 1946 Max left the rural area for the first time to look for work and went straight to Johannesburg. He found work with a construction company at a monthly wage of £15. He stayed for four years and in 1950 went to Messina where he worked for two years as a night watchman. He then returned permanently to the country. With some of his savings he married a third wife who by 1970 had borne him three children, who still live with him. The older children of his first wives have set up their own households. With the rest of his savings Max bought cattle, goats, a bicycle and a plough.

In 1965 the district commissioner informed Max that government had planned to establish an irrigation scheme in the area. Max was displeased and feared that irrigation farming would disrupt the traditional way of life of his people and impose many hardships on them. When, therefore, the district commissioner urged Max to tell his followers to move to the scheme, Max obeyed reluctantly. He also feared that his precarious leadership position in the area might be undermined by the move. Yet his political fears proved unfounded. The Shangaan continued bringing their court cases to him and even gave him some tribute labour, for, like the other Shangaan, Max dislikes working on the land. When his maize has to be planted or when harvesting time comes around, the people work for him without expecting a reward. Max has never yet hired a single labourer but often brews beer to reward his helpers. He himself loves beer and attends all the beer parties in the area.

As a consequence of his personal dislike of agriculture and his reliance on free, often careless, labour, the yields of his fields are very moderate. In 1968–69 he had a gross income of £52.

Irrigation schemes depend on the plotholders' acceptance of the modern cash economy. Yet Max did not settle on the scheme to make money but to remain in control of the Shangaan. The emphasis on money in irrigation farming has worried him from the beginning. Like many plotholders he started off by taking out loans, but he has never repaid any of them. In 1970 he still had an outstanding debt of £50. Because the plotholders' debts to the cooperative society have been transferred to the African Development Fund, Max can now be prosecuted if he refuses to pay, but unless he is prosecuted he will not pay. He has been a stubborn opponent of cooperative marketing and this has won him favour among like-minded Shangaan.

Like most of his people, Max clings to tribal values. As a youth he went to South Africa to be circumcised, and as a married man he installed a *pfuko*, or guardian spirit, in his home. His commitment to traditional values, especially those related to religion and inter-personal relationships in family and tribe, and his opposition to modern institutions is not only confined to his reluctance to settle on the irrigation scheme and his boycott of the cooperative society, but when a new teacher tried to persuade the people to send their children to school, Max saw to it that the teacher was transferred. Max is extremely conservative and if he can prevent it, he will arrest any social change in the area.

(e) Michael, the Mill Owner

Michael, a classificatory brother of Max, was born in 1920 as the fourth of nine children. In his childhood nobody in the area had heard of a school and Michael grew up herding his parents' cattle and goats, and helping them collect wild fruit. As a youth he went to South Africa to earn money for his bride-wealth and found work as a domestic servant.

On his return Michael paid his father-in-law £36, but no cattle for, he argued, 'It is too painful to see the offspring of one's own cattle belonging to someone else.' He stayed a year with his young wife and then went to Johannesburg for six years, working for a building company. Once during this time he went on home leave and found that his wife had given birth to a child. He left her pregnant again but did not take her with him to Johannesburg. He said later that 'the city is a bad place for women'.

In 1956 Michael returned home permanently and married a second wife, paying for her a bridewealth of £37 which he had saved from his wages. By 1970 his first wife had borne him seven children and his second wife two. As soon as his children reached school age, Michael sent them to the local school. He is one of the few Shangaan who welcome education.

Michael had lived a very thrifty life while in South Africa and when he had paid his bridewealth he still had enough money to buy some cattle, a bicycle and a grinding mill. He built the mill close to the local school. Michael stresses that he likes the local school because 'it will enlighten the children'.

But apart from this emphasis on education and his purchase of a mill—a most unusual investment for a local Shangaan and only profitable since the establishment of the irrigation scheme—Michael adheres to all the traditional Shangaan values. Like his neighbours he detests agriculture and in 1968–69 had a gross income from farming of only £29 so that he had to use money from his mill to pay production costs. The extension assistant evaluated Michael as 'lazy' and recorded in his notebook that Michael had sowed only part of his acreage with wheat and at harvest time had reaped only part of the crop. Again, like the other Shangaan, Michael does not count wealth in money but in cattle. He went even further than his neighbours and refused to add any cattle to his bridewealth, yet readily paid his fathers-in-law in cash.

In spite of his low yields Michael has no intention of leaving the irrigation scheme. Zuva is his home area and in this area he wants to stay. If government put up an irrigation scheme, he will try his best to be as little disturbed by it as possible.

(f) Moses, the Cripple

Moses is one of the oldest men in Zuva. Like most Shangaan he is related to Max who is his brother's son. Born in 1885 in a family of seventeen children Moses grew up in the veld, herding cattle, swimming in the river and climbing the mountains. At the age of fifteen he found work in Rhodesia, sweeping the premises of a European businessman. First he earned fifteen shillings, later £1 a month. Moses stayed with his employer for three years and in 1904 he took a similar job in a store where, in addition to sweeping, he was occasionally allowed to sell goods. In 1908 he worked as a cook for African workers employed in a mine and then became a miner himself. During these years he frequently visited his family.

In 1913, after having gained experience as a labour migrant in Rhodesia, Moses went to Johannesburg where again he found employment as a sweeper and occasional shop assistant. In Johannesburg, he said, he earned 'lots of money: £4.15.0 a month'. He saved all he could and married his first wife in 1917. After a month's holiday at home, he again left for Johannesburg and worked there until 1923. On his return he married his second wife and did not leave the rural area again. Moses used all his wages to pay bridewealth and to buy cattle. He was happy. He had all he wanted: wives, children, and a growing herd of cattle.

Then in 1938 he was struck by misfortune. A lion killed one of his donkeys and Moses set a trap for it. The lion returned and was caught. Moses was delighted. He fetched his home-made gun and shot at it twice but failed to kill it. The lion broke loose and attacked him. Moses cried aloud and the lion escaped. He was then taken to hospital where his leg was amputated.

When the scheme was started, Moses was not interested in irrigation farming. Yet he liked his neighbours with whom he had grown up and did not want to be separated from them. He therefore joined the scheme for social, not economic, reasons. His first harvest in Zuva surpassed his expectations: he reaped 36 bags of maize and sold five; he also sold several bags of wheat. But with increasing production costs his profits decreased and he lost all interest. In 1968–69 his gross income was as low as £21. Because he is a cripple he cannot cultivate the land himself and his wives have to do all the work, but this does not strike the local people as a serious handicap since most Shangaan try to avoid agricultural labour. Though Moses is a most unsatisfactory plotholder from an economic point of view, he has no intention of leaving the scheme. Like Michael, he enjoys the company of his relatives and friends and wants to be in Zuva for their sakes, not to make money.

(g) Women Plotholders

Apart from the men, a fifth of all plotholders in Zuva are women. Two case histories have therefore been added of women who are trying to make a living from irrigation farming.

(i) Martha, the Mother

Martha is one of the most industrious women in Zuva. Born in 1919 in the Transvaal of a Venda mother and an Ndebele father, Martha grew up with her parents in Johannesburg. During her youth Martha gave birth to several girls and to one boy, but she never married. Then her father died and Martha went to his family for support. Her son accompanied her, but her daughters remained in South Africa and Martha lost contact with them.

The family of Martha's father lived near Bulawayo. Martha busied herself modelling clay pots and selling them in Bulawayo. On one of her visits to the city, a European commissioned her to sell bananas for him in the African market. Martha accepted the offer and settled in Bulawayo. There she joined an African women's club and learned needlework. She sold the goods she sewed and knitted and soon made enough money to buy two cows and three goats which she kept at her grandparents' homestead. By 1970 her livestock had increased to 23 head of cattle and 60 goats, although she had twice paid a full bridewealth for her son.

In 1966, when the Zuva irrigation scheme was opened, Martha applied for a plot and was accepted by the local district commissioner. Martha is one of the hardest workers on the scheme and highly successful. Unaided she produced in 1968–69 a crop worth £62. She is therefore highly satisfied with the scheme, since for the first time in her life she enjoys economic security. She still lives a very thrifty life and saves as much as she can to provide her son's expanding family with food and cash. Martha is determined to stay in Zuva until she dies.

(ii) Monica, the Widow

Monica is a local woman. Born in 1930 in a tribal trust land ruled by a Shangaan chief, she married in 1947 a man who lived on the present site of the irrigation scheme and was a relative of Max, the scheme leader. Her husband spent most of his life working in the mines around Johannesburg and left her to look after his family. In 1961 he died in a mine accident. By that time Monica had given birth to four children. The mining company paid her a monthly remittance of £10 for a number of years, but then the remittance stopped and Monica had nothing to live on. She had used all the money to buy food and to pay for her children's education.

When therefore, the irrigation scheme was opened and the district commissioner urged her to become a plotholder so that she could grow her own food and make enough money to educate her children, Monica joined it. But she reaped less than she had expected. In 1968–69 she had a gross income of £30. Thus she had no surplus to sell to pay for fertilizer and the water rates. However, both her own family and her husband's family live near the scheme and readily assist her when she is in need. Monica, therefore, knows that her security lies not in her success in irrigation farming but in her kinship relationships.

(5) EVALUATION OF CASE HISTORIES

Table 36 overleaf sets out the most important characteristics of the eight Zuva plotholders.

Unlike Table 35, Table 36 includes no column referring to the agricultural qualifications of Zuva plotholders since none of them has trained as a master farmer. Their poor agricultural skills are reflected in their very low gross incomes, several of which are well below the average production costs of the scheme. Yet I have inserted in this Table a column referring to the residence of the plotholders' families because I stressed in an earlier chapter that many Pfumbi and Venda have divided their families between the scheme and their dry land villages. Of the three Pfumbi whose case histories are here presented, two have half their families living in their home villages and the third is a monogamist. The Shangaan, on the other hand, have no need to split their families since the scheme was started in their home area.

Like the Mvura plotholders, those in Zuva differ very little among themselves in social characteristics, but as a group they differ widely from the Mvura plotholders. All are much older than

TABLE 36

Characteristics of Eight Plotholders on
the Zuva Irrigation Scheme

Name	Tribe	Gross Income £	Year of Birth	Education in Years	Years in Employment	Residence of Family	Past or present leadership position	Attitude to Irrigation Scheme
Martin	Pfumbi	131	1919	2	21	vil. & sch.	committee member of coop. soc.	to stay
Matthew	Pfumbi	123	1910	—	23	vil. & sch.	—	to stay
Maurice	Pfumbi	85	1928	10	14	scheme	rejected leader	to leave
Max	Shangaan	52	1900	—	6	scheme	leader of the scheme	to stay
Michael	Shangaan	29	1920	—	7	scheme	—	to stay
Moses	Shangaan	21	1885		21	scheme	—	to stay
Martha	Ndebele	62	1919	?	?	single	—	to stay
Monica	Shangaan	30	1930	—	—	scheme	—	to stay

the men on the more successful irrigation scheme, and only one has
had any formal education. Though all men have spent many years
in European employment, more years in fact than did the younger
Mvura plotholders, their employment was mainly confined to
unskilled or at most semi-skilled, tasks, except in the case of
Maurice the teacher.

Few of these men have been deeply influenced by their experience as labour migrants, for few accepted European cultural
values. Most invested their earnings in wives and cattle. Schapera,
a well-known social anthropologist and specialist on South
African tribes, wrote as early as 1928 that the desire for cattle,
and through them for wives, was the most powerful driving force
which impelled local Africans to seek European employment.[1]
This is also true of the people now living in Zuva.

None of the men, whose case histories have been presented,
spent much money on himself in town and none set out to enjoy
himself in town as did, for example, Jude, the Mvura plotholder.
This seems to confirm the earlier suggestion that the Shangaan
who worked in South Africa associated more with 'homeboys'
than with educated Africans in order to protect themselves
against urban influences. Also Michael's comment that Johannesburg is a 'bad place for women', points in the same direction.

Whereas only one of the Mvura plotholders was happy to stay
on the irrigation scheme, only one of those in Zuva wants to leave.
This is due to the very different motives with which plotholders
came to the two irrigation schemes. The men in Mvura wanted to
make much money, and to make it quickly. In Zuva only the two
best Pfumbi and Martha the Ndebele woman, came to the scheme
for economic reasons. Two men had come with political ambitions
and the two worst Shangaan plotholders and Monica the Shangaan
widow, had settled primarily to enjoy the presence of their
relatives and the security which the close association with their
kinsmen gave them. Hence even though the gross income of these
people is very low, none of them wants to leave the scheme.

The Pfumbi in Zuva stand economically and culturally half-
way between the Mvura plotholders and the Shangaan. They
are slightly better educated than the Shangaan and they came to
the scheme for economic reasons. Partly because of these factors
and partly because of an agricultural tradition in their own tribe,
they are more successful irrigation farmers than the Shangaan.

[1] Schapera, re-edited 1967, p. 146.

The people in Zuva seem unusual plotholders in Rhodesia, if the comments quoted above from *The Rhodesia Herald* are anything to go by. All of the men are heads of well-established families, and there are hardly any drop-outs. Moreover, the people do not stay on the scheme because they have surrendered their 'soul to the quartermaster's store', but because they are to a large extent indifferent to modern consumer goods. This is both their reason for staying on the scheme and also the reason for their very low agricultural productivity.

(6) CONCLUSION

This study of the two irrigation schemes leads to the same conclusion as the study of the two tribal trust lands and two purchase areas: agricultural success and failure in Rhodesian peasant society is to a very large degree due to sociological factors. The closer the people are involved in their tribal system and the more pervasive the influence of tribal values, especially those of the religious, kinship and marriage systems which are epitomized in the Africans' attitudes towards cattle, the less progressive, in terms of the modern money economy, is the community. Economic success and failure, however, are little related to the satisfaction which peasants derive from living in a particular agricultural settlement.

CONCLUSION

(1) INTRODUCTION

In the Introduction to this book I set out the hypothesis that economic advancement in Rhodesian peasant societies depends on four factors: on government policies, local administrative systems, availability of land and on the peasants' contact with the wider cash economy. I also suggested that these factors may in turn determine the settlement patterns in the various communities and thereby the labour supply of individual families; the election of settlers and thus the agricultural skills they possess; the presence or absence of free markets; and the peasants' ability to invest in the land, which in turn will depend on their readiness to break with the tribal past.

It is seldom if ever possible for social anthropologists to carry out experiments, and hence conduct research, with the same degree of accuracy as can physical scientists in their laboratories. The nearest approach to quasi laboratory conditions social anthropologists can hope for is that of controlled observation. This is the method used in this book, for the successful and unsuccessful communities have been chosen with a view of keeping their ecological environment constant. The only group for which this could not be done are the plotholders in Zuva. Yet by the time I analysed this community I had already established that agricultural success and failure are to a large extent determined by social factors. It may therefore be assumed that the ecological differences, and also the different irrigation techniques in Mvura and Zuva, are less important than the social characteristics of the plotholders. The importance of social factors was further borne out by the case histories of Zuva plotholders who were chosen according to criteria other than those of peasant cultivators and peasant farmers: instead of checking that they represented a typical cross section of men and women sharing all the major characteristics of the other members of their communities, attention was paid exclusively to their agricultural income. The sample then showed that those with higher incomes were all Pfumbi, those with lower incomes

Shangaan. This proved again that social characteristics are highly significant in determining agricultural output.

This Conclusion aims at refining the hypothesis set out in the Introduction, and to draw together the suggestions made throughout the book on how to improve peasant agriculture in Rhodesia.

(2) THE EFFECTS OF GOVERNMENT POLICY ON PEASANT DEVELOPMENT

In the Introduction to this book I pointed out that many underdeveloped countries try to raise the living standards of their people through government planned economic development schemes. This study of African agriculture in Rhodesia shows that the Rhodesian government has no overall development plan for the country. This, however, does not mean that African peasants are free to cultivate the land in the way they choose. In fact, the movements of Africans from one agricultural community to another are strictly controlled by civil servants, and within each settlement-type Africans are subject to specific rules and regulations which narrowly circumscribe their agricultural activities.

This book has shown that all African agricultural settlements in Rhodesia are so administered and designed that the government's ideological commitment to white superiority is never endangered, and that separate development has been chosen as the most effective means of serving this ideology. The land separation which at the beginning of the century aimed at protecting evolving Africans from economic exploitation by European settlers, now no longer serves to protect the poor but to preserve the economically superior position of the rich. With a rapidly increasing African population confined to a limited area of Rhodesia, new problems are arising in African agriculture which in time are bound to lead to a political explosion.

The situation is especially serious in the tribal trust lands which have to absorb the surplus population from every part of Rhodesia. Already in 1967, of all men in the sample communities 47·1 per cent were landless, and in the 15–29 age group the percentage of landless men was as high as 80·7. With the high replacement rate of 2·6 in these areas, the problem of a rural landless proletariat is building up. Between 1958 and 1970 the *per capita* income from the land of Rhodesian peasants fell by 50 per cent.[1] At present in

[1] *The Rhodesia Herald*, 28.7.71.

tribal trust lands few economic opportunities exist for men who are not cultivating the land, and even those men who are engaged in farming have to rely to a large degree on other sources of income to support their families.

In South Africa, which follows a similar policy of separate development as Rhodesia, it is estimated that by 1980 only 2·14 million out of 8 million people in the Bantustans can earn a living from the land, the rest must be given other rural employment.[1] But whereas the South African government is establishing border industries and towns in, or adjacent to Bantustans—however inefficient these might be—the Rhodesian government makes no effort on the same scale to help the people in tribal trust lands. The attempts of the Tribal Trust Land Development Corporation, as has been pointed out in this book, have not met with great success. Moreover, government invests little money for tribal development. In 1971 government voted only £165,000 for the African Development Fund, the same sum as in the preceding year. A member of the opposition asked in parliament: 'Does this reflect that there is no intention whatsoever on the side of Government to bring about development in the Tribal Trust area?'[2]

The productivity survey analysed in this book showed that at present the average peasant cultivator reaps four bags of maize per acre in a season of average rainfall. This output could easily be doubled by only slightly more efficient cultivation methods, as the output of master farmers in the tribal areas indicates. This would enable these areas to absorb more people than they do now, or greatly raise the living standards of the present population. If the productivity is not increased and if living standards fall, famine, and consequently political unrest, will inevitably occur.

The Ministry of Internal Affairs, primarily responsible for tribal areas, has decided that the problem of over-population can best be overcome through irrigation schemes. According to the Deputy Secretary for Internal Affairs it is his Ministry's policy

[1] Magura, 1970, p. 181.
[2] *The Rhodesia Herald*, 28.7.71. Not only does government show little concern for tribal areas, progress is also hindered by the Africans' lack of confidence in the Ministry of Internal Affairs, which is responsible for development in the tribal trust lands. In 1971 the agricultural loans vote was reduced from £28,500 to £15,000 because peasants did not draw on it. An African parliamentarian stated that the people are suspicious of the Ministry of Internal Affairs, and proved his statement by drawing attention to the increasing demands for loans made by Africans on the private African Development Corporation. *The Rhodesia Herald*, 6.8.71.

'to place as many people on as little land as possible'.[1] Irrigation schemes, therefore, are seen as the answer to coping with an increasing population without abandoning the government policy of separate development.

Irrigation schemes, because of the very intensive cultivation methods practised on wet land, give higher yields per acre than dry land farming so that the government policy of confining increasing numbers of Africans on limited land results in a higher productivity per cultivated unit. Yet as this study has shown, irrigation schemes are not readily accepted by the African people. On the economically successful Mvura irrigation scheme most plotholders have decided to leave because of the encroachment on their personal freedom by the scheme administration. Although yields per acre are high on irrigation schemes, the heavy initial investment in a scheme and the recurrent production costs make it doubtful whether such capital is profitably invested. Not only are economic considerations sacrificed for ideological considerations, but the social aspirations of the African people are also completely disregarded, so that dissatisfaction is widespread.

The only settlements free from population pressure are the purchase areas. Earlier this century it was government policy to set aside this land on which an African middle class might emerge. Purchase area farmers are at present the most satisfied group of rural Africans who earn a living from the land.

Should government decide at a later date, when the population pressure in the tribal trust lands increases in excess of their carrying capacity, to sub-divide purchase area farms into smaller holdings, or even to turn them into tribal areas, the dissatisfaction so widespread among African peasants would also engulf these areas. Until recently purchase areas have been a symbol of hope for progressive African peasants, but by 1970 most Africans realized that their chances of buying their own farms were negligible.

Dangers to the existence of purchase areas arise also from the success of some African farm owners. As some purchase areas become highly productive,[2] European farmers begin to fear competition from Africans. Should this competition become acute, steps might be taken to safeguard the European market. Throughout Rhodesian history Africans have only been advanced 'as long as their advancement did not conflict with powerful white interest

---

[1] *The Rhodesia Herald,* 14.7.71.   [2] See footnote 1, p. 42.

groups'.[1] This underlying policy has repeatedly been touched upon in this book, for example, when attention was drawn to the vacant farms in Mutadza purchase area where asbestos can be found, or to the assurance to Europeans by the chairman of the Tribal Trust Land Development Corporation that Africans will not be assisted in growing crops which might compete with those grown by European farmers.

These incidents show that European economic interests are considered to be always dominant in Rhodesia, and that government will not allow any developments in African areas which might be harmful to Europeans. In 1970 the Ministry of Internal Affairs even forbade the Association of Rhodesian Industries to consider ways and means of promoting development in tribal areas.[2] Because of this dominant concern, government only suggests those changes which either contain African peasants at subsistence level in their own communities, as happens on irrigation schemes, or allow them to advance in such a way that they do not threaten white interests.

These considerations may be summarized as follows:

i. The government policy of separate development determines the form of all agricultural settlements of Rhodesian Africans. Its overriding concern is to keep Africans within their own areas. African economic advancement is welcomed only as long as it does not threaten European interests.

The success or failure of government policy, however, cannot simply be measured in terms of economic returns. The great dissatisfaction of African peasants with irrigation schemes shows that social costs at present outweigh any economic benefits. Only when settlements give rise to both high economic returns and to satisfaction among the settlers, can they be considered successful.

[1] Gann and Duignan, 1970, p. 134.
[2] *The Rhodesia Herald*, 28.7.71. On July 30th 1971, *The Rhodesia Herald* reported that European settlers on the Middle Sabi river had been using Sabi river water intended for 700 African plotholders on an irrigation scheme lower down the river when their own dam had dried up, with the result that the wheat harvests of these 700 Africans was in jeopardy. The following day the editorial of *The Rhodesia Herald* commented that the irrigation scheme adversely affected was 'more than an irrigation project. It is one of Rhodesia's most important social experiments ... In 1966 there were seven plotholders. This year reports speak of 700 ... Why, when the river fell below the recognized safety margin, did Middle Sabi (a settlement of 22 European farmers) go on pumping—at the apparent expense of Chisumbanje (the irrigation scheme with 700 African plotholders)? Who is responsible?' *The Rhodesia Herald*, 31.7.71.

(3) THE ADMINISTRATIVE SYSTEM

Government control is tightest in those areas in which population densities are greatest. This may be deemed necessary in the interests of national security, but it gives rise to much discontent. Irrigation schemes, which have the highest population density of all African areas in Rhodesia, are more disliked than any other settlement type. The main reasons are the complete control over the scheme by managers who often know little about irrigation farming, and even less about African peasants. The second reason is the extreme insecurity of plotholders who can be evicted from a scheme if they fail to comply with any of the many rules and regulations governing their lives. Economically successful plotholders claim that they would only stay if they were given a say in the running of their communities and title deeds to the land they cultivate. Presently both the Mvura and Zuva irrigation schemes have failed, the first because its settlers leave after a short time, and the second because it has attracted only peasants with few agricultural skills and little interest in agriculture.

Since the irrigation schemes are very expensive to establish and run, financial investment in a scheme like Zuva, where the average plotholder has an annual net income of only £32, seems highly questionable. The economic failure of this scheme is due to the strong traditional values held by the plotholders, and since government is emphasizing that Africans should preserve their traditional customs—an African member of parliament stated that government tried to mould the African as a person bound by tradition[1]—changes in attitude which might predispose peasants towards an active participation in cash cropping are unnecessarily delayed.

In tribal trust lands the control of external supervision is less strict than on irrigation schemes. This gives peasant cultivators a greater freedom than plotholders and explains the reluctance of tribesmen to settle on irrigation schemes. Moreover, since the average master farmer in a tribal trust land has an annual net income of £128, and the average plotholder on as good an irrigation scheme as Mvura has a net income of only £162, there is little reason for him to give up his relative freedom in the midst of his kinsmen for complete dependence on scheme personnel in an unknown area.

[1] *The Rhodesia Herald*, 28.7.71.

Obstacles to development in tribal areas are partly increased by the return of responsibility for the land to African chiefs, the most tradition-bound group of tribesmen. This book showed that the stronger the chief's influence over agriculture is in a community, the less likely is development to take place. In Shoko Museamwa, where progressive peasant cultivators repeatedly tried to organize themselves in order to increase their production, all efforts were crushed by the chief. In 1971 *The Rhodesia Herald* commented: 'It is useless to say, as the Prime Minister has done, that the Land Tenure Act has placed the problem of the TTLs "squarely where it belongs", with the inhabitants of these areas [especially with the chiefs]. You might as well expect slum dwellers to tackle and finance slum clearance schemes.'[1]

This book has amply shown that it is mainly those who are marginal to the tribal system and who want to move out of it, such as master farmers, who make the fullest use of the land and earn the highest income. As on irrigation schemes, so in tribal trust lands, only those who have freed themselves from tribal values, especially those centring around the cattle complex, become successful participants in the cash economy.

Yet the artificial preservation of tribal values under the guardianship of the chiefs is not the whole problem. The tight control by the Ministry of Internal Affairs over all development works in tribal areas is equally harmful. Though the research was concluded before the technical and administrative functions were again united in the hands of district commissioners, a streamlining of extension work had already begun. For example, the agricultural youth clubs, started on the initiative of a missionary in the Shiri-Ngara tribal trust land and supported by the extension staff, were absorbed on the instruction of the district commissioner in the national movement of young farmers' clubs, with the result that all closed down. The study of the two tribal trust lands indicates that progress is fastest where individuals, who show a strong interest in peasant progress, take a lead in agricultural development, or where a religious ethos, be it Catholic, Seventh Day Adventist or any other, stimulates interest in economic progress. None of these forces are easily squared with bureaucratic administration and where administrators insist on regimentation and uniformity, initiative will be stifled and development will come to an end.

[1] *The Rhodesia Herald*, 28.7.71.

Peasant farmers in purchase areas are free from many of the handicaps suffered by peasant cultivators and plotholders. Their freedom to administer their own communities gives rise to great satisfaction and makes these areas the most desired settlement-type among Rhodesian peasants. Purchase area farmers are free men who, if they want to make a good living from the land, are generally able to do so. The great interest in agricultural progress, which has given rise to many voluntary agricultural societies in Guruuswa, shows that self-administration can greatly stimulate production. In purchase areas, however, where farm owners have been selected for criteria other than farming ability, such freedom may result in negligent farming and low output. In fact, the failure of the Mutadza purchase area can be explained as resulting from the selection procedure of farm owners: the great majority were completely unqualified to farm on a larger scale, 78·3 per cent had come from an adjoining overcrowded tribal trust land and settled in Mutadza in order to continue their traditional way of life with the minimum of interference from government officials.

These considerations can be summarised as follows:

ii.   The participation of peasants in the administration of their communities is an essential factor, making for economic progress, but links with the tribal past tend to arrest such progress.

   If all other factors are equal, local development is faster where enterprising individuals, be they civil servants, missionaries or peasants, are given freedom to experiment than where uniform requirements are made of the people.

(4) POPULATION INCREASE AND LAND SCARCITY

Population increase is one of the most serious problems in Rhodesia. So far it has only been satisfactorily solved in purchase areas where legislation limits the family units on the land. The effect, however, is an acute labour shortage and a consequent superficial use of the land.

The most unsatisfactory situation exists in tribal trust lands which are misused by government as a dumping ground of all Africans not needed in other parts of Rhodesia so that agricultural development becomes impossible.

Irrigation schemes can only be viewed as a partial solution of the land problem, for not only are they very capital intensive, but there is also a limit to irrigable land. Moreover, at present these schemes are not accepted by African peasants as a solution to their problems, because peasants feel insecure and deprived of their freedom in these settlements.

The Rhodesian government has also sought to overcome population pressure by population control. Clinics and hospitals run family planning programmes, and the Minister of Health even employs African women in the tribal trust lands to sell contraceptive pills to their neighbours,[1] yet in spite of this Africans reject family planning as a threat to their very existence.[2] Some see it as a political weapon of Europeans to weaken African opposition to white domination and so see in larger families their only hope of gaining political independence.[3]

Yet even if political factors were not complicating the issue, family planning would not solve the problem of tribal areas. Too many deeply rooted values are at stake, and only if African living standards rise considerably and if Africans find a new economic security, will the population increase less rapidly.

It can therefore be said that:

iii. Birth control programmes will not solve the population pressure in tribal trust lands. Only far-reaching agricultural reforms, leading to the establishment of a socially satisfied and economically viable peasant community, can solve the problem.[4]

(5) EFFECTS OF THE WIDER CASH ECONOMY

The more successful farming communities studied in this book have abandoned labour migration. Only ordinary peasant cultivators still derive a third of their total annual income from salaries and wages. It has been shown that without the possibility of these men leaving their tribal areas for wage employment, population pressure would be still more serious and that without the income from wages few families could live above subsistence level. Yet these figures also show that wage labour alone is insufficient to support rural families. The system of labour migration is therefore in itself inefficient since it lowers the efficiency of individual workers. Only a permanent rural population achieves

[1] *The Rhodesia Herald,* 24.4.71.
[2] *The Rhodesia Herald,* 19.3.71, records the results of a survey including 806 Africans (552 men and 254 women), listing their reasons for rejecting birth control.
[3] See, for example, *The Rhodesia Herald,* 5.6.71.
[4] For detailed suggestions, see the last pages of this Conclusion.

high agricultural success, as the output of master farmers in tribal trust lands indicates. Labour migration brings advantages only to employers who require cheap and unskilled labour, and to those Africans who have access to tribal land. Since the great majority of Africans will soon no longer have land in the tribal areas, they will depend exclusively on wage labour. Their wages must therefore be living wages, but unless they become permanent and skilled labourers, few employers will pay them adequately.

Until now labour migration has brought advantages to tribal trust lands. Not only did it decrease population pressures and inject money into tribal areas, it also introduced urban values into the country and so acted as a strong force making for social change. This social change also affected peasant attitudes towards agriculture since villagers, who are weaned from tribal values, are more ready to experiment with modern farming methods.

Since farm owners in purchase areas are not allowed to seek urban employment, only their sons can work in towns. Hence the urban influence is less strong in purchase areas than in tribal trust lands. However, peasant farmers have an important link with the wider economy through the marketing of their surplus crops. Since the average Guruuswa farm owner sells £65 worth of crops annually, about half of which finds its way into the national economy, and sells cattle worth £57 a year, these sales make a significant contribution to the national economy.

Irrigation schemes are even more geared to the national market than are purchase areas. Since maize is the only locally consumed crop—few peasants have taken to eating wheat—wheat and cotton are almost entirely sold outside the local communities. Moreover, plotholders are not only tied to the wider cash economy through their own sales but also through their large purchases of fertilizer, seed and insecticides. While peasant farmers can exist without the European market because most of their crops can be sold to families in the tribal trust lands, plotholders on irrigation schemes are absolutely dependent on the wider economy.

All the communities studied in this book derive the greater part of their income from the land, though their degree of dependence on agriculture varies. While plotholders on irrigation schemes derive about 92 per cent of their total income from farming, and peasant farmers in purchase areas and master farmers in tribal trust lands 70 to 80 per cent, peasant cultivators in tribal trust lands derive only 57 per cent of their income from the land.

Moreover, while master farmers in tribal areas, peasant farmers in purchase areas and plotholders on irrigation schemes derive the rest of their income mainly from cattle and other agricultural pursuits, ordinary peasant cultivators in tribal trust lands rely heavily on wage labour.[1] Yet even master farmers in tribal trust lands, successful peasant farmers in purchase areas and plotholders on irrigation schemes profit from their earlier experience as labour migrants for, as the case histories showed, those who were first successful in European employment, were later successful in farming.

Since the dependence of peasants on the wider Rhodesian economy varies, these considerations can be summarized as follows:

iv.   Labour migration relieves the population pressure only temporarily, and only in those settlements which derive the lowest proportion of their income from agriculture. The more progressive a farming community is the lower is its rate of labour migration.
      Peasants who succeed in gaining a satisfactory living from the land are bound to the wider economy through purchases and sales, not through hiring out their labour. Yet even these men have profited from labour migration, since it familiarized them with the modern cash economy and weaned them from tribal values.

(6) FACTORS MAKING FOR HIGH INCOMES

This book has shown that successful peasants possess certain social characteristics. The most successful men are younger than their neighbours, are better educated, are often strongly influenced by Christian beliefs, possess special training in modern agricultural methods and come from tribal communities with traditions of agriculture. Almost all of them have emancipated themselves to a large degree from tribal values, especially from an attachment to chiefs.

Men who possess these personal characteristics are likely to earn more money even outside agriculture, than those who lack

[1] This dependence on wage labour, which is widespread in Africa, led Kamarck to observe that Africans are not really peasants and do not behave as such, that they are much more open and receptive to change than peasants generally are, and that they are not attached to the soil but to social and economic security; it is for this reason, he claims, that they combine their agriculture with other economic activities. Kamarck, 1967, p. 101.

these qualities, and so are able to acquire better farming implements, larger herds of cattle, and often also more land. But access
to arable land in itself is one of the less important factors making
for a high farming income. This can be seen from Table 37.

The most striking correlation exists between agricultural success and the possession of a master farmer's certificate. The income of master farmers in tribal trust lands is twice as large as
that of ordinary peasant cultivators; so is the income of Guruuswa
farm owners, all of whom are master farmers, as compared with
Mutadza farm owners of whom only 30 per cent possess a farming
qualification. On the irrigation schemes the income of master
farmers is about five times as high as that of ordinary plotholders.

These men with master farmer's certificates are also those who
have more decisively broken their bonds with the tribal past than
their neighbours. As Table 37 shows, the expenditure on seed,
fertilizer, insecticides and labour is closely related to the possession
of an agricultural qualification, and the use of these items is an
indication of the adoption of modern means of production.

An important factor determining agricultural productivity is the
availability and use of labour. Table 37 shows further that families
who provide most of their own labour force are the most successful. Those who rely most heavily on communal work parties are
the least successful, for work parties, as has been stressed repeatedly,
are concerned with getting a job done rather than with doing it
accurately. Yet the size of a family's labour force does not determine the overall labour input. For whereas both master farmers
and ordinary peasant cultivators, and also Mvura plotholders,
have about one labourer available per acre, their labour input
per acre varies greatly. So does the labour input of purchase area
families: although there is about one worker available for every
two acres of land cultivated, the labour input of Mutadza families
is much lower than that of Guruuswa families. Zuva plotholders
who have about two persons at hand for every acre under crops,
exert themselves least. This uneven application of peasant
families to agricultural labour is directly reflected in the output,
as can be seen when the labour input on maize and the bags harvested are compared.

It has been suggested that settlement patterns, which are
determined by government officials, affect the labour supply.
It is true that the dispersed farm households in purchase areas
face special labour problems because of their relative isolation,

TABLE 37

Factors Influencing Agricultural Income

Factors Influencing Agricultural Income	Tribal Trust Lands		Purchase Areas		Irrigation Schemes	
	M. Farmer	O.P. Cultiv.	Guruuswa	Mutadza	Mvura	Zuva
Net family income	£128	£61.10.0	£234.5.0	£112	£162	£32
Acres cultivated	7·5	4·4	23·2	16·9	3·5	2
Adequate farming implements[1]	100%	54%	100%	100%	100%[2]	25%
Production costs	£7	£2.10.0	£13.15.0	£7.10.0	£115.10.0	£37
Master Farmer's certificate	100%	nil	100%	30%	100%[3]	nil
Percentage of family labour on total crop labour input	86·5	79·0	81·2	59·9	86·2	77·0
Labour input per acre	529	480	313	232	675	594
Labour input per acre of maize	291	253	262	211	318	249
Bags of maize per acre	9·3	3·9	5·7	2·7	33·3	12·1

[1] At least one plough.   [2] Tractor ploughing.   [3] Including master farmer trainees

yet the compact settlements around irrigation schemes do not necessarily overcome this problem, as the low labour input of the Zuva scheme shows.

One factor, difficult to tabulate, is the peasants' access to markets. No community, except that at Zuva, experiences any difficulty in selling its surplus crops. All, except plotholders on irrigation schemes, are free to choose their buyers. Controlled marketing, therefore, does not play an important role in Rhodesian peasant agriculture, and as the high outputs of Mvura plotholders show, does not give rise to apathy—though it does create much bitterness.

(7) CONCLUSION

This book has shown the great complexity of problems facing any reformer of peasant agriculture in Rhodesia. It has emerged from the analysis that a true solution can only be found through a basic alteration of the fundamental structure of Rhodesian society. The present capitalist system has failed because it is almost exclusively geared to preserve the superior status of a racial minority. An effective reform must remove all racial barriers and provide equal training facilities and job opportunities to members of all races. If this is done, those not really interested in agriculture will leave the land, and agricultural reforms can then be implemented.

As there is as yet no indication that the Rhodesian government will accept such radical change, only partial solutions may be offered. But these will only postpone, and thereby intensify, the inevitable final conflict. Some such possible half-measures are the following:

1. In view of the rapidly increasing African population, traditional attitudes towards the land must be abandoned and the rural population must be separated into those who regard farming as a vocation and those who merely use the land to produce enough food for their families. These latter must be employed in other occupations. To make this possible far-reaching legislative changes have to be made to enable Africans to train and perform skilled work.

Many will argue that short of a miraculous expansion of industry the majority of Africans cannot be gainfully employed. But until they are removed from the land no successful agricultural reform will be possible.

2. To encourage peasants in their agricultural tasks, each man or woman should be given exclusive responsibility for a particular plot of land, not only in purchase areas but also in tribal trust lands and on irrigation schemes. Whether this exclusive responsibility be expressed in the handing over of title deeds or not, is of minor importance. As peasants break with tribal values, such requests will become frequent[1] and at present are already made on irrigation schemes. The introduction of individual land tenure, and the fixing of minimal holdings for peasant cultivators, is the only solution to the abuse of tribal trust lands as the dumping ground for the African 'surplus population'. For unless it can be clearly shown that no vacant land is left, the myth will remain alive among white Rhodesians that all Africans could have a home in the tribal areas if they so desired. The Land Husbandry Act, now abandoned, was an important step in this direction and could have helped solve a problem which by now has become seemingly insuperable.

3. Since land is scarce, those who cultivate it must do it well, otherwise they must be told to surrender the land to those likely to make better use of it. Such a rule ought to be enforced not only in African but also in European areas, as much of the land currently owned by Europeans is not used at all. If unused land is not directly alienated, it should be taxed so highly that its owners will be selling it of their own accord.

4. Those Africans who have a vocation for farming must be given the necessary training, since the analysis of all three settlement-types discussed in this book showed that men who possess a master farmer's certificate produce consistently more than those who have no such qualification. As long as agricultural extension workers are too few in number to give personal attention to each cultivator, they should concentrate their limited resources on the most progressive peasants in their areas, or on small groups whose members are united by bonds of kinship, neighbourhood or friendship, and are therefore ready to cooperate.

5. This study has shown that peasant cultivators and farmers have different needs to increase their output: peasant cultivators still living at subsistence level must be helped to acquire sufficient land, cattle and implements, and also be taught basic farming skills; peasant farmers who possess all these requirements, must

---

[1] A request for freehold tenure in African areas was made by an African member of parliament in 1971. *The Rhodesia Herald*, 6.8.71.

be assisted continually to increase their agricultural knowledge, encouraged to apply themselves whole-heartedly to their work, to invest their earnings in the land and to club together with friends or neighbours to buy larger farm machinery.

6. If irrigation schemes are ever to succeed, plotholders must be given a say in the running of their own communities. It is necessary that in the first years plotholders are strictly supervised by experienced extension staff who can teach them the art of irrigation farming. But such staff must itself be well qualified. It is not sufficient that a scheme manager be a European; previous work as an assistant on a European owned farm does not in itself qualify a man to take on responsibility for an irrigation scheme, as the failure of European scheme managers in Mvura bears out. Unless plotholders have confidence in the competence of the scheme personnel, they will only work with them under duress.

After some years of close supervision by experienced agricultural staff, plotholders should be handed over full responsibility for their scheme. By this time unsuccessful plotholders ought to have been weeded out and only the best retained. These should then be offered the opportunity to take out title deeds to the irrigated land and, if possible, take on additional irrigation plots. Unless successful plotholders are given this opportunity, they will not stay, and unless irrigation schemes become attractive to successful peasants, they will remain failures.

It is essential that African peasants are treated as free people and given the opportunity to administer their own communities. Constant supervision, interference in their daily lives and regimentation bring forth nothing but bitterness and resentment. Africans, like most people, prefer wealth to poverty, but they are not yet so materialistic as to be ready to trade their freedom and human dignity for money. Most prefer to live in freedom in an economically less productive community than on scheduled production schemes where personal decision-making and self-administration are unknown.

In the early 1970s Rhodesia is standing at the brink of a crisis. The country is not merely faced with the choice of slower or faster progress, higher or lower output in its peasant sector, but with steadily lowering living standards among its African people brought about by government attempts to preserve present social structures, and forced development which requires a radical break with the tribal system. As the case histories of progressive peasant cultivators, farmers and plotholders have shown, a break with tribal values is possible in Rhodesia. In fact, most Rhodesian Africans have shown a great ability to adapt themselves to new social and economic conditions.

As Nash observes, 'economic systems are among the most dynamic parts of society',[1] and Rhodesian Africans have shown themselves prepared to accept far-reaching changes in their economic system. But unless drastic reforms are carried out, Rhodesia will surely face a peasant revolt in the not too distant future.

[1] Nash, 1967, p. 11.

APPENDIX

TABLE 38

Percentage of Landless Men in Two Tribal Trust Lands
by Age Groups (N=902)

Age in Years	Total Number of Men	Number of Landless Men	Percentage of Landless Men
15–29	415	335	80·7
30–44	268	78	29·1
45 and over	219	12	5·5
Total	902	425	47·1

Tables 39, 40 and 41 on facing pages overleaf.

TABLE 42

Labour Input per Household on Crops in Tribal Trust Lands (N=55)

Crop	Master Farmer		Other Peasant Cultivator	
	Hours	Per cent	Hours	Per cent
Maize	1,107	27·9	403	19·1
Millet	1,024	25·8	663	31·4
Groundnuts	801	20·2	426	20·1
Groundbeans	389	9·8	291	13·8
Other Crops	647	16·3	330	15·6
	3,968	100·0	2,113	100·0

The labour input per crop is worked out for the average household. It does not represent the labour input per acre, since it is the family, not the land unit, on which this survey was based. A comparison with Table 9 shows that maize needs less labour per acre than most other crops. The fact that master farmers spend most time on maize, and that other peasant cultivators spend most time on millet, is due to the larger acreages of these crops grown by master farmers and other peasant cultivators.

TABLE 39

Percentage of Working Hours Contributed by Family Labour, Work Parties and Hired Labour on Crop Production in Tribal Trust Lands (N=55)

Composition of Labour Force	Ploughing		Sowing		Weeding		Harvesting		All Activities	
	M.F.[1]	P.C.[2]	M.F.	P.C.	M.F.	P.C.	M.F.	P.C.	M.F.	P.C.
Family labour	96·7	84·0	97·8	98·5	80·7	77·4	82·0	69·4	86·4	79·0
Work parties	1·9	13·5	—	1·0	13·1	21·9	17·0	28·7	10·8	19·4
Hired labour	2·4	1·5	2·2	0·5	6·2	0·7	1·0	1·9	2·7	1·6
Total	100·0	100·0	100·0	100·0	100·0	100·0	100·0	100·0	100·0	100·0

[1] M.F = master farmer.   [2] P.C. = other peasant cultivator.

TABLE 40

Percentage of Working Hours Contributed by Men, Women and Children on Crop Production in Tribal Trust Lands (N=55)

Composition of Labour Force	Master Farmers	Other Peasant Cultivators
Men	30·9	25·3
Women	32·3	39·9
Children	36·8	34·8
Total	100·0	100·0

TABLE 41

Labour Input per Household on Crop Production (N=55)

Month	Ploughing		Sowing		Weeding		Harvesting		Total Hours		Percentages	
	M.F.	P.C.	M.F.	P.C.	M.F.	P.C.	M.F.	P.C.	M.F.	P.C.	M.F.	P.C.
October	132	27							132	27	3.3	1.3
November	282	196	275	191					557	387	14.1	18.2
December	168	114	289	115	539	300			996	529	25.1	25.0
January			11		568	311			579	311	14.6	14.7
February					200	40			200	40	5.0	1.9
March					32	15	257	139	289	154	7.3	7.3
April							550	294	550	294	13.9	13.9
May							336	260	336	260	8.5	12.3
June							214	64	214	54	5.4	3.0
July–September	61	30					54	17	115	47	2.8	2.2
Total	643	367	575	306	1,339	666	1,411	774	3,968	2,113	100.0	100.0
Percentage	16.2	17.4	14.3	14.5	33.7	31.5	35.6	36.4	100.0	100.0		

TABLE 43

Labour Input per Household on Cattle Herding (N=55)

Composition of labour force	May–September No. of hours	perc.	October–April No. of hours	perc.	Total Year No. of hours	perc.	Percentage contributed by men, women and children
Men	35	16·0	209	83·0	244	100·0	22·7
Women	65	18·7	281	81·3	346	100·0	33·0
Children	84	17·1	404	82·9	488	100·0	44·3
Total	184	17·1	894	82·9	1,078	100·0	100·0

TABLE 44

Degrees of Soil Erosion in Two Tribal Trust Lands

Degree of erosion	Percentage of total area Shiri-Ngara	Shoko
Nil	8	9
Slight	29	55
Moderate	41	19
Severe	19	11
Very severe	3	6
Total	100	100

Extracted from a publication by Keech, 1966.

TABLE 45

Cattle Sales in Shoko Tribal Trust Land, February, 1963

Price	Cattle on offer No.	Per cent	Cattle sold No.	Per cent	Cattle withdrawn No.	Per cent
£5 –£10	35	10·2	24	8·9	11	15·0
£10.5.0–£15	80	23·3	58	21·5	22	30·1
£15.5.0–£20	159	46·4	124	45·9	35	48·0
£20.5.0–£25	41	12·0	38	14·1	3	4·1
£25.5.0–£30	23	6·7	22	8·1	1	1·4
£30.5.0–£35	5	1·4	4	1·5	1	1·4
Total	343	100·0	270	100·0	73	100·0

TABLE 46

Cattle Sales in the Shiri-Ngara Tribal Trust Land, March 1964

Price	Cattle on offer		Cattle sold		Cattle withdrawn	
	No.	Per cent	No.	Per cent	No.	Per cent
£5 –£10	20	16·4	3	9·7	17	18·7
£10.5.0–£15	37	30·3	8	25·8	29	31·9
£15.5.0–£20	45	36·9	11	35·5	34	37·3
£20.5.0–£25	17	13·9	7	22·6	10	11·0
£25.5.0–£30	3	2·5	2	6·4	1	1·1
Total	122	100·0	31	100·0	91	100·0

Tables 45 and 46 show that the average price paid for African cattle is £15 to £20 in both tribal trust lands. Government sponsored sales are better received in Shoko than in the Shiri-Ngara tribal trust land, for although Shoko has less than half the human and half the cattle population of Shiri-Ngara, its sales are always higher and the number of cattle which are withdrawn from the sales is much lower. Various social and political factors are responsible for this difference.

TABLE 47

Selection of Case Histories of Peasant Cultivators
According to Agricultural Income

Agricultural Income	Master Farmers		Other Peasant Cultivators	
	Per cent in total sample	No. of case histories	Per cent in total sample	No. of case histories
Below £25	5·3	–	66·0	3
£25–£49	15·8	1	23·3	2
£50–£74	26·3	1	4·9	1
£75–£99	26·3	2	2·9	–
£100 and over	26·3	1	2·9	–
Total	100·0[1]	5	100·0[2]	6

N [1] = 19   N [2] = 144

TABLE 48

Years Waited to Obtain a Purchase Area Farm (N=204)

	Guruuswa		Mutadza Master Farmers		O. Peasant Farmers	
Years Waited	Freq.	Per cent	Freq.	Per cent	Freq.	Per cent
Less than 1	—	—	4	22·2	27	64·2
1–4	40	27·8	4	22·2	1	2·4
5–9	45	31·2	3	16·7	4	9·6
10–14	25	17·4	—	—	—	—
15–19	18	12·5	5	27·8	1	2·4
20 and over	11	7·6	2	11·1	2	4·8
Inherited	5	3·5	—	—	7	16·7
Total	144	100·0	18	100·0	42	100·0

TABLE 49

Age of Farm Owners (N=204)

	Guruuswa		Mutadza	
Age	Freq.	Per cent	Freq.	Per cent
20–29	6	4·1	1	1·7
30–39	8	5·6	8	13·3
40–49	44	30·6	18	30·0
50–59	51	35·4	14	23·3
60–69	28	19·4	8	13·3
70 and over	7	4·9	11	18·4
Total	144	100·0	60	100·0

TABLE 50

Percentage of Working Hours Contributed by Men, Women and Children to Crop Production in Purchase Areas (N=132)

		Mutadza	
Composition of labour force	Guruuswa	Master Farmers	Other Peasant Farmers
Men	27·0	29·5	33·3
Women	46·3	32·7	36·7
Children	26·7	37·8	30·0
Total	100·0	100·0	100·0

TABLE 51

Labour Input per Household on Crops in Purchase Areas (N=132)

	Guruuswa		Mutadza Master Farmers		O. Peasant Farmers	
Crops	Hours	Per cent	Hours	Per cent	Hours	Per cent
Maize	1,910	26·3	1,514	34·9	1,132	30·1
Millet	2,096	28·8	1,626	37·8	1,318	35·0
Sorghum	559	7·7	228	5·3	282	7·5
Groundnuts	2,086	28·7	929	21·6	919	24·4
Groundbeans	472	6·5	17	0·4	46	1·2
Other crops	147	2·0	—	—	69	1·8
Total	7,270	100·0	4,314	100·0	3,766	100·0

TABLE 52

Labour Input per Household on Cattle Maintenance in Purchase Areas and Tribal Trust Lands (N=187[1])

	Guruuswa		Mutadza		Tribal Trust Lands	
Herders	Hours	Per cent	Hours	Per cent	Hours	Per cent
Men	1,011	32·0	289	20·6	244	22·6
Women	608	19·2	66	4·8	346	32·1
Children	1,539	48·8	1,036	74·6	488	45·3
Total	3,158	100·0	1,391	100·0	1,078	100·0

[1] 132 households are from the two purchase areas, 55 from the tribal trust lands.

TABLE 53

Selection of Case Histories of Peasant Farmers
According to Agricultural Income

Agricultural Income	Guruuswa		Mutadza Master Farmers		O. Peasant Farmers	
	Perc. in total sample	No. of case history	Perc. in community	No. of case history	Perc. in community	No. of case history
Below £50	1·4	—	16·6	1	19·1	1
£50–£99	—	—	22·2	—	30·9	1
£100–£149	4·2	1	22·2	—	23·8	1
£150–£199	19·4	—	5·6	1	11·9	1
£200–£249	22·2	1	5·6	—	7·1	—
£250–£299	12·5	—	22·2	—	4·8	—
£300–£349	18·0	—	—	—	2·4	—
£350–£399	4·2	1	5·6	1	—	—
£400–£449	11·1	1	—	—	—	—
£450–£499	1·4	—	—	—	—	—
£500–£549	4·2	—	—	—	—	—
£1,000 plus	1·4	1	—	—	—	—
Total	100·0[1]	5	100·0[2]	3	100·0[3]	4

N[1] = 72   N[2] = 18   N[3] = 42

TABLE 54

Selection of Case Histories of Plotholders
According to Agricultural Income

Agricultural Gross Income	Mvura		Zuva	
	Percentage in total sample	No. of case histories	Percentage in total sample	No. of case histories
Below £50	—	—	24·1	3
£50–£99	—	—	58·6	3
£100–£149	—	—	17·3	2
£150–£199	—	—	—	—
£200–£249	41·2	2	—	—
£250–£299	23·5	1	—	—
£300–£349	29·4	2	—	—
£350–£399	5·9	1	—	—
Total	100·0[1]	6	100·0[2]	8

N[1] = 17   N[2] = 29

BIBLIOGRAPHY

AFRICAN FARMING DEVELOPMENT 1968a (March) *African Farming Development: 1964–65 to 1967–68 Seasons.* Cyclostyled Report. Salisbury, African Farming Development.
—— 1968b *African Farming Development: To live or to Subsist?* Salisbury, African Farming Development.
ALLAN, W. 1965 *The African Husbandman.* Edinburgh, Oliver & Boyd.
ALLAN W., GLUCKMAN, M. *et al.* 1948 *Land Holding and Land Usage among the Plateau Tonga of Mazabuka District.* Rhodes-Livingstone Paper No. 14. Cape Town, O.U.P. for Rhodes-Livingstone Institute.
ALVORD INSTITUTE 1965 *Chief's Conservation Conference.* (unpublished) Fort Victoria, Alvord Institute.
ANONYMOUS 1969 (May) What's Happening in the Sabi Valley? Salisbury, *The Shield*, No. 281, pp. 13–14.
AQUINA, SR. MARY O.P. 1964. The Social Background of Agriculture in Chilimanzi Reserve. *Rhodes-Livingstone Journal*, No. 36, pp. 7–39.
BAUM, E. 1968 Land Use in the Kilombero Valley *in* RUTHENBERG, H. (*ed.*) *Smallholder Farming and Smallholder Development in Tanzania.* München, Weltforum Verlag.
BELSHAW, C. S. 1967 *Traditional Exchange and Modern Markets.* Englewood Cliffs, N.J., Prentice-Hall, Inc.
BIEBUYCK, D. 1966 *African Agrarian Systems.* O.U.P. for I.A.I.
BOSERUP, E. 1965 *The Conditions of Agricultural Growth.* London, George Allen & Unwin.
BROWN, K. 1959 *Land in S. Rhodesia.* London, The Africa Bureau.
BYRES, T. J. (*ed.*) 1973 *The Logic of Peasant Agriculture.* London, Frank Cass & Co. Ltd.
CHAMBERS, R. 1969 *Settlement Schemes in Tropical Africa.* London, Routledge & Kegan Paul.
CHENNELS, ANTHONY 1969 (July) The T.T.L. Development Corporation: A Review. Salisbury, *The Shield*, pp. 13, 29.
CLUTTON-BROCK, G. 1969 *Rekayi Tangwena.* Gwelo, Mambo Press.
CONEX 1970 *Nyanyadzi: An African Irrigation Scheme.* Umtali.
CONFERENCE DE REHOVOTH, 1963. Israel, Institut Weizmann des Sciences.
CREDIT UNION NATIONAL COUNCIL 1970 *Schools for Adults: Saving Clubs.* Mission Press, Chishawasha, Rhodesia.
DANCKWERTS, J. P. 1970 Technology and Economic Development of

African Agriculture in Rhodesia. *The Rhodesian Journal of Economics*, Vol. 4, No. 4. pp. 17–30.

DEQUIN, H. 1969 *Agricultural Development in Malawi*. München Weltforum Verlag.

DE WILDE, J. C. 1967 *Experiences with Agricultural Development in Tropical Africa*. Baltimore, Johns Hopkins Press. Vol. 1.

DOBB, M. 1966 *Soviet Economic Development since 1917*. London, Routledge & Kegan Paul.

DUMONT, R. 1967 *False Start in Africa*. André Deutsch Ltd., London.

ELKINGTON, B. D. 1968 The effects of Education or Extension Methods on Traditional Land Tenurial Systems in Rhodesia. *Synoptical Paper, SARCCUS*, Salisbury.

FELDMAN, D. 1969 The Economics of Ideology: Some Problems of Achieving Rural Socialism in Tanzania, *in* LEYS, C. (*ed.*) *Politics and Change in Developing Countries*. Cambridge University Press, pp. 85–111.

FIRTH, R. 1964 A Viewpoint from Economic Anthropology *in* FIRTH, R. and YAMEY, B.C. (*eds.*) *Capital, Saving and Credit in Peasant Societies*. London, Allen & Unwin, pp. 15–34.

FLOYD, B. N. 1959 *Changing Patterns of African Land Use in Southern Rhodesia*. Rhodes-Livingstone Institute Publication.

FORDE, D. *and* DOUGLAS, M. 1967 Primitive Economics *in* DALTON, G. (*ed.*) *Tribal and Peasant Economies*. New York, The Natural History Press, pp. 13–28.

GANN, L. H. *and* DUIGNAN, P. 1970 *Colonialism in Africa*. Vol. II. Cambridge University Press.

GEDDES, W. R. 1963 *Peasant Life in Communist China*. Ithaca, New York, Cornell University'

GLUCKMAN, M. 1951 The Lozi of Barotseland in North-Western Rhodesia *in* COLSON, E. *and* GLUCKMAN, M. (*eds.*) *Seven Tribes of British Central Africa*. Manchester University Press, pp. 1–93.

GULLIVER, P. H. 1967 Labour Migration in a Rural Economy *in* WHETHAM, E. H. *and* CARRIE, J. I. (*eds.*) *Readings in the Applied Economics of Africa*, Vol. 1, pp. 32–37.

HELLEN, J. A. 1968 *Rural Economic Development in Zambia, 1890–1964*. München, Weltforum Verlag.

HOLLEMAN, J. F. 1969 *Chief, Council and Commissioner*. London, O.U.P.

HOWMAN, R. 1967 Changing Social Structure and Land Tenure. *1st Rhodesian Scientific Congress*.

HUGHES, J. A. 1968. *The Border Lands*. Salisbury, Government Printer.

HUNT, A. F. 1966 The Economic Position of the Tribal Trust Land in Relation to Agriculture. Paper presented at the *Conference on the Tribal Trust Lands* at the U.C.R., pp. 1–7.

——1967 The Agricultural Industry. *CONEX* (cyclostyled).

HUNT, N. A. 1963 Age and Land in a Native Reserve. *NADA*, No. 40, pp. 108–112.

JOHNSON, C. E. 1956 African Farming Improvement in the Plateau Tonga Maize Areas of Northern Rhodesia. *Agricultural Bulletin No. 11*. Northern Rhodesia, Department of Agriculture.

JOHNSON, R. W. M. 1959 Budgeting Farm Improvements in African Areas. Rhodesia, *Makoholi Newsletter* No. 11.

——1960 Budgeting Labour Requirements in African Areas. Rhodesia, *Makoholi Newsletter*, No. 14.

——1961 On the Valuation of Subsistence Production. *Occasional Paper No. 1*, Department of Economics, U.C.R.N.

——1963a The Economics of Subsistence. *Technical Paper No. 1* Department of Economics, U.C.R.N.

——1963b Notes on Rural African Population Statistics, Southern Rhodesia. *Technical Paper in Agricultural Economics*, No. 3. Department of Economics, U.C.R.N.

——1963c The Economics of Equality—African Rural Marketing in Southern Rhodesia. *Technical Paper No. 6.* Department of Economics, U.C.R.N.

——1963d African Cattle Problems in the Intensive Agricultural Areas of Southern Rhodesia. *Technical Paper No. 7.* Department of Economics, U.C.R.N.

——1964a An Economic Survey of Native Purchase Areas in the Mount Darwin District, Southern Rhodesia. *Technical Paper No. 16*, Department of Economics, U.C.R.N.

——1964b An Economic Survey of Chitowa Native Purchase Area, Mrewa District, Southern Rhodesia. Part I. *Technical Paper No. 18.* Department of Economics, U.C.R.N.

——1964c The Labour Economy of the Reserves. *Occasional Paper No. 4*, Department of Economics, U.C.R.N.

——1964d An Economic Survey of Chiweshe Reserve. *Rhodes-Livingstone Journal* No. 36, pp. 82–108.

——1964e *African Agricultural Development in S. Rhodesia: 1945–1960.* Stanford University, Food Research Institute.

——1964f The Current State of Agricultural Economics Research and Teaching in Southern Rhodesia. *Technical Paper No. 19*, Department of Economics, U.C.R.N.

——1965 The Labour Economy of Chitowa Native Purchase Area. Part II. *Technical Paper No. 21*, Department of Economics, U.C.R.N.

JORDAN, J. D. 1966 *A Preliminary Report of an Investigation into the Master Farmer Training Scheme.* (unpublished). Fort Victoria, Alvord Institute.

KAMARCK, A. M. 1967 *The Economics of African Development.* New York, Frederick A. Praeger.

KEECH, M. A. 1966 An Objective Survey of Erosion with Particular Reference to the Tribal Trust Land. Paper presented at the *Conference on the Tribal Trust Lands* at the U.C.R., pp. 1–6.

KIRKPATRICK, C. 1968 The Role of the African L.D.C. in the Field of African Agriculture. *The Rhodesian Journal of Economics*, Vol. 2, No. 2, pp. 22–27.

LEYS, C. (*ed.*) 1969 *Politics and Change in Developing Countries.* Cambridge University Press.

LIPTON, M. (ed.) 1973 Livestock and Peasant Agriculture. London, Frank Cass & Co. Ltd.

LONG, N. 1968 Social Change and the Individual. Manchester University Press.

MAGURA, W. 1970 Die Entwicklung der Landwirtschaft in den Bantu Gebieten von Süd- und Südwest Africa. München, Weltforum Verlag.

MANN, H. H. 1968 The Social Framework of Agriculture. London, Frank Cass & Co. Ltd.

MASON, P. 1960 Land Policy in GRAY, R. The Two Nations. O.U.P., pp. 43–88.

MAYER, P. 1961 Townsmen or Tribesmen. O.U.P.

NASH, M. 1967 The Organization of Economic Life in DALTON, G. (ed.) Tribal and Peasant Economies. New York, The Natural History Press.

NATURAL RESOURCES BOARD 1966a Twenty-Fifth Annual Report, 1966. Salisbury.

——1966b Report of the Fifth Annual Conference of Purchase Area, Intensive Conservation Area Committees. Salisbury, 1966.

——1967 Sixth Annual Conference of Purchase Area, Intensive Conservation Area Committees. Salisbury, 1967,

——1968 25 Years of Conservation in Rhodesia. Salisbury.

PALMER, R. H. 1968 Aspects of Rhodesian Land Policy, 1890–1936. The Central Africa History Association, Local Series 22.

PENDERED, A. and VON MEMERTY, W. 1955 Native Land Husbandry Act of Southern Rhodesia. Journ. of Afr. Admin. 7, 3.

PLOWES, D. C. H. 1963 Memorandum on the Land and Fertility Problems of the African Farming Areas. Umtali Regional Conex Dept. Conference. (cyclostyled)

RODER, W. 1965 The Sabi Valley Irrigation Projects. Department of Geography Research Paper 99, Chicago, Illinois.

RUTHENBERG, H. 1964 Agricultural Development in Tanganyika. Berlin, Springer Verlag.

——1968 Smallholder Farming and Smallholder Development in Tanzania. München, Weltforum Verlag.

SABI-LIMPOPO AUTHORITY 1969 Golden Dawn. Salisbury, Graphic Printing & Packaging Industries Ltd.

SCHAPERA, I. 1967 Economic Changes in South African Native Life in DALTON, G. (ed.) Tribal and Peasant Economies. New York, The Natural History Press.

SCHEFFLER, W. 1968 Tobacco Schemes in the Central Region: Production under Close Supervision in RUTHENBERG, H. (ed.) Smallholder Farming and Smallholder Development in Tanzania. München, Weltforum Verlag.

SMITH, G. A. 1963 The Peasant (cyclostyled) Fort Victoria, Alvord Institute.

——1966 Agricultural Extension Work in Rhodesia with particular reference to African Areas (cyclostyled).

STANNING, T. R. 1967 Some Human Problems Encountered by African

Farming Development. *The Rhod. Journ. of Econ.*, Vol. 1, No. 1, pp. 25–29.

STAUNTON, F. A. 1967 Review of the Value and Role of Tribal Land Authority Conservation Committees. *N.R.B., FAS/WRO.*

STAUNTON, F. A. 1969 Good Farming Competition (Grazing Areas). *N.R.B., FAS/MLM.*

THORPE, G. B. 1968 The Development of Financial Credit Institutions for African Farmers in the Tribal Trust Lands of Rhodesia. *Synoptical Paper, SARCCUS*, Salisbury.

TURNER, V. W. 1957 *Schism and Continuity in an African Society.* Manchester University Press.

VAN VELSEN, J. 1964 *The Politics of Kinship.* Manchester University Press.

VICTORIA ASSOCIATION OF YOUNG FARMERS' CLUBS 1965 *Constitution.*

WALKER, K. R. 1965 *Planning in Chinese Agriculture.* London, Frank Cass & Co.

WALLMAN, S. 1969 *Take Out Hunger.* London, Athlone Press.

WATSON, W. 1958. *Tribal Cohesion in a Money Economy.* Manchester University Press.

WHARTON, J. R. 1972 *Subsistence Agriculture and Economic Development.* London, Frank Cass & Co. Ltd.

WEINGROD, A. 1966 *Reluctant Pioneers.* New York, Cornell University Press.

WEINRICH, A. K. H. 1971 *Chiefs and Councils in Rhodesia.* London, Heinemann.

——1973 *Black and White Elites in Rural Rhodesia.* Manchester University Press.

WEINZIERL, T. 1970 Is the Credit Union Movement a Valid Form of Adult Education in Rhodesia? *University of Rhodesia Adult Education Documents Library.*

WILSON, M. *and* MAFEJE, A. 1963 *Langa: A Study of Social Groups in an African Township.* Cape Town, O.U.P.

YUDELMAN, M. 1964 *Africans on the Land.* Harvard U. Press.

THE RHODESIAN GOVERNMENT ACTS:

1967 Tribal Trust Land Act, No. 9. Salisbury, Government Printer.
1967 Tribal Trust Land (Control of Irrigation Schemes) Regulation. Act 9/67. Rhodesia Government Notice No. 856.
1968 Tribal Trust Land Development Corporation Act, No. 47. Salisbury, Government Printer.
1969 Agricultural Land Settlement Act, No. 59.
1969 Land Tenure Act, No. 55.
1970 Land Tenure (Control of Irrigable Areas) Regulations. Act 55/69. Rhodesia Government Notice No. 679.
1970 Land Tenure (Suspension of Irrigation) Regulation. Act 55/69.
1970 Agricultural Research Act, No. 31.

SOUTHERN RHODESIA:

1952 The African Land Husbandry Act. Salisbury, Government Printer.
1960 The African Farmers' Licencing Act.
1963 Rural Land Act, No. 47. Salisbury, Government Printer.

OTHER GOVERNMENT PUBLICATIONS:

1960 *Seminar on Land Policies in East and Central Africa.* Southern Rhodesia Country Paper. Uganda.
1960 *Second Report of the Select Committee on Resettlement of Natives* (Quinton Report). Salisbury, Government Printer.
1960–61 NAD Farmer Service Information Sheets. Salisbury, Government Printer.
1961 *Report of the Secretary for Native Affairs and C.N.C. for the year 1961.* Salisbury, Government Printer.
1961 *1961 Census of the European, Asian and Coloured Population.* Salisbury, Central Statistical Office.
1961 *Southern Rhodesia Constitution, 1961.* London, H.M. Stationery Office.
1962 *Report of the Advisory Committee, 1962.* The development of the economic resources of Southern Rhodesia, with special reference to the role of African agriculture.
1962 Tribal Land Authorities Circular No. 172, file No. Lan. 2/TTL.
1964 *Report of the Rural Land Board.* Salisbury, Government Printer.
1964–70 *Report of the Secretary for Internal Affairs,* for the years 1963 to 1969. Salisbury, Government Printer.
1965 *Constitution of Rhodesia, 1965.* Salisbury, Government Printer.
1967 *Report by J. C. Sadie on Planning for the Economic Development of Rhodesia.* Salisbury, Government Printer.
1969 *Constitution for Rhodesia, 1969.* Salisbury, Government Printer.
1969–70 *1969 Population Censuses, Preliminary Reports.*
1970 *Report of the Secretary for Agriculture for the period 1st October 1968 to 30th September 1969.* Presented to Parliament of Rhodesia 1970. Salisbury, Government Printer.

NEWSPAPERS:

The Rhodesia Herald, Salisbury.
The Sunday Mail, Salisbury.

INDEX